P9-CRL-415

"Men ever had, and ever will have, leave
To coin new words well suited to the age.
Words are like leaves, some wither ev'ry year,
And ev'ry year a younger race succeeds."

Horace, Ars Poetica
Trans., Earl of Roscommon
Wentworth Dillon

The language of science is complex and everchanging. In order to comprehend and appreciate the fascinating world of the scientist and our age of electronics, nuclear energy, and space, one must stay abreast of this language. The YOUNG PEOPLE'S SCIENCE DICTIONARY is the most complete science dictionary available for young people. Its user gains a head start in today's world of mushrooming knowledge. Designed as a companion volume to the YOUNG PEOPLE'S SCIENCE ENCYCLOPEDIA, the new YOUNG PEOPLE'S SCIENCE DICTIONARY is an outstanding contribution to science education that will be welcomed by young and old alike in home, school, or library.

21 Aa My

Young People's Science Dictionary

by the Editors of the

YOUNG PEOPLE'S SCIENCE ENCYCLOPEDIA

in cooperation with

The Science Center

National College of Education
Evanston, Illinois

 CHILDRENS PRESS ™

CHICAGO

Photographs

Page 2: Skylab space station (NASA)

Page 3: *Top to Bottom:*
Wheatfield (U.S.D.A. Photo)
Technician capping Abbokinase (Abbott Laboratories)
Spider (Macmillan Science Company)
View of Earth (NASA)
Space Shuttle (NASA)
Bahama coral reef (Macmillan Science Company)

Cover: Design by Sandra Gelak
Katydid (James P. Rowan)
Claret-Cup Cactus (James P. Rowan)
Apple River: Warren, Illinois (James P. Rowan)

Library of Congress Catalog Card Number: 67-17925

Copyright© 1991 by Childrens Press®, Inc.
Original Copyright© 1963 by Childrens Press, Inc.
All rights reserved. Printed in the U.S.A.
Published simultaneously in Canada.

TABLE OF CONTENTS

EDITED BY
The Science Center
National College of Education • Evanston, Illinois

EDITOR
Dr. Donald A. Boyer
Director, The Science Center
Associate Editor, Young People's
Science Encyclopedia

ASSOCIATE EDITOR
Dr. Helen J. Challand
Chairman, Science Department
Associate Editor, Young People's
Science Encyclopedia

EDITORIAL ADVISORY BOARD

Dr. N. Eldred Bingham
Professor of Education
University of Florida

Dr. Martin Block
Professor of Physics
Northwestern University

Dr. Stanley B. Brown
Professor Education
Indiana University

Dr. Ralph Buchsbaum
Professor of Zoology
University of Pittsburgh

Dr. Hilary J. Deason
Director, Science Library Program
American Association for the
    Advancement of Science

Dr. Krafft A. Ehricke
Centaur Program Director
Astronautics Division
General Dynamics Corporation

Dr. Evan Evans
Executive Director
National Aerospace Education Council

Harry Milgrom
Assistant Director of Science
New York City Public Schools

Dr. W. Ray Rucker
Dean, School of Education
East Texas State College

Dr. Paul Witty
Director, Psycho-Educational Clinic
Northwestern University

THE STAFF

MANAGING EDITOR
Jean F. Blashfield

ARTISTS . . . STUDIO 5
    Charles Omens
    Steven Babecki
    R. Scott
    Ray Schaeffer
    Sam Heller
    J. Sharte

COVER DESIGN
Alex D'Amato

PRODUCTION
    Camilla Bereckis
    Houston Mimms
    Kenneth Roberts
    Sharon Schraudenbach
    Marilynn Warren

EDITORIAL
Joan Soltz
Ruth L. Oldfield

© Copyright 1964, U.S.A., CHILDRENS PRESS, INC.
All rights reserved.   Printed in U.S.A.
Library of Congress Catalog Card #64-25789

EDITOR'S PREFACE

Progress in the comprehension of any science concept begins with understanding the terms in which it is expressed.

The YOUNG PEOPLE'S SCIENCE DICTIONARY defines words and ideas. It also defines groups of words which have meanings in science that are not evident in the single words that make them up.

This work is designed as a tool which will serve the needs of a student in the rapidly changing pattern of modern education, with its increasing demands upon him.

The most important purpose of this Science Dictionary is to afford the student a ready reference source for clear statements of the meaning of science terms and ideas, with profitable use in association with the *Young People's Science Encyclopedia,* current-science news media, leisure reading, and the like.

In the rapid growth of modern science and its vocabulary, many terms have special meanings in particular science fields. Some words have two or more meanings, each one distinct for a special branch of science. Editors and consultants have been careful to research and include the fullest possible inventory of these terms and their useful meanings. New usages for older words have been recognized and included. Definitions are not over-simplified. They are terse and adequate statements at a low and reasonable vocabulary level.

This Science Dictionary aims, also, to help a student spell and pronounce correctly words he meets in the study of science and those he encounters in Science Clubs, hobbies, reading, and television. No attempt has been made, however, to usurp the duties of a general, English-language dictionary.

Evident among the special features of this work, besides the effective use of illustrations and color, is the care that has been taken to foster critical thinking.

In writing many definitions, the editors have added, purposely, phrases such as "as distinguished from . . ." or directions to "contrast with . . ." in order to pinpoint meanings. Often a meaning is clear only when a student knows what a concept *is not,* as well as what it *is.*

The editors chose not to stifle this work with the more than one million popular names of living things in the plants and animal worlds. Numerous published field-guide books adequately cover description and identification.

A more useful policy was adopted when it was decided to define major phyla, classes, and (in most cases) orders, and to include only certain useful names. These additional listings include popular names of some animals or plants, such as common laboratory specimens. These, in each case, are cross-referred to their proper higher level of classification—either the order, class, or phylum.

Consistent care has been taken in dealing with the problems of synonyms, with the less acceptable but still current terms, and with basic scientific abbreviations.

For teachers, parents and librarians, the YOUNG PEOPLE'S SCIENCE DICTIONARY will serve to help them meet the challenge of keeping up with modern scientific vocabulary. It affords them a compact resource for their use with young people.

Donald A. Boyer, Ph.D.
The Science Center

USING THE DICTIONARY

ALPHABETICAL ORDER

A through **zymogen,** words, symbols, and abbreviations, are arranged in strict letter-for-letter alphabetical order, rather than word for word. For example:

> **carbon arc**
> **carbonate**
> **carbonation**
> **carbon cycle**

PARTS OF SPEECH

Most of the words defined are nouns (abbreviated *n.*), verbs (*v.*), or adjectives (*adj.*). Occasionally the word defined is a plural noun (*pl. n.*); the singular form (*sing.*) is then given in parentheses.

Additional useful forms of the word defined appear in **bold type** at the end of the definition. For example, at the end of the definition of **legume,** a noun, appears **leguminous,** an adjective describing all such fruits. Additional forms are also frequently used within the definition itself where they appear in *italics*. Adverbs are rarely shown.

PLURALS

The plural form of a word, or the plural ending, is shown only if the form is different from the standard **-s** or **-ies** ending. For example: the plural of **spectrum** is **spectra** and is shown; the plural of **stage** is **stages** and is not shown. But the plural of **sperm** can be **sperm** or **sperms,** so both are shown, in preferred order.

PLANTS AND ANIMALS

Except for a few common laboratory specimens, the only definitions of living organisms are given under the major classifications, usually down through order. For plants, the common name of the family is cross-referred to the order: **sweet-gale family,** see **Myricales.** For animals, common names of representatives of the group are used as cross references: **bear family,** see **Carnivora; camel,** see **Artiodactyla.**

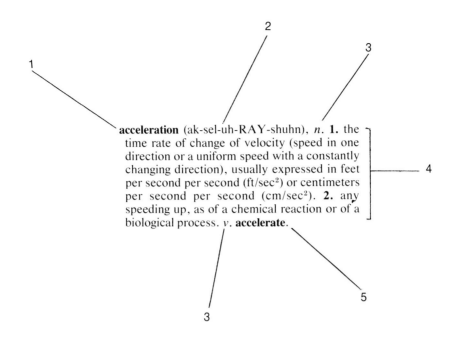

acceleration (ak-sel-uh-RAY-shuhn), *n.* **1.** the time rate of change of velocity (speed in one direction or a uniform speed with a constantly changing direction), usually expressed in feet per second per second (ft/sec²) or centimeters per second per second (cm/sec²). **2.** any speeding up, as of a chemical reaction or of a biological process. *v.* **accelerate**.

1. **ENTRY WORD** appears in bold face type.

2. **PRONUNCIATION** appears enclosed in parentheses. The syllable that is to be stressed in the pronunciation is printed in large type.

3. **PART OF SPEECH** is printed in italic type. Part of speech shows how the word is used.

4. **DEFINITIONS** tell the meaning of the entry word. If a word has more than one meaning each definition is set off by a number 1, 2, etc.

5. **RUN-ON WORDS** appear at the end of the definition in bold face type. The word is undefined because its meaning is similar to the entry word. Part of speech is indicated in italics.

6. **CROSS-REFERENCES** also appear in bold face at the end of the definition. They refer the reader to other entries for further information.

anthropoid ape (AN-thruh-poyd), *n.* any man-like ape: the orangutan, gorilla, gibbon, and chimpanzee; all have thumbs on each of their 4 feet; also called *pongid* apes; see **Primates**.

PRONUNCIATION KEY

(stress is put on syllable in LARGE LETTERS)

VOWELS

a—*a* as in *lap* or *Al*
ah—*a* as in *calm, o* as in *constant*
ai—*a* as in *care*
ay—*a* as in *late*
ee—*e* as in *deep*
ey—*i* as in *iris,* when standing alone in syllable
i—*i* as in *pin*
ih—*i* as in *pin,* when standing alone in syllable
oh—*o* as in *stone*
oy—*oi* as in *coil, oy* as in *boy*
uh—*u* as in *but, e* as in *matter*
y—*i* as in *line,* when part of a syllable
yoo—*u* as in *fuse*

CONSONANTS

f—*ph* as in *phase*
g—*g* as in *gap*
j—*g* as in *gem*
k—*c* as in *cat*
kw—*qu* as in *quake*
s—*c* as in *cell, s* as in *slip*
sh—*sh* as in *shell*
z—*s* as in *please, x* as in *xenon*
zh—*si* as in *fusion, ti* as in *equation*
Remainder of consonants are said as written

A, 1. abbreviation for **angstrom.** 2. former symbol for **argon.**

AAM, abbreviation for **air-to-air missile.**

aardvark (AHRD-vahrk), see **Tubulidentata.**

abdomen (AB-duh-muhn, ab-DOH-muhn), *n.* in mammals, the large cavity between the pelvis and the muscular diaphragm, containing digestive, excretory, reproductive, and other organs. *adj.* **abdominal.**

abductor (ab-DUK-tuhr), *n.* a muscle that moves a body part away from its median position, as one that moves the arm from a position beside the body; contrast with **adductor.** *v.* **abduct.**

aberration (ab-uh-RAY-shuhn), *n.* 1. in optics, failure of light rays to meet at a common point; caused by lens curvature (*spherical aberration*) or by the different distances that dispersed light

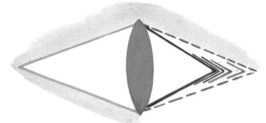

Chromatic aberration in a lens: light passing through is broken into its component wavelengths

rays of differing wavelengths must travel (*chromatic aberration*). 2. in astronomy, the difference between the position in which a star is seen and its true position, caused by the earth's motion during the time it takes for light to travel from the star to the telescope.

abiogenesis (ab-ee-oh-JEN-uh-sis), *n.* the development of living organisms from nonliving substances; a disputed theory among early scientists; also called *spontaneous generation.*

ablation (ab-LAY-shuhn), *n.* 1. in astronautics, the melting of some of the surface of a nose cone in friction with atmosphere; helps to reduce temperature of reentry. 2. in geology, loss of part of glacial ice by evaporation and melting. 3. surgical removal of an organ; prevention of an organ's functioning. *v.* **ablate.**

abnormal (ab-NAWR-muhl), *adj.* not according to the usual pattern or standard: cancer is an *abnormal* cell growth. *n.* **abnormality.**

A-bomb, shortened term for **atomic bomb.**

abort (uh-BAWRT), *v.* to fail to complete a mission, said especially of missiles or spacecraft. *n.* **abort.**

abortion (uh-BAWR-shuhn), *n.* 1. failure to achieve complete development. *adj.* **abortive.** 2. premature expulsion of a fetus from the uterus; in women, during the first 28 weeks of pregnancy.

abrasion (uh-BRAY-zhuhn), *n.* the wearing away of a surface by friction (rubbing). The skin injury in a "skinned" knee is an abrasion.

abrasive (uh-BRAY-siv), *n.* any substance that wears away or polishes another substance, such as emery. *adj.* **abrasive.**

abscess (AB-ses), *n.* an accumulation of pus in a body part, usually due to bacterial infection.

abscission layer (ab-SIZH-uhn), a layer of separation cells that develops at the point where a leaf petiole joins a stem, causing the leaf to fall off.

absolute (AB-suh-loot), *adj.* 1. fundamental; without regard to other characteristics, as *absolute humidity,* without regard to temperature. 2. practical, as *absolute* electrical units.

absolute altimeter, see **altimeter.**

absolute humidity, see **humidity.**

absolute magnitude, the luminosity, or brightness, of a star calculated as if the star were 10 parsecs (more than 32 light years) away from Earth. Figured in this manner, our sun is seen as a faint star with an absolute magnitude of 4.7; contrast with **visual magnitude.**

absolute temperature scale, see **Kelvin, Rankine.**

absolute zero, the lowest possible temperature at which all molecular motion stops, resulting in the complete absence of heat energy. This temperature, 0° on the Kelvin and Rankine scales, is $-273.16°$ C and $-459.7°$ F.

absorption (ab-SAWRP-shuhn), *n.* the receiving of one substance or form of energy by another substance. Cells absorb foods and chemicals; ceilings and walls absorb sound waves; this page absorbs all light waves striking the page wherever there is printing, making the letters appear black. *v.* **absorb.** *adj.* **absorbent.**

absorption band, a dark line in a continuous spectrum caused by the selective absorption of certain wavelengths by some substances; see also **Fraunhofer lines.**

abyssal plain (uh-BIS-uhl), the lowest ocean depths, where almost no light can penetrate.

Ac, symbol for **actinium.**

AC, a.c., or **a-c,** abbreviation for **alternating current.**

acceleration (ak-sel-uh-RAY-shuhn), *n.* 1. the time rate of change of velocity (speed in one direction or a uniform speed with a constantly changing direction), usually expressed in feet per second per second (ft/sec^2) or centimeters per second per second (cm/sec^2). 2. any speeding up, as of a chemical reaction or of a biological process. *v.* **accelerate.**

acceleration of gravity, acceleration due to gravitational force; bodies falling in a vacuum near the earth's surface have such an acceleration of about 32 ft/sec^2 or 980 cm/sec^2; see also **g.**

accelerator (ak-SEL-uh-ray-tuhr), *n.* 1. a device for changing the speed of an automotive engine by regulating amounts of air and fuel admitted to the cylinders. 2. a device for increasing the energy and speed of an electron or nuclear particle; see also **synchrotron. 3.** a substance that increases the speed of polymerization.

accelerometer (ak-sel-uh-RAHM-uh-tuhr), *n.* an instrument for measuring the acceleration of aircraft or spacecraft in flight.

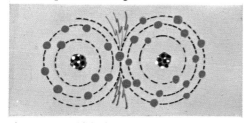

Acceptor atom (right) borrows a "spare" electron from donor, taking on a charge that bonds it to the donor

acceptor atom (ak-SEP-tuhr), an atom which becomes electrically negative by capturing an electron from another atom.

accessory fruit (ak-SES-uh-ree), a fruit composed of tissues derived from other floral parts as well as from the ovary; any botanical type of fruit may be included; common ones are pomes, false berries, and accessory aggregates (strawberry, blackberry); see **fruit** picture.

acclivity (uh-KLIV-uh-tee), *n.* land that slopes upward.

accommodation (uh-kahm-uh-DAY-shuhn), *n.* an adjustment made automatically by the eye in viewing objects at different distances.

accretion (uh-KREE-shuhn), *n.* increase in an object's size due to addition at the surface, not to internal growth: a snowball rolled over fallen snow grows by *accretion.* *v.* **accrete.**

acet-, a word part indicating presence of an *acetyl* radical.

acetaldehyde (as-uh-TAL-duh-hyd), see **aldehyde.**

acetate (AS-uh-tayt), *n.* **1.** a salt or ester of acetic acid, such as sodium acetate, ethyl acetate. **2.** cellulose acetate, a type of rayon made by treating cellulose with acetic acid.

acetic acid (uh-SEE-tik), a colorless organic acid with a sharp, sour odor, found in vinegar; an important intermediate product in manufacture of chemicals; formula, CH_3COOH. The clear, pure acid is called *glacial* acetic acid.

acetone (AS-uh-tohn), *n.* a colorless liquid with a penetrating, fruity odor; the simplest ketone, used as a solvent and as an intermediate product in preparing other chemicals; formula, CH_3COCH_3.

acetyl (uh-SEE-tuhl, AS-uh-tuhl), *n.* the organic radical of acetic acid, CH_3CO-.

acetylcholine (as-uh-tuhl-KOH-leen), *n.* a chemical neurohumor produced by ends of a nerve cell at the synapse, acting to set up the impulse in the next neuron; also produced at nerve effectors on skeletal muscle, playing a role in muscle contraction. It is prepared from ergot, a fungus, to use medicinally.

acetylene (uh-SET-uh-luhn), *n.* a colorless, flammable gas with a strong, sharp odor, used in welding and organic synthesis; the simplest hydrocarbon in the acetylene series; formula, C_2H_2.

acetylsalicylic acid (as-uh-tuhl-sal-uh-SIL-ik), chemical name for aspirin, a common pain-relieving organic chemical; formula, $C_9H_8O_4$.

achene (ah-KENE), *n.* a dry, indehiscent fruit formed from one carpel, and bearing only one seed; the seed coat and pericarp are not fused; examples are dandelion and sunflower.

Achernar (AY-kuhr-nahr), *n.* a star in the southern constellation Eridanus, ninth brightest star in the sky in visual magnitude.

Achilles' tendon (uh-KIL-eez), the tendon joining the calf muscle, the *gastrocnemius,* to the heel.

achromatic lens (ak-ruh-MAT-ik), a lens that prevents chromatic aberration; it is ground to a special shape or is a combination of lenses; see also **aberration.**

Achromycin (ak-roh-MY-sin), *n.* a trade name for *tetracycline,* a broad-spectrum antibiotic (useful against many kinds of germs).

acid (AS-id), *n.* **1.** any of a group of chemical compounds that taste sour, turn blue litmus red, and can neutralize bases. Many, such as citric and lactic acids, occur naturally. **2.** a compound containing hydrogen ions that can unite with hydroxyl ions to form water. **3.** a proton donor.

acidity (uh-SID-uh-tee), *n.* **1.** the state of being acid: said of a substance with a pH of less than 7. **2.** in physiology, **hyperacidity.**

acidosis (as-uh-DOH-sis), *n.* in medicine, loss of the normal amount of body alkalinity, often due to excessive production of acids.

aclinic line (ay-KLIN-ik), an imaginary line roughly parallel to and near the earth's equator, along which a magnetized needle does not dip in response to the earth's magnetic field.

acne (AK-nee), *n.* a skin inflammation especially common in adolescence; involves clogging of oil glands, ducts, and hair follicles. Pimples, blackheads, and whiteheads commonly accompany it.

acorn worm, see **Hemichordata.**

acoustic (uh-KOOS-tik), *adj.* having to do with sound, or with the organs that sense it.

acoustics, *n.* **1.** the science dealing with all aspects of sound. **2.** the special branch dealing with sound absorption or reflection by rooms or building materials.

acquired characteristic, a characteristic of a living organism produced in response to environment; an example is tanned skin from exposure to the sun; acquired characteristics should not be confused with *inherited* characteristics.

acquired immunity, the accumulation in the blood of antibodies preventing the recurrence of a disease; develops when the blood has produced antibodies in response to the disease.

acre (AY-kuhr), *n.* a unit measure of area, especially of land: 43,560 square feet; see also **hectare.**

acromegaly (ak-roh-MEG-uh-lee), *n.* a disease of adults in which bones of the face, feet, and hands become enlarged; usually caused by an overactive anterior lobe of the pituitary gland.

acronical rising (uh-KRAHN-uh-kuhl), rising of a star, planet, etc., at sunset.

acrylic (uh-KRIL-ik), *n.* a plastic made by polymerizing chemicals related to *acrylic acid,* an organic chemical ($C_3H_4O_2$) that readily forms polymers; usually transparent; examples are Lucite and Plexiglas. *adj.* **acrylic.**

ACTH, *adrenocorticotropic hormone,* an anterior pituitary gland secretion used in treating rheumatic and other disorders. ACTH stimulates activity of the adrenal cortex.

actin (AK-tuhn), *n.*　a globulin present in muscle that works together with myosin in causing muscles to contract; see also **globulin.**

actinide series (AK-ti-nyd), the chemical elements with atomic numbers 89 through 103 in the periodic table: actinium, thorium, protactinium, uranium, and the transuranium elements.

actinium (ak-TIN-ee-uhm), *n.*　a radioactive chemical element formed by protactinium decay; symbol Ac; *at. no.,* 89; mass number of most stable isotope, 227; discovered by Debierne in 1899.

actinometer (ak-ti-NAHM-uh-tuhr), *n.*　an instrument for measuring radiation, such as light rays.

activated (AK-ti-vay-tuhd), *adj.*　being ready to do a particular job, or to go from a stable state to a state which may or may not be stable.

active immunity (im-YOO-ni-tee), an organism's immunity to disease, brought about by its own production of antibodies.

active repeater satellite, a satellite, such as *Telstar,* that picks up a signal and rebroadcasts it, usually

Active repeater, or relay, satellite receives signals from a broadcasting station on Earth and retransmits them on command beyond the curvature of Earth

on command, with greater signal strength; also called *relay satellite.*

active transport, the active use by a cell of energy to bring certain chemicals, such as glucose, through the membrane when there is already a greater concentration of the chemical inside the cell than outside.

acute (uh-KYOOT), *adj.* **1.** of a disease, reaching a crisis rapidly and often severely: infectious hepatitis is an *acute* liver infection. **2.** of an angle, measuring less than 90°.

Adam's apple, the projection of the thyroid cartilage at the front of the human throat, normally more prominent in males than females.

adapt (uh-DAPT), *v.*　to adjust to environment: the coat of the ermine becomes white in winter and cannot be seen against snow. *n.* **adaptation.**

addiction (uh-DIK-shuhn), *n.*　habitual dependence on some outside source of satisfaction; usually refers to narcotics, though sometimes to alcohol, tobacco, or other things.

Addison's disease, *n.*　a disorder of the adrenal gland cortex, causing weakness, low blood pres-

sure, a peculiar brown skin, and kidney damage; named for Thomas Addison, English physician.

additive (AD-uh-tiv), *n.*　a substance added in small amounts to another substance to produce some improvement in properties. A food additive may be a tiny amount of preservative, flavoring, or coloring matter.

adductor (uh-DUK-tuhr), *n.*　a muscle that moves a body part toward its median position: *adductors* draw the arms toward the body; contrast with **abductor.** *v.* **adduct.**

adenine (AD-uh-neen), *n.*　a purine-type base, one of the 4 fundamental units of nucleic acids; always pairs with thymine; formula, $C_5H_3N_4NH_2$.

adeno-, a word part meaning *gland.*

adenoid (AD-uh-noid), *n.*　a large mass of lymphatic tissue in the pharynx. Inflamed adenoids

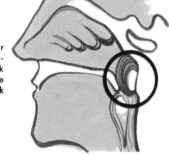

Adenoids, or *pharyngeal tonsils,* at the back of the soft palate (within black circle)

may interfere with normal breathing and may need removal.

adenovirus (ad-uh-noh-VY-ruhs), *n.*　one of a virus group that attacks the respiratory system; highly infectious, often affecting lymphatic tissue.

ADF, abbreviation for *aircraft direction finder;* see **direction finder.**

adhesion (ad-HEE-zhuhn), *n.*　the force that binds unlike molecules, as of 2 liquids, 2 solids, or a liquid and a solid. *v.* **adhere.** *adj.* **adhesive.**

adiabatic (ad-ee-uh-BAT-ik), *adj.*　occurring without exchange of heat between an object and its surroundings. A perfectly *adiabatic* process requires perfect insulation and has not been achieved; see also **isothermal.**

adipic acid (uh-DIP-ik), a solid organic acid with 2 carboxyl radicals; formula, $C_6H_{10}O_4$; one of the major components of nylon.

adipose tissue (AD-uh-pohs), a specialized connective tissue that has animal fat stored within the cells; see **connective tissue.**

adolescence (ad-uh-LES-uhns), *n.*　the period in human development between the end of childhood (puberty) and the beginning of adulthood; in girls, roughly ages 12 to 18; in boys, roughly 14 to 20. *adj.* **adolescent.**

ADP, see **ATP.**

adrenal gland (uh-DREE-nuhl), either of 2 endocrine glands found in vertebrates, one above or on each kidney. The adrenal *cortex* surrounds the *medulla.* Among the hormones produced are aldosterone, cortisone, and corticosterone from the cortex, and adrenalin from the medulla; also called *suprarenal gland;* see **endocrine gland.**

adrenalin (uh-DREN-uh-lin), *n.*　a hormone from the medulla of the adrenal gland; acts to increase heart action and blood sugar, and decrease movements of the digestive tract. It is one of the few hormones the secretion of which is stimulated by nerve cells; also called *epinephrine.*

adrenal virilism (VEER-uhl-izm), a condition in which male secondary sex characteristics (deep voice, beard, and others) develop in a female; caused by increased amount of male hormone produced by the adrenal cortex; usually started by tumors of the cortex.

adsorption (ad-SAWRP-shuhn), *n.* the collecting of particles of one substance on the surface of another substance, often done to purify fluids. Poison gas is *adsorbed* on tiny charcoal grains. *v.* **adsorb.**

adventitious (ad-vuhn-TISH-uhs), *adj.* of or pertaining to a root growing from a plant part other than from the primary root, as the aerial roots of ivy and prop roots of corn.

aeolipile (EE-uhl-uh-pyl), *n.* an ancient reaction engine described about 2,000 years ago. When water in a hollow metal sphere is heated from below, steam escapes from 2 or more bent tubes, forcing the sphere to rotate.

aeration (air-AY-shuhn), *n.* exposure of a substance to plentiful supplies of air to purify it or to add oxygen. Water is often purified by spraying it into the air; sewage is *aerated* by bubbling air into it.

aerial (AIR-ee-uhl), **1.** *adj.* in the air. **2.** *n.* the antenna of a radio or television transmitter or receiver.

aerial root, a root attaching a plant to a support in the air, such as to a tree. Many orchids have aerial roots attaching them to other plants.

aero-, a word part meaning *air* or *airplane.*

aerobic (air-OH-bik), *adj.* depending on, or not harmed by, air or oxygen: *aerobic* bacteria grow in the presence of oxygen.

aerodynamic heating (air-oh-dy-NAM-ik), heating of a surface traveling at high speed, due to friction with the air; a severe problem for human safety with jets flying at supersonic speeds and with missiles and spacecraft.

aerodynamics, *n.* the study of gases in motion and of objects moving in gases; especially, the study of airplane, rocket, and spacecraft behavior while traveling through the air. *adj.* **aerodynamic.**

aerodyne (AIR-uh-dyn), *n.* any aircraft heavier than air that is kept in the air by aerodynamic forces; contrast with **aerostat.**

aeronautics (air-uh-NAW-tix), *n.* **1.** the study of aircraft, including design, building, and operation. **2.** navigation in the air. *adj.* **aeronautical** or **-nautic.**

aerosol (AIR-uh-sohl), *n.* **1.** a colloid system of solid particles or liquid droplets in a gas: smoke and fog are aerosols. **2.** any substance in a spray can or "squeeze-bottle," whether colloidal or not.

Aerosol can: compressed gas is mixed with the fluid, or fills the space above it; when valve is opened, the gas expands, forcing the fluid through the tube and out the nozzle which breaks it into a fine spray

aerospace (AIR-oh-spays), **1.** *n.* all area above the earth's surface; the atmosphere and all of space above it. **2.** *adj.* pertaining to research and production of devices for use above the earth's surface, as the *aerospace* industry that works on air travel and space travel.

aerospacecraft, *n.* any vehicle operating both in air and in space, such as the *X-15.*

aerostat (AIR-uh-stat), *n.* any aircraft lighter than air, supported by its buoyancy; helium-filled balloons are *aerostats;* contrast with **aerodyne.**

A.F., abbreviation for **audio frequency.**

afferent (AF-uh-ruhnt), *adj.* carrying anything toward an organ: *afferent* nerves carry impulses from receptors to the central nervous system.

afterbirth (AF-tuhr-burth), *n.* the placenta, when expelled from the uterus after the birth of the mammal.

afterburner (AF-tuhr-buhrn-uhr), *n.* a device that injects added fuel into a jet engine's exhaust gas, providing additional thrust.

afterglow, *n.* **1.** the light that a phosphor continues to emit after the electromagnetic or particle irradiation is removed; also called *persistence;* see also **phosphorescence. 2.** continued brightness in the sky after the sun has disappeared below the horizon.

Ag, symbol for **silver** (from Latin, *argentum*).

agar (AH-guhr), *n.* a culture medium for growing bacteria and other organisms, made from a jelly-like substance (*agar-agar*) found in red algae.

agate (AG-uht), *n.* a type of quartz with colors formed in regular bands; see **quartz.**

agave family (uh-GAY-vee), see **Liliales.**

Agena (uh-GEE-nuh), *n.* **1.** an alternate name for **Beta Centauri. 2.** the second stage of some launch vehicles, of which one type is planned for use as a rendezvous vehicle in Project Gemini; see **Gemini.**

agglomerate (uh-GLAHM-uh-ruht), **1.** *n.* any rock made up of volcanic particles naturally cemented together. **2.** *adj.* of flowers, tightly clustered together, but not joined.

agglutinin (uh-GLOO-ti-nin), *n.* any antibody that causes clumping of particles, especially bacteria or blood cells, in an organism. Important agglutinins cause clumping (*agglutination*) of bacteria with specific antigens on their surfaces. These are called *immune* agglutinins. A specific antigen is agglutinated only by a specific agglutinin.

agglutinogen (ag-loo-TIN-uh-jen), *n.* an antigen that is agglutinated (clumped together) by an agglutinin.

aggregate (AG-ruh-guht), **1.** *n.* any rock made up of small particles bonded together; the particles are often of different kinds. **2.** *adj.* with tightly clustered flowers, or with fruits formed from several ovaries of a single flower.

aggregate fruit (AG-ruh-guht), a fruit developing from a cluster of simple ovaries produced by one flower on one base or receptacle; examples are raspberry, blackberry, and strawberry.

agonic line (ay-GAHN-ik), the imaginary line on the earth's surface connecting points at which the earth's magnetic declination is zero.

agouti (uh-GOO-tee), see **Rodentia.**

agravic (ay-GRAV-ik), *adj.* without gravity; weightless.

agriculture (AG-ri-kuhl-chuhr), *n.* the growing of plants and raising of livestock by man; the theory and practice of farming. *adj.* **agricultural.**

agronomy (uh-GRAHN-uh-mee), *n.* the science of crop management and soil treatment, including conservation; a branch of scientific agriculture.

aileron (AY-luh-rahn), *n.* a hinged flap, usually on the rear (*trailing*) edge of an airplane wing, controlling the plane's flight by forcing the wing up or down; a control surface.

aircraft, *n.* any vehicle that travels through the air, usually excluding space vehicles although they must travel through air to reach space; classified as lighter-than-air (blimps or *aerostats*) and heavier-than-air (airplanes or *aerodynes*).

air-cushion vehicle, an alternate term for **ground-effect machine** (because of the cushion of air on which the vehicle travels).

airfoil, *n.* a surface that provides aerodynamic lift by means of the differences in pressure of the air

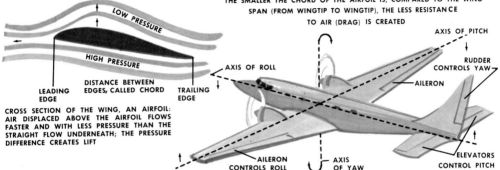

THE SMALLER THE CHORD OF THE AIRFOIL IS, COMPARED TO THE WING SPAN (FROM WINGTIP TO WINGTIP), THE LESS RESISTANCE TO AIR (DRAG) IS CREATED

LOW PRESSURE

HIGH PRESSURE

LEADING EDGE — DISTANCE BETWEEN EDGES, CALLED CHORD — TRAILING EDGE

CROSS SECTION OF THE WING, AN AIRFOIL: AIR DISPLACED ABOVE THE AIRFOIL FLOWS FASTER AND WITH LESS PRESSURE THAN THE STRAIGHT FLOW UNDERNEATH; THE PRESSURE DIFFERENCE CREATES LIFT

AXIS OF PITCH

AXIS OF ROLL

RUDDER CONTROLS YAW

AILERON

AILERON CONTROLS ROLL

AXIS OF YAW

ELEVATORS CONTROL PITCH

air, *n.* the gaseous mixture that surrounds Earth, extending above the surface for roughly 100 miles, with half its weight in the 2½ miles just above the earth. In this denser area, air is about 78% nitrogen, 21% oxygen, with small amounts of carbon dioxide, hydrogen, argon, water vapor, neon, helium, krypton, and a few other substances.

air bladder, 1. an air-filled organ in true fishes, serving as a balancing organ; changes in volume adapt the fish to changes in depth of water. **2.** in lungfish, an organ serving as a lung. **3.** a hollowed organ in certain algae that keeps the thallus above water; a *float.*

air-breathing missile, any missile with an oxygen-burning engine depending on air; range is limited to altitudes low enough for an oxygen supply.

air column, a column or tube of air in which vibrations such as sound waves can be controlled and

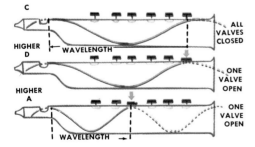

C

HIGHER D — WAVELENGTH

ALL VALVES CLOSED

HIGHER A

ONE VALVE OPEN

WAVELENGTH

ONE VALVE OPEN

altered. Many musical wind instruments have such columns; pitch depends on tube length.

air compressor, any of various machines that increase the pressure of air above atmospheric pressure; see also **compressor.**

air conditioning, the treatment of air to make it more suitable for any special purposes. Cleaning is achieved by passing it through a filter; temperature is changed by blowing air around coils with heated or cooled liquids; humidity is increased by spraying or other water contact, and decreased by adsorption or absorption.

currents traveling around it. An airplane's wings and ailerons are *airfoils.*

air hammer, a pneumatic tool with hammering action caused by the force of compressed air on a sliding piston; often used in breaking pavement.

air lock, a chamber used to adapt workers in compressed air, such as in a tunnel, to the pressure changes caused by entering and leaving the working area. The men usually sit in the air lock while pressure is slowly increased or decreased.

air mass, any large body of air with fairly uniform moisture and heat conditions, the movement of which brings weather changes.

airplane, *n.* any aircraft that is heavier than air and that uses aerodynamic lift against its wings and other surfaces to keep it aloft, and has an engine for movement.

air plant, a common term for **epiphyte.**

air pocket, an inaccurate term for **downdraft.**

air pollution (puh-LOO-shuhn), contamination of the atmosphere by chemical fumes, chimney smoke, engine exhaust gases, and other particles; see **smog.**

airport, *n.* an area for the landing and takeoff of airplanes, equipped for flight control and passenger and freight handling.

air pressure, the pressure exerted by the mass of the air. At sea level this pressure has a force of 14.7 pounds per square inch, called *one atmosphere.* In a closed system, air pressure may be reduced to a near vacuum or increased by compression.

air resistance, the force the air exerts against any object in motion through it; drag.

air speed, the speed with which an object moves through the air; contrasted with *ground speed,* which may be greater or less than air speed because of winds.

air-speed indicator, an instrument for measuring a vehicle's speed in relation to the air, consisting of a Pitot tube connected to a gauge.

airtight, *adj.* so free of holes, cracks, or other openings that air or other gases cannot enter or escape; a vacuum chamber must be airtight.

air-to-air missile, a missile fired from a carrier aircraft to encounter a target also in the air; usually a short-range missile, such as the *Falcon* or *Sidewinder. abbr.* **AAM.**

air-to-surface missile, a missile fired from a carrier aircraft at a target on land or on the surface of the water, such as the *Zuni, Hound Dog,* and *Shrike;* also called *air-to-ground missile. abbr.* **ASM.**

air traffic control, the system for accurate check on location, flight, and identity of all planes in the air at any given time; especially concerned with safe operation during landing, takeoff, or flight; administered by the Federal Aviation Agency.

Al, symbol for **aluminum.**

alabaster (AL-uh-bas-tuhr), *n.* **1.** a fine-grained gypsum, often nearly white, used for ornamental purposes. **2.** a type of banded calcite.

albatross (AL-buh-traws), see **Procellariiformes.**

albino (al-BY-noh), *n.* any plant or animal lacking the pigment that normally provides color. Albino mammals usually have pink eyes, pale skin, and white hair. *Albinism* is a recessive hereditary trait. *adj.* **albino.**

albumen (al-BYOO-muhn), *n.* **1.** the clear or white portion of an egg. **2.** the protein in egg white, also known as *ovalbumin.* **3.** the food deposit in a seed.

albumin (al-BYOO-min), *n.* any of certain proteins commonly found in many vegetable and animal tissues. They are water-soluble and readily coagulated by heat; important in blood serum, and in many plant tissues; secreted by glands in some animals and deposited around eggs.

alchemy (AL-kuh-mee), *n.* the forerunner of modern chemistry, which combined a few chemical facts with much magic. *Alchemists* tried to transmute cheap metals like lead into gold or silver, and also sought the "philosopher's stone," supposed to bring immortality and good health.

alcohol (AL-kuh-hawl), *n.* **1.** ethyl (grain) alcohol (C_2H_5OH). **2.** poisonous methyl or wood alcohol (CH_3OH). **3.** any organic chemical, like these 2, having a hydroxyl radical attached to a carbon atom linked only to other carbon atoms or to hydrogen atoms. Many such alcohols have been synthesized and some occur in nature.

Aldebaran (al-DEB-uh-ruhn), *n.* the 13th brightest star in the sky in visual magnitude, found in the northern constellation Taurus; long familiar for its bright orange-red color.

aldehyde (AL-duh-hyd), *n.* any of a group of organic compounds containing the carbonyl (-CHO) radical attached either to hydrogen (as in formaldehyde) or to another organic radical (as in acetaldehyde or benzaldehyde, oil of bitter almonds). Aldehydes can be oxidized to acids and reduced to alcohols.

aldosterone (al-DAHS-tuh-rohn), *n.* a hormone from the cortex of the adrenal glands, controlling the body's salt balance.

aleurone (AL-oo-rohn, -yuh-rohn), *n.* a protein occurring in granules or grains within the outermost layer, the *aleurone layer,* of the endosperm of a grain seed, such as corn or wheat.

Alfven wave (ALF-vuhn), a low-frequency, oscillating wave produced in a plasma along magnetic lines of force; occurs naturally in the ionosphere.

alga (AL-guh), *n., pl.* **algae** (AL-jee). any of the simplest green plants, ranging in size from one-celled diatoms to huge kelp. They are divided

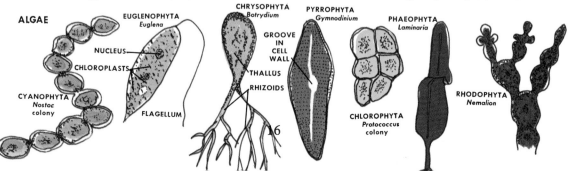

ALGAE — CYANOPHYTA *Nostoc* colony — NUCLEUS — CHLOROPLASTS — EUGLENOPHYTA *Euglena* — FLAGELLUM — CHRYSOPHYTA *Botrydium* — THALLUS — RHIZOIDS — GROOVE IN CELL WALL — PYRROPHYTA *Gymnodinium* — CHLOROPHYTA *Protococcus* colony — PHAEOPHYTA *Laminaria* — RHODOPHYTA *Nemalion*

16

into 7 divisions according to pigmentation, within subkingdom *Thallophyta: Chlorophyta, Euglenophyta, Chrysophyta, Phaeophyta, Rhodophyta, Schizophyta,* and *Pyrrophyta.*

algal fungus, see **Phycomycetes.**

algin (AL-jin), *n.* an industrial gum extracted from brown algae by treatment with alkalies, used as a stabilizer in various products.

Algol (AL-gahl), *n.* a double star in northern constellation Perseus, especially noted for its variable brightness, caused by the dim star obscuring the bright one during their rotation around each other; see also **binary star.**

alignment chart (uh-LYN-muhnt), an alternate term for **nomograph.**

alimentary canal (al-i-MEN-tuh-ree), the passage taken by food from its entry into the mouth to the point at which undigested portions leave the body; includes much of the digestive system; see also **digestive system.**

aliphatic (al-i-FAT-ik), *adj.* referring to a group of hydrocarbons (as paraffins and olefins) that have carbon atoms arranged in an open chain rather than a ring; contrast with **aromatic.**

alkali (AL-kuh-ly), *n., pl.* **-lies, -lis. 1.** generally, one of several inorganic chemical bases, such as calcium, sodium, and potassium hydroxides. **2.** specifically, a hydroxide of ammonium or of an alkali metal; see **base.**

alkali metal, any of the chemical elements in group IA of the periodic table: lithium, sodium, potassium, rubidium, cesium, francium; generally soft, highly-reactive, low-melting-point metals; see also **periodic table.**

alkaline earths (AL-kuh-lin), the oxides of calcium, strontium, and barium, the heavier alkaline-earth metals in group IIA of the periodic table. The metals are medium-soft, brittle but malleable, and chemically reactive; see also **periodic table.**

alkaloid (AL-kuh-loyd), *n.* any of a group of complex organic compounds found in plants, such as caffeine, nicotine, ephedrine, and morphine; all are nitrogen-containing bases that react with acids to form salts.

alkyl (AL-kil), *n.* an organic radical containing only carbon and hydrogen (such as methyl, CH_3, and ethyl, C_2H_5) and not aromatic in nature.

alkylation (al-kuh-LAY-shuhn), *n.* **1.** in chemistry, addition of an alkyl radical to an organic compound. **2.** in petroleum processing, the combination of an olefin with a branched-chain hydrocarbon to form a higher molecular weight hydrocarbon useful in gasoline for improved anti-knock qualities.

allantois (uh-LAN-toh-is), *n., pl.* **-toides.** a membrane between the outer chorion and inner amnion in embryos of reptiles, birds, and mammals. In mammals it usually develops into part of the umbilical cord and is one source of the mammalian placenta; in reptiles and birds, it functions in respiration; see also **amnion.**

allele (uh-LEEL), *n.* one of 2 or more contrasting genes located in identical positions on pairs of chromosomes. If *A* represents a gene for color-blindness and *a* the gene for normal color-vision, the pair *Aa* are alleles; also called *allelomorph.*

allergen (AL-uhr-jen), *n.* any substance, usually entering the body from outside, that causes an allergy; a substance to which the body is hypersensitive.

allergy (AL-uhr-jee), *n.* an illness caused by strong reaction of antibodies to allergens; much *allergic* discomfort is caused by histamine production; symptoms often include sneezing, difficulty in breathing, itching, and skin eruptions.

alligator (AL-uh-gay-tuhr), see **crocodile.**

allotropic (al-oh-TRAH-pik) *adj.* pertaining to a chemical element or compound that exists in 2 or more different forms: carbon exists in the *allotropic* forms of graphite, lampblack, charcoal, and diamond. *n.* **allotrope.**

alloy (AL-oy), *n.* a uniform mixture of 2 or more metals (as in bronze), or of metals and nonmetals (as in steel), usually prepared in molten form; used to introduce or improve special properties: zinc and copper are both soft, but their *alloy,* bronze, is hard. *v.* **alloy** (uh-LOY).

REPRESENTATIVE ALLOYS		
NAME	COMPOSITION (percentage)	PROPERTIES
Alnico-4	Fe-55; Ni-28; Al-12; Co-5	Permanent magnetism
Babbitt metal	Sn-89; Sb-9; Cu-2	Antifriction
Brass	Cu-70; Zn-30	Malleable; corrosion resistant
Bronze	Cu-90; Zn-10	Malleable; durable
Chromel-A	Ni-80; Cr-20	Highly heat-resistant
Dow-metal-F	Mg-95.7; Al-4; Mn-0.3	High ductility
Inconel	Ni-80; Cr-14; Fe-6	Withstands low and high temperature extremes
Monel metal	Ni-67; Cu-28; Fe-2; C, Si-traces	Corrosion-resistant; malleable; elastic
Stainless steel	Varies; example— Fe-74; Cr-18; Ni-8	Heat resistant; corrosion resistant

alluvium (uh-LOO-vee-uhm), *n.* sand, gravel, or other sediment carried to its present position by a stream of water at some previous time: a river delta is an *alluvium. adj.* **alluvial.**

almandine (AL-muhn-deen), see **garnet.**

alpha (AL-fuh), *n.* the first letter of the Greek alphabet (A or α), used to indicate that something is first: *Alpha* Orionis is the brightest star in the constellation Orion.

Alpha Centauri (AL-fuh sen-TAW-ry), a triple star in the constellation Centaurus; brightest star in the southern sky and third brightest of all stars in visual magnitude. *Proxima Centauri,* one of its members, is the star closest to the solar system.

Alpha Crucis (AL-fuh CROO-sis), a star in the constellation Crux; 14th brightest star in the sky in visual magnitude; useful for navigation in the Southern Hemisphere.

alpha particle, a helium nucleus; a high-energy particle formed by radioactive decay of atoms; consists of 2 protons and 2 neutrons.

Altair (al-TAIR), *n.* a bluish star in the northern constellation Aquila; 12th brightest star in the sky in visual magnitude.

alternate leaves, an arrangement of leaves on a stem in which one leaf occurs at each node; see **leaf** picture.

alternating current, electric current that reverses direction periodically. Almost all modern power generators produce alternating-current energy because equipment is simpler and transmission more economical than DC. *abbr.* **AC, a-c,** or **a.c.**

alternation of generations, 1. in plants, sexual reproduction (fertilization of ova by sperm) in

17

one generation with half the chromosome number (n), followed by asexual reproduction (formation of spores) in the next generation with the full number of chromosomes (2n). **2.** in animals, alternation of diploid asexual and sexual generations with asexual reproducing by budding instead of gamete formation; also called *metagenesis.*

alternation of hosts, the transfer of a parasite, at different stages in its life cycle, from one type of host to another, as in the liver fluke cycle.

altimeter (al-TIM-uh-tuhr), *n.* an aircraft instrument that measures altitude. An *absolute altimeter* measures a plane's actual height above the terrain, as indicated by radio or radar echoes from the ground. A *barometric altimeter* operates by air pressure, and shows only elevation above sea level; see also **barometer.**

altitude (AL-ti-tyood), *n.* height above a line used as a base; usually measured from a base of sea level, and expressed in feet and miles or meters and kilometers.

altocumulus (al-toh-KYOO-myuh-luhs), *n.* whitish clouds in large balls or tufts, roughly 12,000 feet high, usually indicating rain within a few hours; see **cloud.**

altostratus (al-toh-STRAY-tuhs), *n.* moderately high, bluish-gray clouds in the form of a sheet or veil, often indicating approaching snowstorms.

alum (AL-uhm), *n.* any aluminum sulfate double salt such as potassium aluminum sulfate, $KAl(SO_4)_2 \cdot 12H_2O$; used as astringents, in paper-sizing, and in leather-tanning.

alumina (uh-LOO-mih-nuh), *n.* aluminum oxide, Al_2O_3, found in the minerals corundum and bauxite; prepared from bauxite as a source of metallic aluminum.

aluminium (al-oo-MIN-ee-um), British spelling of **aluminum.**

aluminum (uh-LOO-muh-nuhm), *n.* a silvery-gray, metallic chemical element that is a good electrical conductor; used for construction where lightness and strength are desired; symbol Al; *at. no.,* 13; *at. wt.,* 26.9815; discovered in the early 1800's.

alveolus (al-VEE-uh-luhs), *n., pl.* **-oli.** one of many small air sacs in the lungs, the points at which lungs give up oxygen to the capillaries and receive carbon dioxide; see **respiratory system.**

Am, symbol for **americium.**

AM, abbreviation for **amplitude modulation.**

A.M., a.m., abbreviation for the period of time between midnight and noon; from Latin *ante meridiem,* meaning *before noon.*

amalgam (uh-MAL-guhm), *n.* any alloy of mercury and other metals; used as electrodes, dental fillings, and for silver backings on mirrors.

amaryllis family (am-uh-RIL-uhs), see **Liliales.**

amazonite (AM-uh-zuh-nyt), see **feldspar.**

amber (AM-buhr), *n.* a pale yellow, brittle fossil resin from ancient evergreens, used for ornamental objects; found chiefly on the southeastern shore of the Baltic Sea.

ambergris (AM-buhr-grees), *n.* a rare, dark-gray, fatty substance from the sperm whale's digestive tract, found in killed whales, floating on the sea in clumps, or washed ashore; used in perfumes.

ameba (uh-MEE-buh), *n., pl.* **amebas, -bae. 1.** any of a genus of rhizopod protozoans, including a species *Ameba proteus,* usually studied in

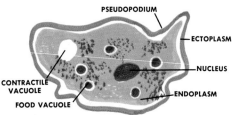

Ameba proteus, a common laboratory protozoan

classrooms because it is easily grown and shows many protozoan characteristics; also spelled **amoeba. 2.** any other ameba-like species, as the dysentery-producing *Entameba.*

amebic dysentery (uh-MEE-bik), see **dysentery.**

ameboid (uh-MEE-boyd), *adj.* moving or changing shape by means of pseudopodia or false feet, as an ameba or white blood cell.

ament (AM-uhnt), an alternate term for **catkin.**

americium (am-uh-RISH-ee-uhm), *n.* a radioactive chemical element in the actinide series, formed by neutron capture in plutonium; symbol Am; *at. no.,* 95; mass number of most stable isotope, 243; first made by Seaborg, James, and Morgan in 1944.

amethyst (AM-uh-thist), *n.* a violet quartz gem, with color caused by traces of manganese; gem-quality stones mined chiefly in Brazil, India, and Ceylon.

amine (uh-MEEN), *n.* any of a group of basic organic compounds derived from ammonia: *primary* amines have one ammonia hydrogen replaced by an organic radical, *secondary* amines have 2, and *tertiary,* 3.

amino acid (uh-MEE-noh), any of certain vital, complex organic acids found in all living things, having an amino (NH_2) group; about 20 amino acids are the basic links in building peptide and protein chains. The simplest amino acid is glycine (aminoacetic acid), CH_2NH_2COOH.

ammeter (AM-ee-tuhr), *n.* an instrument for measuring electrical current in amperes, usually indicated by movement of a needle around a dial.

ammonia (uh-MOHN-yuh), *n.* a colorless, flammable gas with a strong, irritating odor; formula, NH_3; used as an intermediate stage in the preparation of other chemicals; dissolves readily in water to form *ammonium hydroxide,* a common household cleaning agent.

amnion (AM-nee-uhn), *n.* a sac containing serous *amniotic fluid,* enclosing the embryo in reptiles,

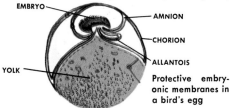

Protective embryonic membranes in a bird's egg

birds, and mammals; serves as a cushion for the embryo, and normally ruptures at time of birth or hatching.

amoeba (uh-MEE-buh), alternate spelling of **ameba.**

amorphous (uh-MAWR-fuhs), *adj.* without definite shape: an *amorphous* solid is noncrystalline.

amp, abbreviation for **ampere.**

amperage (AM-puhr-uhj), *n.* electrical current strength, indicated in amperes.

ampere (AM-peer), *n.* unit of measurement for electrical current: the amount of current flowing through a conductor when the emf is one volt and the resistance is one ohm. *abbr.* **amp.**

Ampère's law, any of several statements regarding electrical and magnetic currents made by André Marie Ampère, French physicist: **1.** 2 currents traveling in the same direction through parallel conductors cause the conductors to attract each other; if the currents are in opposite directions, the conductors repel each other. **2.** magnetic flux produced in a wire by current directed toward the observer travels counterclockwise. **3.** intensity of magnetic force at a certain distance from a circuit is proportional to current in the circuit multiplied by the length of circuit, and is inversely proportional to the distance squared.

Amphibia (am-FIB-ee-uh), *n.* a class of vertebrates that spend the earlier stages of life in water, but mature into air-breathing animals that can live on land. Frogs and toads, salamanders, and the wormlike caecilians are *amphibians.*

amphibious (am-FIB-ee-uhs), *adj.* **1.** able to live in water and on land. **2.** of military forces, equipment, etc., operating on land and in water.

amphibole (AM-fi-bohl), *n.* any of a group of silicate minerals with elongated crystals, white to black or dark green, with hardness 5-6; includes hornblende and a type of asbestos.

Amphineura (am-fi-NOO-ruh), *n.* a class in the phylum Mollusca of animals with elongated bodies and reduced head; has radula, flat ventral foot

CAECILIAN
Ichthyophis glutinosus
Order Apoda

COMMON TOAD
Bufo Woodhousei
Order Anura
(also called *Salientia*)

BULLFROG
Rana catesbriana
Order Anura

PAINTED SALAMANDER
Ensotina Eschscholtzi
Order Caudata

Representatives of the 3 orders of amphibians

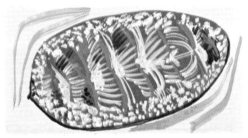

Fuzzy chiton, *Acanthopleura granulata*, of amphineuran order Polyplacophora

(sometimes absent), and a shell usually composed of 8 dorsal plates; one order is segmented; includes the chitons; see also **Mollusca.**

amphioxus (am-fee-AHK-suhs), see **Cephalochordata.**

amphoteric (am-foh-TAIR-ik), *adj.* reacting chemically either as an acid or a base, depending on what other chemical is present: zinc hydroxide, $Zn(OH)_2$, forms salts with both strong acids and strong bases.

amplifier (AM-pluh-fy-uhr), *n.* any device that increases the value of a wave impulse such as sound. Most amplifiers are electronic and increase the strength of signals, usually by means of a vacuum tube or transistor. *n.* **amplification.**

amplitude (AM-pli-tood), *n.* the range from the midpoint or zero value of any wave, such as sound, to its peak, or from the dead center of a pendulum to its extreme swing; see **wave.**

amplitude modulation (mah-dyoo-LAY-shuhn), variation in the characteristics of a radio carrier wave produced by change in amplitude; *abbr.*

AM. AM radio broadcasting uses a carrier wave that transmits a steady signal, modulated by an audio-frequency wave that transmits the program; contrast with **frequency modulation.**

ampule (AM-pyool), *n.* a sealed glass tube or bulb containing a sterile drug solution to be injected under the skin by a hypodermic syringe; also spelled **ampul** or **ampoule.**

ampulla (am-PUL-uh), *n., pl.* **ampullae.** the expanded end of a semicircular canal in the ear, lined with tiny hairs. When the fluid in the canal (*endolymph*) is disturbed, otoliths strike the hairs, and the impulse is transmitted to the brain. The whole structure forms the balancing organ.

amylase (AM-uh-lays), *n.* any digestive enzyme that breaks down starches into simpler carbohydrates; often refers to the specific enzyme in pancreatic juice that changes starch to maltose.

anabolism (uh-NAB-uh-lizm), *n.* the phase of metabolism in which complex materials are built from simpler materials, as in photosynthesis; contrast with **catabolism.** *adj.* **anabolic.**

anaerobic (an-uh-ROH-bik), *adj.* not harmed by absence of oxygen, or requiring its absence for development. Some *anaerobic* bacteria develop only in the absence of free oxygen; others develop either with or without oxygen.

anaesthetic, alternate spelling of **anesthetic.**

anal (AY-nuhl), *adj.* near or of the anus (the external opening for digestive wastes).

analgesia (an-uhl-JEE-zee-uh), *n.* a condition in which no sense of pain exists, often induced by narcotics. An *analgesic* is a drug that reduces or eliminates pain.

analog computer (AN-uh-lawg), any computer that converts physical measurements into numerical data for processing. They serve many purposes; some calculate the area of irregular curved bodies, and some control the flight of missiles.

analogous (uh-NAL-uh-guhs), *adj.* **1.** similar or comparable. **2.** in biology, describing a structure with the same function as another structure in a different kind of organism, but with the 2 structures having different evolutionary origins: bird wings and insect wings are *analogous;* contrast with **homologous.**

analyze

analyze (AN-uh-lyz), *v.* to study the separate parts of which a thing is composed; especially, in chemistry, to discover what simpler substances make up a complex substance, and, often, the amounts of simpler substances present. *n.* **analysis.** *adj.* **analytical.**

anaphase (AN-uh-fayz), see **mitosis.**

anatomy (uh-NAT-uh-mee), *n.* **1.** the structure of an organism. **2.** the study of all the structural details of the various parts of a body; a branch of biology. *adj.* **anatomical.**

andradite (AN-druh-dyt), *n.* a form of garnet mineral containing calcium and iron, often found in limestone and connected with fluorite; occurs in a wide color range.

androgen (AN-druh-jen), *n.* any of several male sex hormones, secreted by the testes and the adrenal glands, including testosterone and androsterone.

Andromeda (an-DRAHM-uh-duh), *n.* a northern constellation near the great spiral galaxy called *Andromeda's nebula,* the only galaxy in northern skies clearly visible without a telescope.

anemia (uh-NEE-mee-uh), *n.* an insufficient amount of hemoglobin in the blood, often caused by destruction of red blood cells or by improper blood formation. Inadequate iron content in the diet or faulty metabolism of consumed iron causes some anemias; see also **pernicious anemia.** *adj.* **anemic.**

anemometer (an-uh-MAHM-uh-tuhr), *n.* an instrument for measuring wind speed; usually a *cup anemometer,* with 3 cups mounted on a shaft. The number of revolutions the cups make in a standard time is counted and wind speed calculated, usually in miles per hour.

aneroid barometer (AN-uh-roid), a barometer usually in the form of a metal box from which almost all the air has been removed, and with an elastic cover that moves in or out as atmospheric pressure changes. The movement operates a dial graduated to read atmospheric pressure. The altimeter is an aneroid barometer showing attitude in feet.

anesthesiology (an-es-thee-zee-AHL-uh-jee), *n.* the medical science dealing with anesthetics and the techniques of administering them; also spelled **anaesthesiology.**

anesthetic (an-uhs-THET-ik), *n.* any substance that produces loss of feeling by chemical action on a nerve. *General* anesthetics produce complete unconsciousness; *local* anesthetics eliminate feeling only in a specific region; also spelled **anaesthetic.** *adj.* **anesthetic.**

aneurysm (AN-yuh-rizm), *n.* abnormal enlargement of a blood vessel, often caused by arteriosclerosis.

angina (an-JY-nuh), *n.* **1.** an inflammation of the throat and surrounding areas. **2.** *angina pectoris,* a sudden attack of severe chest pain, often caused by diseased arteries cutting off the blood supply to the heart muscle.

angiosperm (AN-jee-uh-spuhrm), *n.* any plant of class *Angiospermae* in subdivision *Pteropsida* containing flowering plants; seeds are enclosed in the ovary of the flower; leaves have linear or netted venation; includes 2 subclasses: *Monocotyledoneae* and *Dicotyledoneae.*

angle of incidence, the angle between a ray of light striking a surface and the line normal (perpendicular) to the surface at that point.

angle of reflection, the angle between a ray of light reflected from a surface and the line normal (perpendicular) to the surface at that point. A

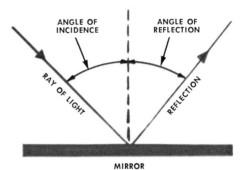

basic law of optics states that the angle of reflection always equals the angle of incidence.

angle of refraction, in optics, the angle between a line normal (perpendicular) to a surface and a ray of light refracted at the surface as the ray passes from a medium of one density to that of another; see **index of refraction.**

angstrom (ANG-struhm), *n.* a unit used for very small linear measurements, such as wavelengths of light, atomic measurements, etc.: one 10-billionth of a meter, or one 250-millionth of an inch. *abbr.* **A.**

anhydride (an-HY-dryd), *n.* a compound formed by removing water from another compound; such compounds react readily with water: *basic anhydrides,* such as calcium oxide, CaO, form bases, such as $Ca(OH)_2$; *acid anhydrides,* such as sulfur dioxide, SO_2, form acids, such as H_2SO_3.

animal (AN-uh-muhl), *n.* any living thing lacking cellulose cell walls, and generally moving about actively; a member of kingdom *Animalia.* Unlike plants, animals (with few exceptions) cannot manufacture food from sunlight and must eat plants or other animals that eat plants.

animalcule (AN-uh-muhl-kyool), *n.* any of the microscopic organisms described by van Leeuwenhoek; most are now known as protozoans.

animal husbandry, the care of animals, especially of livestock; the branch of agriculture dealing with livestock breeding, nutrition, and health.

anion (AN-ey-uhn), *n.* an ion with a negative charge, attracted to the anode in an electrolytic solution; contrast with **cation.**

anisotropic (an-ey-suh-TRAH-pik), *adj.* **1.** in physics, having distinct properties under stresses acting in different directions, as some crystals. **2.** in geology, exhibiting differing conditions for transmission of earthquake tremors, electrical current, etc. **3.** in botany, taking different positions as a reaction to a stimulus from outside the organism.

anneal (uh-NEEL), *v.* to heat metals, glass, or other objects and then slowly cool them; removes internal stresses set up by original uneven cooling from a molten state; makes substances harder and less brittle.

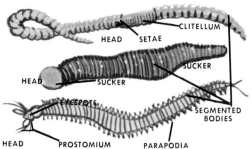

1. Common earthworm, *Lumbricus terrestris*, class Oligochaeta; 2. medicinal leech, *Hirudo medicinalus*, class Hirudinea; 3. clam worm *(Nereis)*, a marine sandworm, class Polychaeta

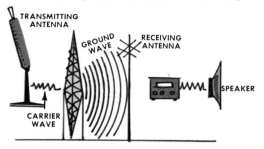

Annelida (uh-NEL-uh-duh), *n.* a phylum of segmented, soft-bodied worms; each segment, called a *metamere,* has a separate set of many organs. *Annelids* are grouped into 3 main types: sandworms, earthworms, and leeches.

annual (AN-yoo-uhl), **1.** *adj.* lasting one year or occurring once each year. **2.** *n.* a plant that normally completes its entire life cycle in a single growing season, then dies; cultivated annuals are planted each year. The growing season may range from a few weeks to several months.

annual ring, any of the concentric marks in a tree trunk cross section, each with a light and dark band. Usually only one set of circles appears each year, so counting the pairs of rings should indicate the tree's age.

anode (AN-ohd), *n.* a positively charged electrode, toward which electrons move; examples are the plate of a vacuum tube and the positive terminal post of a battery.

anodize (AN-uh-dyz), *v.* to deposit a thin protective coat of metal oxide on a metal object (usually aluminum or magnesium). The coat is often only 1/1,000 inch thick, and may be dyed for decorative purposes.

Anopheles (uh-NAHF-uh-leez), see **mosquito.**

Anoplura (an-uh-PLOO-ruh), *n.* an order of small insects with piercing, sucking mouth parts, no wings, and no metamorphosis. Examples are head, body, and crab lice.

Anseriformes (an-suhr-uh-FAWR-meez), *n.* an order of swimming birds with broad, flattened beaks, webbed feet, compact bodies, and short legs; includes ducks, geese, and swans.

ant, see **Hymenoptera.**

antacid (ant-AS-id), *n.* a chemical that can reduce the acidity of the stomach by absorbing some of the acid or by neutralizing it; used to counteract hyperacidity.

antagonist (an-TAG-uh-nist), *n.* any muscle counteracting the effects of another muscle: a flexor muscle is the *antagonist* of an extensor.

antarctic (ant-AHRK-tik, -AHR-tik), **1.** *adj.* of or near the South Pole. **2.** *n.* the *Antarctic* or *Antarctica,* the ice-covered land mass and ocean around the South Pole; coldest spot on Earth.

Antares (an-TAIR-eez), *n.* the 15th brightest star in the sky in visual magnitude; in the southern constellation Scorpius; a bright-red double star, one of the largest known.

anteater, see **Edentata.**

antelope (AN-tuh-lohp), see **Artiodactyla.**

antenna (an-TEN-uh), *n.* **1.** *pl.* **-nas.** the part of a radio, television, or radar transmitter or receiver that sends electromagnetic waves into the air or captures them from the air. **2.** *pl.*

-nae. one of the threadlike sense organs (feelers) on the heads of insects, crustaceans, and other animals; jointed and occurring in pairs.

anterior (an-TEER-ee-uhr), *adj.* toward the front or forward part of the body; contrast with **posterior.**

anther (AN-thuhr), *n.* the pollen-bearing tip of the stamen in a flower.

antheridium (an-thuh-RID-ee-uhm), *n., pl.* **-ridia.** the male organ in gametophyte plants (such as ferns and mosses) that contains sperm cells; when mature, it releases the sperm.

anthocyanin (an-thoh-SY-uh-nin), *n.* a pigment found in cytoplasm of plant cells; often responsible for color in flowers and other plant parts, such as beet roots.

anthogen (AN-thoh-jen), *n.* a fatty substance obtained from flowering plants; used as a spray for rapid leaf growth and earlier blooming.

Anthozoa (an-thuh-ZOH-uh), *n.* a large class of marine coelenterates in which the tentacled, tubular, polyp stage is well developed and the medusa stage absent; most species are attached; digestive cavity is divided by 8 or more septa. Corals and sea anemones are examples of flowerlike *anthozoans;* see also **Coelenterata.**

anthracite (AN-thruh-syt), *n.* hard coal, containing at least 86% carbon; burns with little smoke and leaves little ash. This kind of coal has lost most of its volatiles.

anthrax (AN-thraks), *n.* a highly infectious disease of cattle and men; the first disease for which bacterial origin was proved. Cattle are vaccinated to prevent anthrax.

anthropoid ape (AN-thruh-poyd), any manlike ape: the orangutan, gorilla, gibbon, and chimpanzee; all have thumbs on each of their 4 feet; also called *pongid* apes; see **Primates.**

anthropology (an-thruh-PAHL-uh-jee), *n.* the study of man's development and ways of living. The *anthropologist,* usually on the staff of a museum, university, or research group, may study: **anthropography**—man's geographical distribution; **anthropometry**—measurement of the human body; **ethnology**—the races of man; **cultural anthropology**—the history of man's social life and arts; **physical anthropology**—the physical development of man from his evolutionary ancestors. *adj.* **anthropological.**

anthropomorphism (an-thruh-poh-MAWR-fizm), *n.* the giving of human form, character, or attributes to things and organisms not human;

the assigning of purpose or motivation to biological actions that can be explained as responses to stimuli. *adj.* **anthropomorphic.**

anti-, a word part meaning *against, opposed to,* or *not;* also **ant-** before a vowel.

antibiotic (an-tee-by-AHT-ic), **1.** *adj.* preventing, destructive to, or opposed to, life. *n.* **antibiosis. 2.** *n.* any chemical, produced by microorganisms or synthetically, that destroys or prevents the growth of bacteria or other microorganisms; *penicillin* is an *antibiotic.*

antibody (AN-ti-bah-dee), *n.* a substance made in the body that counteracts an outside substance called an *antigen.* Antibodies are defense mechanisms against many diseases, and are usually specialized chemicals neutralizing specific antigens.

anticline (AN-ti-klyn), *n.* a fold in rock layers, with both sides sloping down from the peak of the fold. These roughly dome-shaped rock formations may show the presence of petroleum below ground. *adj.* **anticlinal.**

anticyclone (an-ti-SY-klohn), *n.* movement of a large air mass around a high-pressure center; the motion is a clockwise spiral in the Northern Hemisphere, counterclockwise in the Southern.

antidote (AN-ti-doht), *n.* any substance that counteracts a poison; works by causing expulsion of the poison (often by vomiting), by chemical neutralization, or in other ways; see also **universal antidote.**

anti-electron, an alternate term for **positron.**

antifreeze, *n.* a chemical that, added to a liquid, causes it to freeze at a lower temperature. Water-cooled engines (as in automobiles) need antifreeze in cold weather. Permanent antifreezes, such as ethylene glycol, do not boil away in summer.

antigen (AN-tuh-juhn), *n.* any substance not normally present in the body which, when supplied, stimulates antibody production. Some antigens cause infections, but others are deliberately introduced to create immunity; these are called *vaccines.*

antigravity, *n.* negative gravity, a theoretical concept. Just as gravity involves the attraction exerted by 2 bodies, antigravity involves the repulsion between 2 bodies; not yet experimentally produced.

antihistamine (an-ti-HIS-tuh-meen), *n.* any drug that offsets the effects of histamine, providing relief from many allergic reactions.

antiknock, *adj.* referring to a chemical additive (as tetraethyl lead) for gasoline that levels out the pressure generated in an engine by explosion of the gasoline.

antimatter, *n.* the exact opposite, in electrical charges, of matter; in theory, it would consist of positrons rather than electrons, antiprotons rather than protons, and antineutrons rather than neutrons (if present). Though physicists have produced some antiparticles, complete antimatter is unconfirmed. If created, it could react with matter, releasing large amounts of energy.

antimetabolite (an-ti-muh-TAB-uh-lyt), *n.* a substance that replaces an essential metabolite, interfering with the metabolic process; sulfa drugs, for example, act as antimetabolites against certain bacteria; see also **metabolite.**

antimissile missile (MIS-uhl), a missile used to destroy another missile in flight, such as the *Nike-Hercules.*

antimony (AN-ti-moh-nee), *n.* a semi-metallic chemical element used to increase hardness in alloys; symbol Sb; *at. no.,* 51; *at. wt.,* 121.75; known since ancient times.

antinode (AN-ti-nohd), *n.* a point of maximum amplitude in a regularly recurring wave; in electricity, the point of maximum amplitude in a voltage or current wave; see **wave.**

antiparticle, *n.* the antimatter particle corresponding to any given particle of ordinary matter, including positrons (positive electrons), antiprotons (negative protons), antineutrons, antimesons, and others.

antiseptic, *n.* any chemical that kills microorganisms; generally destructive to human tissue and used only on instruments, clothing, etc.; see also **asepsis, disinfectant.** *adj.* **antiseptic.**

antitoxin (an-ti-TAHK-sin), *n.* an antibody that will counteract a toxin (poison). Most vaccines operate by stimulating antitoxin formation.

antler (ANT-luhr), *n.* a large, solid bone growing in pairs on the foreheads of male members of the deer family. They are usually shed at the end of each mating season, and grow again the following spring; contrast with **horn.**

anus (AY-nuhs), *n.* the opening at the end of the alimentary canal through which an animal discharges undigested food or waste materials; see **digestive system.** *adj.* **anal.**

anvil (AN-vuhl), a common term for **incus.**

aorta (ay-AWR-tuh), *n.* the largest and most vital artery of the human body; begins at the left ventricle of the heart, extends upward a short length, and then forms into ascending and descending branches which supply blood for the entire body.

aortic arch (ay-OHRT-ik), a branch of the vertical aorta that originally supplied gills. With the evolutionary replacement of gills by lungs, some aortic arches were lost, while others, or parts of them, persisted as pulmonary and carotid arteries and as the large single or paired arch connecting the heart and dorsal aorta.

apatite (AP-uh-tyt), *n.* any mineral consisting of calcium phosphate with fluorine, chlorine, or hydroxyl present; especially, $Ca_5F(PO_4)_3$, with hardness 5; usually green; important as a phosphate fertilizer; see **mineral** picture.

ape, see **Primates.**

aperture (AP-uhr-chuhr), *n.* **1.** an opening. **2.** in optics, an opening, sometimes changeable, limiting the size of the light ray that can pass through an optical instrument, such as in a camera.

apex (AY-pex), *n.* the tip or extreme end of a structure, such as the growing point of a stem or root, or the top of a pyramid. *adj.* **apical.**

aphelion (uh-FEE-lee-uhn), *n.* the point farthest from the sun reached by a planet, comet, or artificial satellite during its orbit; contrast with **perihelion.**

aphid (AY-fid, AF-id), see **Homoptera.**

apical (AY-pi-kuhl), *adj.* located at, or referring to, the extreme tip, as: **1.** *apical meristem,* the young, actively growing cells at the tip of a shoot or root. **2.** *apical dominance,* the suppression of development in lateral buds by a terminal bud through the action of a hormone.   3. *apical organ,* the anterior ciliated tip and eyespot of the trochophore larva.

Apodiformes (uh-poh-di-FAWR-meez), *n.*   an order of birds capable of flying at great speed, never known to rest on ground or in trees; when not flying they cling to vertical structures; includes swifts and hummingbirds.

apogee (AP-uh-jee), *n.*   that point in the orbit of a satellite (natural or artificial) at which it is farthest from the body around which it orbits.

Apollo (uh-PAHL-oh), *n.*   an American lunar aerospace project to use a 3-man craft scheduled for earth orbit, lunar orbit, and lunar landing. The craft will consist of 3 parts: command unit, service unit, and lunar excursion module.

apoplexy (AP-uh-plek-see), *n.*   a sudden partial or severe loss of consciousness, often with some paralysis; caused by the breaking of brain arteries; a type of stroke.

apothecaries' measure (uh-PAHTH-uh-kair-eez), **1.** alternate term for **liquid measure. 2.** the system of weight units used in pharmacy, similar to the troy system in its base unit of one pound = 12 ounces; see measurement tables on page 214.

apparatus (ap-uh-RAT-uhs), *n., pl.* **-tus, -tuses.** the equipment necessary to do an experiment; especially, equipment arranged in a way to do a

hairlike feathers, strong legs, and nostrils located at the tip of the long curved beak; includes kiwis

aquaculture (ah-kwa-KUL-chur), see **hydroponics.**

aquamarine (ak-wah-muh-REEN), *n.* a blue, almost transparent gem type of beryl; prize stones mined chiefly in Brazil and Siberia.

aqua regia (ah-kwah REE-jee-uh), a mixture of one part nitric acid to 3 (or 4) parts hydrochloric acid; will dissolve gold and platinum.

Aquarius (uh-KWAIR-ee-uhs), *n.* the *Water Bearer,* a large zodiacal constellation of the northern sky, with no particularly bright stars; clearly seen from late summer to mid-autumn.

aquatic (uh-KWAHT-ik), *adj.* living or growing in the water; referring to a water habitat.

aqueous humor (AY-kwee-uhs), watery liquid between cornea and lens of eye; aids in preserving constant pressure within eye; see **eye.**

Aquila (AK-wuh-luh), *n.* the *Eagle,* a constellation of the northern sky, in the Milky Way, clearly seen in summer; its 4 major stars form a rough cross, with the brightest star, Altair, at the crossing point.

Ar, symbol for **argon.**

Ara (AY-ruh), *n.* the *Altar,* a southern constellation just south of the "tail" of Scorpius.

Arachnida (uh-RAK-ni-duh), the class of animals in phylum *Arthropoda,* including spiders, scor-

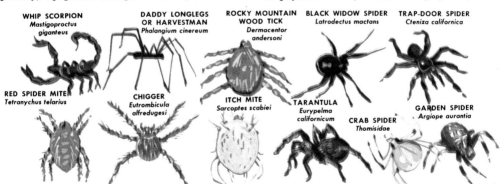

WHIP SCORPION
Mastigoproctus giganteus

DADDY LONGLEGS OR HARVESTMAN
Phalangium cinereum

ROCKY MOUNTAIN WOOD TICK
Dermacentor andersoni

BLACK WIDOW SPIDER
Latrodectus mactans

TRAP-DOOR SPIDER
Cteniza californica

RED SPIDER MITE
Tetranychus telarius

CHIGGER
Eutrombicula alfredugesi

ITCH MITE
Sarcoptes scabiei

TARANTULA
Eurypelma californicum

CRAB SPIDER
Thomisidae

GARDEN SPIDER
Argiope aurantia

particular job, as gas-absorption *apparatus.*

appendage (uh-PEN-dij), *n.*   a structure attached to a major structure; wings, arms, legs, fins, antennae, tail, nose, and outer ears are all animal appendages with special functions.

appendectomy (ap-uhn-DEK-toh-mee), *n.* the surgical removal of the *appendix,* usually because of inflammation.

appendicitis (uh-pen-duh-SY-tis), *n.* inflammation of the appendix, often due to bacterial infection and usually accompanied by severe pain in the lower right part of the abdomen.

appendix (uh-PEN-diks), *n.*   a fingerlike sac attached to the large intestine; found on the right in the lower part of the abdomen; has no known function in man, so is considered vestigial; also called *vermiform appendix;* see **digestive system.**

applied science, practical science; science put to direct use for man, as in egineering, medicine, and agriculture.

apterous (AP-tuh-ruhs, *adj.* without wings, as certain primitive insects and birds.

Apterygiformes (ap-tuh-rij-uh-FAWR-meez), *n.* an order of flightless New Zealand birds with

pions, mites, ticks, and daddy longlegs; *arachnids* have 4 pairs of jointed legs, no wings, and no antennae.

arachnoid (uh-RAK-noyd), see **meninges.**

aragonite (uh-RAG-uh-nyt), *n.* an orthorhombic form of calcium carbonate, white and slightly harder than calcite with hardness 3½-4; found in sea shells, pearls, and stalagmites.

Arales (uh-RAY-leez), *n.* an order of monocot plants with small flowers on a fleshy spike surrounded by an often showy spathe. The order includes the aquatic duckweed family (*Lemnaceae*) with few flowers showing, and the arum family (*Araceae*) with spathes often mistaken for flowers, as in jack-in-the-pulpit and skunk cabbage.

arboreal (ahr-BOHR-ee-uhl), *adj.* living in trees; applies to monkeys, opossums, squirrels, etc.

arboretum (ahr-buh-REE-tuhm), *n.* a botanical garden planted with trees and shrubs for purposes of scientific research and education.

arc (AHRK), *n.* **1.** any part of the circumference of a circle. **2.** the bright bridge formed when electrical current "jumps" the gap between 2 conductors; yields intense light and concentrated heat. Electric furnaces for making alloy steels, and arc welding depend on the heat of the arc; see also **arc lamp.**

Archean (ahr-KEE-uhn), *adj.* referring to the oldest of the earth's rocks, possibly more than 3 billion years old, free of fossils that might indicate living things; also spelled **Archaean.**

archegonium (ahr-kuh-GOH-nee-uhm), *n. pl.* **-gonia.** the vessel containing the eggs of gametophyte plants (as ferns and mosses); a sperm enters the archegonium in fertilizing an egg.

archeopteryx (ahr-kee-AHP-tuhr-iks), *n.* one of the first feathered, winged animals, from about 125 million years ago; about the size of a pigeon, and with a structure between that of reptiles and birds; also spelled **archaeopteryx.**

Archeozoic (ahr-kee-oh-ZOH-ik),*n.* formerly, the era when the first forms of life appeared on earth; term no longer used. No fossils known, but limestone deposits may be result of decayed algae. This period is now referred to as the Precambrian; see **geologic time table.**

archetype (AHRK-uh-typ), *n.* the type of specimen or specimens from which the original description and name of a species was derived.

Archimedes' principle (ahr-kuh-MEE-deez), a principle used in finding the density or specific gravity of solids; a solid object immersed in a liquid is buoyed up by a force equal to the weight of the liquid displaced. If the solid is less dense than the liquid, it floats; the buoyant force then equals the weight of the solid; stated by Archimedes, Greek scientist.

archipelago (ahr-kuh-PEL-uh-goh), *n.* **1.** any region containing many islands in a body of water. **2.** the islands in such a region.

arc lamp, a light source formed by electrical current "jumping" the gap between electrodes; the

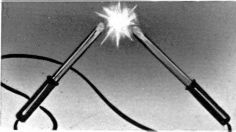

Flame-arc lamp: the brilliant light burns in the arc itself rather than around a carbon electrode; volatile chemicals are driven into the arc from the carbon

intense light is used for photography; see also **mercury-vapor lamp.**

arctic (AHRK-tik, AHR-tik), *adj.* **1.** of the far northland near the North Pole or within the Arctic Circle (66½° North Latitude). **2.** very cold.

Arcturus (ahrk-TOOR-uhs), *n.* a bright red star in the northern constellation Boötes; the fourth brightest star in the sky in visual magnitude, many times larger than the sun.

are (AIR, AHR), *n.* a unit of area in the metric system: 100 square meters, or about 120 square yards; see also **hectare.**

argentite (AHR-juhn-tyt), *n.* a silver-bearing dark gray mineral, silver sulfide, Ag_2S, with hardness 2-2½.

argon (AHR-gahn), *n.* a chemical element in the rare gas family; colorless, odorless, highly unreactive; used in light bulbs; symbol Ar; *at. no.,* 18; *at. wt.,* 39.948; identified by Ramsay and Rayleigh in 1894.

argon dating, see **potassium-argon dating.**

argyrodite (ahr-JIR-oh-dyt), *n.* a silver-germanium-sulfide, Ag_8GeS_6, mined chiefly in Germany and Bolivia; major source of germanium.

arid (AIR-uhd), *adj.* hot and dry, referring chiefly to desert regions

Aries (AIR-eez), *n.* the *Ram,* a zodiacal constellation, most clearly seen in the fall; has no extremely bright stars; but Hamel, one of the eyes, is useful to navigators.

armadillo (ahr-muh-DIL-oh), see **Edentata.**

armature (AHR-muh-chuhr), *n.* the part of an electric generator in which induction occurs, made of a soft iron core around which coils of insulated wire are wound. In AC generators, the field magnet rotates around a stationary armature; the magnetic field cutting across a wire generates current in the wire; see **motor.**

aromatic (ar-uh-MAT-ik), *adj.* referring to a group of hydrocarbons (especially benzene derivatives) that have carbon atoms arranged in a ring; important in synthesis; contract with **aliphatic.**

arrowroot family, see **Musales.**

arroyo (uh-ROY-oh), *n.* a steep-edged flood plain, usually having a flat watercourse that is dry except after heavy rains.

arsenic (AHR-suh-nik), *n.* a poisonous, semimetallic chemical element used to harden alloys; its compounds are used in pesticides; symbol As; *at. no.,* 33; *at. wt.,* 74.9216; known since ancient times.

arterial (ahr-TEER-ee-uhl), *adj.* of an artery; often said of blood in the arteries.

arteriole (ahr-TEER-ee-ohl), *n.* a small branch of an artery; carries blood to capillaries.

arteriosclerosis (ahr-teer-ee-oh-skluh-ROH-sis), *n.* hardening of artery walls, failure of the walls to expand and contract normally; appears commonly with age, may be caused by faulty cholesterol or fat metabolism; see **atherosclerosis.**

artery (AHR-tuh-ree), *n.* a vessel carrying blood away from the heart; the oxygenated blood is bright red (due to color of oxygen-hemoglobin compound) except in the pulmonary arteries; formed of 3 layers of elastic tissue.

artesian well (ahr-TEE-zhuhn), a well from which water flows without added mechanical pressure; flow is caused by the hydrostatic pressure.

arthritis (ahr-THRY-tis), *n.* a painful condition in which skeletal joints are inflammed, with many possible causes; some forms are infectious, traceable to influenza and other diseases; *rheumatoid arthritis,* one of the severest types, is usually related to aging. *adj.* **arthritic.**

Arthropoda (ahr-THRAP-uh-duh), *n.* a large phylum of animals with jointed legs and horny exoskeleton (outer shell); four-fifths of all known animal species are *arthropods;* includes fossil trilobites and major classes *Arachnida, Crustacea, Insecta, Onychophora, Chilopoda,* and *Diplopoda.*

articulation (ahr-tik-yuh-LAY-shuhn), *n.* **1.** a point of junction between animal parts, especiall**'** bones; a joint. **2.** a node or joint in a plant.

artifact (AHR-ti-fakt), *n*. useful object made by humans that does not occur naturally. Arrowheads and pottery are artifacts.

artificial horizon, an aircraft instrument showing the angle the craft is making with the horizon; its position tells the pilot whether he is flying level, even when there is no visibility.

artificial intelligence, the ability of a computer to learn, plan, recognize patterns, translate, etc.; its ability to learn as an intelligent being learns.

artificial respiration, *n*. stimulation of natural breathing in a person whose breathing is impaired by forcing air into and out of the person's lungs.

artificial satellite, see **satellite.**

Artiodactyla (ahr-tee-oh-DAK-til-uh), *n*. an order of mammals with even-toed hoofs; many of them are ruminants (cud-chewers). *Artiodactyls* include antelope, bison, buffalo, camel, deer, giraffe, hippopotamus, and others.

arum family (AIR-uhm), see **Arales.**

As, symbol for **arsenic.**

asbestos (as-BES-tuhs), *n*. any of several minerals occurring in fiber form; amphibole asbestos and chrysotile (a form of serpentine) are examples; because they do not burn, they are often used for insulation and for fireproof clothing.

Ascomycetes (ask-uh-my-SEET-eez), *n*. a class of thallophytes including the sac fungi; an *ascomycete* forms spores in a saclike sporangium (ascus); has filamentous hyphae with walls be-

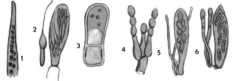

Yeasts: (1) *Dipodassus albidus*, (2) *Nematospora phaseoli*; (3) leaf curl—*Taphrina deformans.* Blue-green molds: (4) *Penicillium roqueforti* (used in making Roquefort cheese), (5) back knot in cherries—*Dibotryon morbosa*, (6) black spot in apples—*Diplocarpon earliana*

tween nuclei; reproduces asexually by conidia; when fruiting body is present, it is cup-shaped, club-shaped, and honey combed, or spherical and warty, growing underground. Examples are yeasts, blue-green molds (as penicillium), mildews, truffles, and many plant disease-producing pests.

ascorbic acid (as-KAWR-bik), vitamin C, a white crystalline solid occurring naturally in many plants; deficiency in diet produces scurvy; formula, $C_6H_8O_6$.

asepsis (ay-SEP-sis), *n*. the process of destroying all microorganisms (as on surgical instruments) accompanied by procedures to prevent access of other microorganisms. *adj.* **aseptic.**

asexual (ay-SEK-shoo-uhl), *adj.* not reproducing by sexual means; not divided into male and female sexes with their respective organs; fission and budding are types of *asexual* reproduction.

Asian flu (AY-zhuhn), a form of influenza believed to be caused by a virus imported from Asia; first prevalent in 1957, and designated virus type A-2 because the previous virus type A gives no antigenic immunity.

ASM, abbreviation for **air-to-surface missile.**

aspirator (AS-puhr-ay-tuhr), *n*. **1.** an apparatus that produces suction, as the laboratory pumps

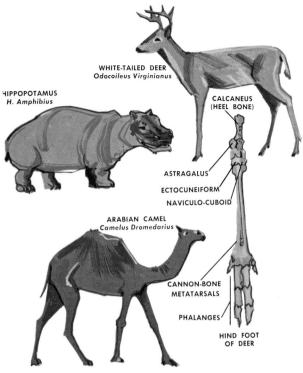

WHITE-TAILED DEER
Odocoileus Virginianus

HIPPOPOTAMUS
H. Amphibius

CALCANEUS
(HEEL BONE)

ASTRAGALUS

ECTOCUNEIFORM

NAVICULO-CUBOID

ARABIAN CAMEL
Camelus Dromedarius

CANNON-BONE
METATARSALS

PHALANGES

HIND FOOT
OF DEER

Representative artiodactyls

used to produce a partial vacuum. **2.** in medicine, an instrument used to remove body fluids by suction.

asphyxia (as-FIK-see-uh), *n*. a condition in which body cells do not receive the oxygen they require; may be caused by interference with breathing, as by choking; by insufficient oxygen in the air; or by carbon monoxide or other poisons. *v.* **asphyxiate.**

assay (AS-ay, uh-SAY), **1.** *v.* in chemistry, to analyze a substance to determine what its components are and in what proportions they occur. *n.* **assaying. 2.** *n.* the measured amount of a desired element that occurs in a substance, used especially in mining and metallurgy.

assimilation (uh-sim-uh-LAY-shuhn), *n*. the taking of the final products of digestion into the body's cells; the final change of food into living protoplasm. *v.* **assimilate.**

astatic (ay-STAT-ik), *adj.* unstable; not taking a permanent position: *astatic* needles can be used on measuring devices because they change position with changing forces.

astatine (AS-tuh-teen), *n*. a radioactive chemical element in the halogen family, usually made by bombarding bismuth with alpha particles; symbol At; *at. no.*, 85; mass number of most stable isotope, 210; first astatine isotope identified in 1940 by Corson, MacKenzie, and Segrè.

aster (AS-tuhr), *n*. **1.** either of the 2 star-shaped clusters, made up of fibers, around the centrioles of a cell during mitosis; see **mitosis, meiosis. 2.** a late-blooming flower of the composite family.

asteroid (AS-tuh-royd), *n*. any very small planet of the solar system. Most of the thousands observed are in orbits between those of Mars and Jupiter; the largest known, Ceres, has a diameter of about 475 miles; also called *minor planet* or *planetoid.*

25

asthma

asthma (AZ-muh), *n.* a partial blocking of the bronchial tubes, resulting in very little air reaching the lungs; may be due to allergy, respiratory infection, or psychological reasons.

astigmatism (uh-STIG-muh-tizm), *n.* an imperfect image caused by parallel rays of light coming into the eye being focused at different angles;

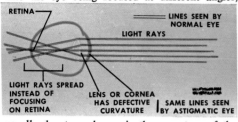

usually due to a change in the curvature of the cornea or outer membrane of the eye; sometimes due to a defect in lens curvature.

astral (AS-truhl), *adj.* of a star or like a star.

astringent (uh-STRIN-juhnt), *n.* a substance that causes tissues to contract or pucker, such as alum; used to stop bleeding from small cuts by shrinking capillary vessels, and to shrink swollen nasal passages. *adj.* **astringent.**

astrionics (as-tree-AHN-iks), *n.* the use of electronic devices in space science.

astro-, a word part meaning *star.*

astrogation (as-troh-GAY-shuhn), *n.* navigation in space.

astrolabe (AS-troh-layb), *n.* an instrument that measures the exact altitude of stars, used in navigation and surveying; one type has a fixed altitude and depends on exact timing of the instant a star reaches that altitude.

astrology (uh-STRAHL-uh-jee), *n.* the belief that observing stars, planets, the sun, and moon can reveal a man's fate; not a science.

astronaut (AS-truh-nawt), *n.* anyone traveling outside the earth's atmosphere; *astronaut* is the American term; *cosmonaut,* the Russian term.

astronautics (as-truh-NAW-tiks), *n.* the science and techniques involved in space flight.

astronomical unit (as-truh-NAHM-uh-kuhl), a common measure of distance in astronomy: the average distance from Earth to the sun: about 150 million kilometers or 92,880,000 miles. *abbr.* **a.u.**

astronomy (uh-STRAHN-uh-mee), *n.* the science of celestial bodies. Most *astronomers* work in observatories, and are on university or governmental staffs. Major subdivisions include: **astrophysics**—use of the methods of physics; **celestial mechanics**—study of celestial motion; **cosmog-**

ony—study of the origin and development of celestial bodies; **radio astronomy**—use of the radio telescope to get signals from stars that give no observable light. *adj.* **astronomical.**

astrophysics (as-troh-FIZ-iks), *n.* the branch of physics dealing with the physical properties and motions of stars and other celestial bodies.

asymmetrical (ay-suh-MET-ruh-kuhl), *adj.* not symmetrical; see **symmetry.** *n.* **asymmetry.**

At, symbol for **astatine.**

atavism (AT-uh-vizm), *n.* the reappearance in an individual organism of characters found in early ancestors but not its immediate ancestors; also called *regression.*

atherosclerosis (ath-uh-roh-skluh-ROH-sis), *n.* a stage in hardening of the arteries in which cellular cholesterol is deposited in the artery walls; see **arteriosclerosis.**

athlete's foot, a fungus infection usually found between the toes; a form of ringworm in which skin is cracked and spongy; so-called because it is readily transmitted in shower rooms.

atmosphere (AT-muhs-sfeer), *n.* **1.** a mass of gas surrounding a celestial body; especially, the air around Earth that occurs in regions or layers with different characteristics: (from Earth out) *troposphere, stratosphere, stratopause, mesosphere,* and *ionosphere;* see also **air.** *adj.* **atmospheric. 2.** a unit of pressure: 14.7 pounds pressure per square inch; see **air pressure.**

atmospheric pressure, the pressure produced by air; decreases with increased altitude because a column (vertical section) of air gets smaller and weighs less; pressure also changes with changing weather, as indicated on a barometer.

at. no., abbreviation for **atomic number.**

atoll (AT-awl), *n.* a small island built of coral skeletons growing on top of undersea volcanoes or mountain tops. Atolls are circular or horseshoe-shaped, and enclose calm lagoons.

atom (AT-uhm), *n.* the smallest part of a chemical element that can exist by itself or in combination with other atoms; composed of a nucleus with one or more protons and, often, neutrons, and one or more electrons orbiting about the nucleus.

atomic (uh-TAHM-ik), *adj.* **1.** referring to an atom or to atoms. **2.** a loose term for *nuclear,* as in *atomic* fission, accurately *nuclear* fission.

atomic bomb, a bomb that explodes by the chain reaction of nuclear fission; depends on fission of either uranium-235 or plutonium; more accurately called *fission bomb.*

atomic clock, a very accurate electric clock with its frequency regulated by vibrating atoms.

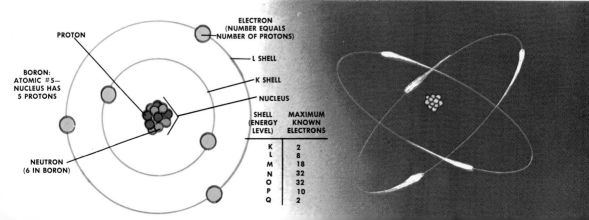

atomic energy, a common term for **nuclear energy.**

atomic number, the number of protons in the nucleus of an atom; equal to the mass number minus neutron number; the position of a chemical element in the periodic table depends on its atomic number; see also **periodic table.** *abbr.* **at. no.**

atomic pile, name for the first **nuclear reactor.**

atomic theory, the idea that all matter is composed of tiny particles, called *atoms;* first proposed by John Dalton, an English physicist, in 1805; see also **Bohr theory, Rutherford theory.**

atomic time clock, popular name for methods of dating by radioactive decay, such as carbon-14 dating, potassium-argon dating, and others.

atomic weight, the weight of an atom relative to the weight of carbon-12, defined as exactly 12. This carbon isotope was adopted in 1961 as the atomic weight standard; previously, oxygen was the standard, with a defined weight of 16. *abbr.* **at. wt.**

atomizer (AT-uh-my-zuhr), *n.* a device for scattering liquids as a spray of fine droplets; most atomizers make use of air pressure to divide the liquid into tiny particles.

atom smasher, popular but inaccurate term for any device that accelerates nuclear particles; see **accelerator.**

ATP, *adenosine triphosphate,* a chemical compound that regulates body metabolism. *Adenosine diphosphate,* ADP, absorbs energy in becoming ATP; when ATP arrives at a point in the cell where energy is required, the ATP gives up energy and reverts to ADP.

atrium (AY-tree-uhm), *n.* in medicine, a chamber of the heart that pumps blood into the ventricles; one of 2 in mammals; the right atrium is larger than the left; in zoology, called *auricle.*

atrophy (AT-ruh-fee), *n.* a wasting away or decrease in size of a cell, tissue, or organ; may result from disease or injury, and often accompanies aging. *v.* **atrophy.**

atropine (AT-ruh-peen), *n.* an alkaloid obtained from plants of the nightshade family, important in medicine; it causes the pupils of the eyes to enlarge (dilate).

attenuation (uh-ten-yoo-AY-shuhn), *n.* **1.** in botany, the gradual tapering of a structure to a narrow tip. **2.** in bacteriology, the reduction of a disease-producing ability (*virulence*) of bacteria in order to produce a serum capable of producing immunity-giving antibodies without transmitting the disease. *v.* **attenuate.**

attitude (AT-i-tyood), *n.* the position of an air or space vehicle with respect to the horizon, Earth, or other stable object; *level attitude* usually means one parallel to the horizon.

attitude stabilization, the system for keeping a space vehicle right side up, especially important in communications and weather satellites where special equipment must face Earth.

attraction (uh-TRAK-shuhn), *n.* the force between 2 bodies tending to pull or draw them together. Oppositely charged particles have *attraction* for one another. *v.* **attract.**

at. wt., abbreviation for **atomic weight.**

atypical (ay-TIP-i-kuhl), *adj.* not typical; having characteristics different from others of the same species or category; *atypical* pneumonia shows symptoms different from the usual.

a.u., abbreviation for **astronomical unit.**

Au, symbol for **gold** (from Latin, *aurum*).

audible (AW-duh-buhl), *adj.* capable of being heard.

audio frequency (AW-dee-oh), any frequency for electromagnetic waves in the range from about 20 to 20,000 cycles per second; this is the frequency range for sound waves audible to humans. *abbr.* **A.F.**

audiometer (aw-dee-AHM-uh-tuhr), *n.* an instrument for measuring the acuteness of hearing.

auditory canal (AW-di-tohr-ee), the passage from the external ear to the eardrum; lined with bone and cartilage, covered with thin, glandular, hairy skin; brings sound waves to the eardrum (tympanic membrane); see **ear.**

augite (AW-jyt), see **pyroxene.**

auk (AWK), see **Charadriiformes.**

aureomycin (aw-ree-oh-MY-sin), *n.* an antibiotic obtained from soil microbes; a yellow crystalline chemical useful against many infectious organisms; also called *chlortetracycline.*

auricle (AW-ri-kuhl), *n.* **1.** the zoologists' term for **atrium.** **2.** the lateral, earlike lobes in the head region of flatworms, as planaria.

Auriga (aw-RY-guh), *n.* the *Charioteer,* a northern constellation best seen in winter; has the bright star Capella as its most distinctive feature.

aurora (aw-ROH-ruh), *n.* a display of moving, colored lights in the night sky, usually green to yellow. In northern skies, it is *aurora borealis;* in southern skies, *aurora australis;* probably caused by solar electric particles striking gas particles in the near vacuum above Earth and affected by the outer region of the Van Allen belt; may affect radio transmission.

Australopithecus (aws-tray-loh-pi-THEE-kuhs, -PITH-uh-kuhs), *n.* a prehistoric African ape, like man in being erect and in tooth formation. Only skulls and crude chipped stone tools have been found; name means *southern ape;* also called the *pebble-culture man;* one of the most primitive creatures called "human."

autogiro (aw-tuh-JY-roh), *n.* an aircraft with an overhead-mounted horizontal propeller, as well as the usual front-mounted vertical one.

Attitude stabilization: after alignment with the sun and Earth, the satellite is stabilized about 3 axes by a sun sensor, horizon scanner, and yaw sun sensor that activate gyroscopes, gas jets, etc.

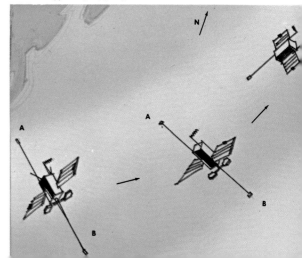

automatic (aw-tuh-MAT-ik), *adj.* operating in a way that entirely or partially eliminates the need for conscious effort.

automatic pilot, a control device depending on gyroscopes to keep aircraft on course and level; once adjusted, it flies the plane itself.

automation (aw-tuh-MAY-shuhn), *n.* the use of automatic devices (usually electronic) to regulate and control machine operations.

automotive (aw-tuh-MOH-tiv), *adj.* operating under the power of a self-contained engine, such as an automobile.

autonomic nervous system (aw-tuh-NAHM-ik), the nerves and ganglia that regulate normal body functions requiring no thinking; controls heartbeat, breathing, digestion, and similar involuntary tasks; see **nervous system.**

autopsy (AW-tahp-see), *n.* study of a body after death, usually to discover the cause of death.

autoradiograph, *n.* a "picture" of a radioactive substance made by exposing photographic film to the substance but not to light; the image appears black. Deposits of tracer isotopes in the body can be located by autoradiographs.

autorotation (aw-toh-roh-TAY-shuhn), *n.* **1.** the uncontrollable rotation of an aircraft around an axis parallel to the wind direction; cause of tailspin. **2.** in helicopters and autogiros, rotor movement causing pure aerodynamic lift.

autotomy (aw-TAHT-uh-mee), *n.* an animal's ability to rid itself of damaged or trapped structures, often appendages. In some animals, the lost appendage grows back again by regeneration.

autumn (AW-tuhm), *n.* the season between the autumnal equinox and the winter solstice (about September 22 to December 21 in the Northern Hemisphere); characterized by fewer hours of daylight each day.

autumnal equinox (aw-TUHM-nuhl EE-kwi-nahks), one of the dates (about September 22) when night and day are of the same length; see also **vernal equinox.**

autunite (AW-tuh-nyt), *n.* a common radioactive mineral of calcium, phosphate, and uranium oxide; a source of uranium. It is fluorescent, and occurs in tetragonal, yellow flakes.

auxiliary system (aug-ZIL-yuh-ree), any secondary system, often applied to power supply for lights, etc., on planes, as distinguished from the *primary* power system; may also be a standby system for use in emergencies, when the major system fails.

auxin (AWK-sin), *n.* a growth-regulating plant hormone, present in minute amounts in many parts of plants; synthetic auxins have many special uses including cellular elongation and early bloom in flowers.

Aves (AY-veez), *n.* a vertebrate class of phylum Chordata including birds; all are warm-blooded, feathered, and egg-laying; two groups include flying and flightless birds.

avian (AY-vee-uhn), *adj.* referring to, found in, or resembling, a bird: *avian* tuberculosis is a type found among birds.

aviation (ay-vee-AY-shuhn), *n.* the whole range of activity involved in man's flight in the air, including design, manufacture, testing, and flying, as well as related ground activities.

Avogadro's law (ah-voh-GAH-droh), the statement that all gases have the same number of molecules in the same volume, measured at the same temperature and pressure; fairly accurate at temperatures well above boiling points; calculated number of molecules in a gram molecule is about 6×10^{23}; named for Italian chemist Amedeo Avogadro (1776–1856).

avoirdupois system (av-uhr-duh-POYZ, -wahr-doo-PWAH), the system of weights generally used in Great Britain, Canada, and the United States; the basic unit of weight is the *pound* (abbreviated *lb.* or symbolized by $\#$), equal to 16 ounces; see measurement tables on page 214.

axial (AK-see-uhl), *adj.* in line with the central axis of an organism; in the human body, skull, ribs, breastbone, and backbone make up the *axial* skeleton.

axil (AK-sil), *n.* the angle between a leaf and a stem.

axillary bud (AK-suh-lair-ee), see **bud.**

axis (AK-sis), *n., pl.* **axes** (-seez). **1.** an ideal line extending through the center of a body; the line connecting Earth's poles is the imaginary axis around which Earth rotates. **2.** a central line in plants or animals, around which the body of the organism may show symmetry. **3.** the second neck vertebra, around which the head turns.

axis of rotation, the line drawn through a body around which the body rotates; in a hinged door, the axis of rotation is a line through the centers of the hinges.

axle (AK-suhl), *n.* a rigid rod through the center of a wheel; see **wheel and axle.**

axon (AK-sahn), *n.* the smooth threadlike extension of a nerve cell (neuron). Axons carry impulses away from the cell body, may be quite long, and have myelin sheaths; see **neuron.**

azimuth (AZ-i-muhth), *n.* the clockwise angle a line makes with true north or true south; navi-

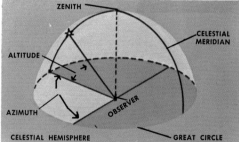

gators measure azimuth from the north; astronomers and surveyors measure it from the south; used, with altitude, to locate objects in space.

azo (AZ-oh), *adj.* containing a radical of 2 nitrogen atoms joined to each other and also to carbon atoms. Azo compounds occur in some dyes.

Azoic (ay-ZOH-ik), *n.* formerly, a geologic time before any plant or animal life existed on earth; term is no longer used. This period is now referred to as the Precambrian; see also **geologic time table.**

azurite (AZH-yoo-ryt), *n.* a blue, copper-containing mineral, with hardness 3½-4; basic copper carbonate, found in Arizona and in southern Africa; see also **malachite.**

REPRESENTATIVES OF 28 BIRD ORDERS
(not drawn to same scale)

FALCONIFORMES
Bald Eagle
Haliaetus leucocephalus

PASSERIFORMES
Superb Bird of Paradise
Laphorina superba

PASSERIFORMES
Vermilion Flycatcher
Pyrocephalus rubineus

STRIGIFORMES
Screech Owl
Megascops asio

PSITTACIFORMES
Macaw
Ara ararauna

CUCULIFORMES
Yellow-billed Cuckoo
Coccyzus americanus

PICIFORMES
Pileated Wood pecker
Ceophloeus pileatus

CORACIIFORMES
Belted Kingfisher
Ceryle alcyon

PASSERIFORMES
Wood Thrush
Hylocichla mustelina

PROCELLARIIFORMES
Laysan Albatross
Diomedea immutabilis

ARCHAEOPTERYGIFORMES
Archaeopteryx
lithographica

COLUMBIFORMES
Mourning Dove
Zenaidura macroura

CHARADRIIFORMES
Spotted Sandpiper
Actitis macularia

SPHENISCIFORMES
King Penguin
Aptenoides patigonicus

APODIFORMES
Ruby-throated Hummingbird
Trochilus colubris

PASSERIFORMES
Baltimore Oriole
Icterus galbula

CAPRIMULGIFORMES
Whip-poor-will
Antrostomus vociferus

GALLIFORMES
Wild Turkey
Meleagris gallopavo silvestris

APTERYGIFORMES
Kiwi
Apteryx australis mantelli

PELECANIFORMES
Brown Pelican
Pelecanus Occidentalis

RHEIFORMES
Common Rhea
Rhea americana

GAVIIFORMES
Pacific Loon
Gavia pacifica

GRUIFORMES
Whooping Crane
Grus americana

PODICIPEDIFORMES
Western Grebe
Aechmophorus occidentalis

CICONIIFORMES
Great Blue Heron
Ardea herodias

ANSERIFORMES
Wood Duck·
Aix sponsa

CASUARIIFORMES
Common Cassowary
Casuarius casuarius

STRUTHIONIFORMES
South African Ostrich
Struthis camelus

B, symbol for **boron.**

Ba, symbol for **barium.**

baby teeth, *n.*   the first set of 20 teeth in humans, normally erupting through the gums beginning when the baby is about 6 months old; replaced by permanent teeth beginning when the child is about 6 years old; see also **tooth.**

bacillus (buh-SIL-uhs), *n., pl.* **-cilli.   1.** any rod-shaped bacterium; may appear singly or in long chains.   **2.** a rod-shaped bacterium that requires free oxygen; some are responsible for serious illnesses, such as tuberculosis.

backbone, see **spinal column, vertebra.**

background radiation, radiation coming from sources other than radioactive material that is being studied or measured; usually due to bombardment by cosmic rays.

bacteria, plural of **bacterium.**

bactericide (bak-TEER-uh-syd), *n.*   any chemical that kills bacteria.

bacteriology (bak-teer-ee-AHL-oh-jee), *n.*   the study of bacteria, their ways of living, their effects on humans, other animals and plants, and methods of making use of them.

bacteriophage (bak-TEER-ee-uh-fayj), *n.*   any virus that attacks bacteria. Each kind of bacterium appears to have a specific bacteriophage, or "phage."

bacterium (bak-TEER-ee-uhm), *n., pl.* **-teria.** any of numerous one-celled plants of division *Schizomycophyta,* visible only by microscope; classified by 3 basic shapes: *coccus* (spherical), *bacillus* (rod-shaped), and *spirillum* (spirals); may also be grouped according to how they react to a complex test called a *Gram stain:* gram-positive and gram-negative bacteria respond differently to specific antibiotics. Some bacteria are injurious to man (causing disease or spoiling food), some are beneficial (important in fermentation and antibiotics), and some have no known effect.

baking soda, a common term for **sodium bicarbonate.**

balance (BAL-uhns), *n.*   **1.** a device for weighing objects; depends on the principle of the seesaw. In the *analytical balance,* a horizontal bar is balanced on a fine edge called a *knife-edge;* a pan hangs from each side of the bar. The object to be weighed is placed in one pan, and weights are added to the other until the pans balance.   **2.** an alternative term for **equilibrium.**

balanced forces, a set of forces acting on an object in such a way that no acceleration or other change takes place. If the object is stationary, it will remain stationary; if it is moving, it will continue moving in the same direction with no change in velocity.

balance of nature, plants, animals, geographical features living in harmony with each other.

bald eagle, eagle, *Haliaetus leucocephalus.* Adults are white on head and tail, wingspread is about 8 feet (2.5 meters).

baleen (bah-LEEN), *n.*   whalebone, a hard, layered skin occurring in cetaceans without teeth; see **Cetacea.**

ball-and-socket joint, the union of 2 bones in which the rounded head of one bone (the ball) fits into cavity in the other (the socket), offering the greatest possible freedom of movement; see also **joint.**

ballast (BAL-uhst), *n.*   **1.** a weight with the sole function of keeping a ship, balloon, etc., upright.   **2.** in electricity, a resistor used to compensate for voltage change or to limit current applied to a device.

ball bearing, a bearing in which friction is reduced by contact of a shaft or similar moving part with steel balls free to rotate but confined to a track or *raceway.*

ballistic missile (buh-LIS-tik), a missile powered for part of its flight; after power cutoff, its flight path (trajectory) is that of a body in free fall; see also **intercontinental ballistic missile.**

ballistics, the study of the motion of projectiles, such as cannon shells, missiles, and bullets; especially, study of their paths (trajectories) and energy relations.

balloon (buh-LOON), *n.*   a bag containing hot air or gas less dense than air. If the bag is airtight, the balloon can rise from the earth into the atmosphere, often carrying heavy materials attached to it; has no engine for guiding flight.

ORDER NAME	SHAPE	ACTION
SOME BACTERIA THAT HELP AND HARM		
Actinomycetales		
Mycobacterium leprae	rod	causes leprosy
M. tuberculosis	rod	causes tuberculosis
Streptomyces griseus	branching rods	produces streptomycin antibiotic
Chlamydobacteriales		
Sphaerotilus natans	rod	decomposes waste
Eubacteriales		
Acetobacter	rod	ferments acetic acid
Bacillus anthracis	rod	causes anthrax
B. licheniformis	rod	produces bacitracin antibiotic
Bacteroides fragilis	round chain	abundant in acute appendicitis
Clostridium botulinum	rod	produces botulinus toxin
Proteus	rod	produces urease
Staphylococcus aureus	round	causes pneumonia
Streptococcus hemalyticus	round	causes scarlet fever
Str. thermophilus	round	used in making Swiss cheese
Spirochaetales		
Treponema pallidum	spiral	causes syphilis

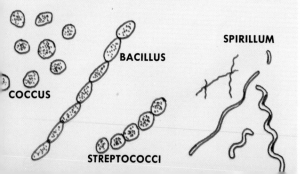

COCCUS   BACILLUS   SPIRILLUM   STREPTOCOCCI

battery

balsam (BAWL-suhm), *n.* **1.** a spicy, pleasant-smelling resin from various evergreen trees, as *Canada balsam*. **2.** an evergreen tree, the balsam fir, which grows in northern North America and produces Canada balsam. **3.** any plant of the garden balsam family.

banana family (buh-NAN-uh), see **Musales**.

bank-and-turn indicator, an instrument that shows an airplane pilot the plane's angle of turn and tilt, or bank, from the horizontal.

bar, *n.* a unit of pressure: one million dynes per square centimeter, equal to the normal sea-level atmospheric pressure of 29.53 inches of mercury.

barb, *n.* **1.** any beardlike growth on a plant or animal. **2.** a small, brightly colored, tropical fresh-water fish, popular for home aquaria. **3.** part of a feather; see **feather**.

barbel (BAHR-buhl) *n.* a long, thin feeler, found on the mouth of some fishes, notably the catfish.

barberry family, see **Ranales**.

barbicel (BAHR-buh-sel), see **feather**.

barbiturate (bahr-BITCH-uh-rayt), *n.* any drug derived from barbituric acid, $C_4H_4N_2O_3$; most are used as sedatives.

barbule (BAHR-byoo-uhl), see **feather**.

barite (BAIR-eyt, *n.* a dense, usually white, crystalline mineral, $BaSO_4$, with hardness 3-3½; chief source of barium.

barium (BAIR-ee-uhm), *n.* a yellowish-white, heavy, metallic chemical element in the alkaline-earth family; used chiefly in chemical compounds; barium salts are used to help read X-rays of the stomach and intestines; symbol Ba; *at. no.,* 56; *at. wt.,* 137.34; isolated by Davy in 1808.

bark, *n.* the tough outer covering of woody roots and stems, made up of 2 layers: an outer protective coating, usually cork, and an inner *phloem* layer, which carries food from leaves to the rest of the plant.

barnacle (BAHR-nuh-kuhl), see **Crustacea**.

barograph (BAHR-uh-graf), *n.* a recording barometer; a pen traces pressure changes on paper attached to a revolving drum; this records pressure continuously.

barometer (buh-RAHM-uh-tuhr), *n.* an instrument for measuring pressure, usually air pressure. The most accurate barometer is a column of mercury in a glass tube, sealed at the top, and connected at the bottom with a well of mercury. A scale alongside the tube shows the height of the column in inches and fractions, or in millimeters; see also **aneroid barometer**.

barometric altimeter (bahr-uh-MET-rik), an altimeter showing elevation above sea level, usually an aneroid barometer; used in airplanes and in obtaining mountain heights.

baryon (BAIR-ee-ahn), *n.* an atomic particle with a mass 1,835 times the mass of an electron or more; nucleons (neutrons and protons) and hyperons are baryons; the hyperons decay into neutrons and other particles.

basal metabolism (BAY-sul), the minimum level of cellular activity; measured indirectly by combining the rate of oxygen consumption with carbon dioxide elimination some hours after eating and with the body at rest. It is an important guide in medical diagnosis.

basalt (buh-SAWLT), *n.* a finely crystalline igneous rock of high density and deep-gray to black color; the most widespread volcanic rock.

base, *n.* **1.** a chemical compound that feels slippery, turns red litmus blue, and reacts with acids to form salts; also called *alkali*. **2.** a compound containing hydroxyl ions ($^-$OH) that can combine with hydrogen ions (H^+) to form water. **3.** a proton acceptor. *adj.* **basic**.

Basidiomycetes (buh-sid-ee-oh-my-SEET-eez), *n.* a class including the club fungi; a *basidiomycete* forms spores in a clublike sporangium; has filamentous hyphae with cell walls between nuclei; reproduces asexually by modified conidia; when

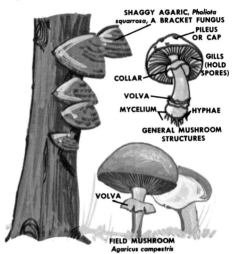

SHAGGY AGARIC, *Pholiota squarrosa*, A BRACKET FUNGUS
PILEUS OR CAP
GILLS (HOLD SPORES)
COLLAR
VOLVA
MYCELIUM
HYPHAE
GENERAL MUSHROOM STRUCTURES
VOLVA
FIELD MUSHROOM
Agaricus campestris

fruiting body is present, it is umbrella-like with gills; includes mushroom, toadstool, puffball, morel, and bracket or shelf fungi.

bat, see **Chiroptera**.

batholith (BATH-uh-lith), *n.* a large body of igneous rock far below the earth's surface; a type of intrusion; see **intrusion**.

bathyscaphe (BATH-uh-skaf), *n.* a vessel used for exploring the depths of the sea, attached to a gasoline tank on the surface. When the vessel is filled with gasoline, it is very buoyant. Pumping out gasoline and replacing it with sea water causes the bathyscaphe to sink in the water; also spelled **bathyscaph**.

bathysphere (BATH-uh-sfeer), *n.* a large steel globe, designed for human observations under water; this vessel, which must be attached to a ship, has been replaced by the bathyscaphe.

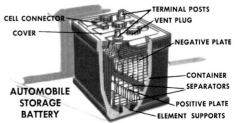

TERMINAL POSTS
CELL CONNECTOR
VENT PLUG
COVER
NEGATIVE PLATE
CONTAINER
SEPARATORS
AUTOMOBILE STORAGE BATTERY
POSITIVE PLATE
ELEMENT SUPPORTS

battery (BAT-uh-ree), *n.* a device of 2 or more electric cells that changes chemical energy to electrical energy. Most batteries have 3 parts: a metal *cathode,* an *electrolyte* (liquid or solid),

31

and a metal oxide or carbon *anode*. The electron flow from cathode to anode produces electrical current; see also **dry cell.**

bauxite (BAWK-syt), *n.* a mineral ore composed mainly of aluminum oxides and hydroxides; the chief ore of aluminum.

bay, n. 1. a shoreline indentation, so a body of water is partially surrounded by land. **2.** the sweet bay, a laurel tree with leaves used for flavoring.

bayberry family, see **Myricales.**

Be, symbol of **beryllium.**

beach, *n.* area of sand or pebbles along water.

beacon (BEE-kuhn), *n.* any signal for guiding aircraft or ships. Light beacons usually flash on and off in regular patterns, and have varying colors, so that a navigator can identify any beacon he sees and keep his craft on course.

beak, *n.* the horny jaw covering of a bird; the

FISH SPEAR (SNAKEBIRD)

FLOWER PROBE (HUMMINGBIRD)

SEED CRACKER (CARDINAL)

MEAT TEARER (EAGLE)

GENERAL-PURPOSE (RAVEN)

NUT CRACKER (PARROT)

WATER STRAINER (DUCK)

bill. Beaks vary extensively in size and shape, largely determining a bird's feeding habits.

beaker (BEE-kuhr), *n.* a piece of laboratory glassware with straight sides and, usually, a pouring lip; used to measure liquids.

bear family, polar, grizzly, black, kodiak, and others; see **Carnivora.**

bearing, *n.* **1.** a surface designed to reduce friction between moving and stationary machine parts; may be roller bearings, ball bearings, oiled wooden blocks, or metal or plastic objects; nylon is often used for lightweight bearings. **2.** in navigation, the angle between north or south and the direction a ship or plane is traveling: a *bearing* of 45 degrees is northeast.

beat, 1. *v.* to combine 2 waves (such as sound or electric) such that the resulting wave is the difference or sum of the original waves. **2.** *n.* each regular pulse of the sound or frequency resulting from such a combination.

Beaufort scale (BOH-fuhrt), a chart for comparative wind speeds, graduated from 0 (dead calm) to 12 (over 75 mph or 120 kph); some scales go to 17 (over 130 mph or 273 kph); devised by Sir Francis Beaufort (1774-1857), British admiral.

beaver (BEE-vuhr), see **Rodentia.**

Becquerel ray (BEK-uh-rel), radiation given off by a radioactive element such as uranium, radium, thorium; named for Henri Becquerel, French physicist, now called *alpha, beta,* or *gamma* rays.

bed, *n.* **1.** in geology, a layer or stratum. **2.** the bottom of a present or former body of water, as a riverbed.

bedrock, *n.* solid, massive rock, usually covered by soil or broken pieces of rock.

bee, see **Hymenoptera.**

beebread, *n.* a food made by worker bees from pollen; fed to the young bees.

beech family, see **Fagales.**

beeswax, *n.* a wax produced by worker bees who have fed heavily on honey; used to build the comb; preserves woodwork and leather.

beet, see **Centrospermales.**

beetle (BEE-tuhl), see **Coleoptera.**

begonia family (bi-GOHN-yuh), see **Parietales.**

bel (BEL), *n.* the unit used in power measurement (especially in sound) to express loudness by the ratio of one sound's intensity to that of another. The logarithm to base 10 of the ratio is the number in bels; see also **decibel.**

bellflower family, see **Campanulales.**

bends, *n.* an illness caused by working in compressed air and coming back to normal pressures too rapidly; nitrogen forms gas bubbles in body tissues; also called *caisson disease* and *decompression illness.*

benign tumor (bi-NYN), **1.** a tumor that does not spread rapidly from its point of origin. Benign tumors can usually be removed surgically with no complications. **2.** any noncancerous tumor; contrast with **malignant.**

benthic zone (BEN-thik), the ocean floor, when regarded as the habitat of plant and animal life; certain forms of life are characteristic of this region, although they vary greatly depending on the depth of the ocean to the floor.

benthos (BEN-thohs), *n.* the plant and animal life found in the benthic zone.

benzaldehyde (ben-ZAL-duh-hyd), see **aldehyde.**

benzene (BEN-zeen), *n.* a colorless, flammable liquid with a characteristic odor; the most important aromatic hydrocarbon; used as a solvent and to manufacture hundreds of synthetic chemicals; formula, C_6H_6; also called *benzol.*

BEAUFORT SCALE

Wind Force No.	Weather Bureau Name	Signs and Indications	Miles Per Hour	Kilometers per Hour*
0	Calm	Smoke rises vertically	less than 1	under 1.6
1	Light air	Direction shown by smoke but not by vanes	1-3	1.6-5
2	Slight breeze	Leaves rustle; vanes move	4-7	6-11
3	gentle breeze	Leaves and twigs are moved	8-12	12-19
4	moderate breeze	Dust raised; small branches moved	13-18	20-29
5	fresh breeze	Small trees sway	19-24	30-39
6	strong breeze	Large branches are moved; telephone wires whistle	25-31	40-50
7	high wind	Whole trees in motion	32-38	51-61
8	fresh gale	Twigs are broken off; walking is difficult	39-46	62-74
9	strong gale	Slight structural damage; roof slate removed	47-54	75-87
10	whole gale	Trees uprooted; great structural damage	55-63	88-102
11	storm	Widespread damage	64-75	103-120
12	hurricane	Countryside devastated	over 75	120+

*approximate velocity

32

benzene ring, the structural formula of benzene, consisting of a 6-carbon regular hexagon with alternating double bonds, and with a hydrogen attached to each carbon; the basis for the structural formulas of many aromatic chemicals.

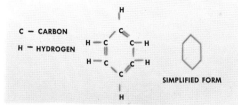

benzine (BEN-zeen), *n.* a colorless, flammable liquid with an odor like kerosene; composed of hydrocarbons from petroleum; used as a solvent.

benzoic acid (ben-ZOH-ik), a white, crystalline organic acid used in dyes, medicines, and food preservatives; formula, C_6H_5COOH.

beriberi (BAIR-ee-BAIR-ee), *n.* a disease caused by a vitamin B_1 deficiency that is common to people whose chief food is polished rice; symptoms are swollen limbs, partial paralysis, and, sometimes, heart disease.

berkelium (buhr-KEE-lee-uhm), *n.* a man-made, radioactive chemical element in the actinide series; symbol Bk; *at. no.,* 97; mass number of most stable isotope, 249; first prepared in 1949 by Thompson, Ghiorso, Street, and Seaborg.

Bernoulli's principle (buhr-NOO-lee), as the speed of fluid flow increases, pressure decreases; the basis of aerodynamic lift; named for the Swiss scientist Daniel Bernoulli.

berry, *n.* a fruit with a completely fleshy pericarp; currants, grapes, and tomatoes are true berries, but many fruits called berries are not.

beryl (BAIR-uhl), *n.* a hard mineral composed of beryllium aluminum silicate, $Be_3Al_2Si_6O_{18}$, with hardness 8; usually light green or white; the chief source of beryllium and gems such as aquamarine and emerald.

beryllium (buh-RIL-ee-uhm), *n.* a grayish-white, metallic chemical element; light and brittle; used chiefly to harden alloys; symbol Be; *at. no.,* 4; *at. wt.,* 9.0122; isolated independently by Wöhler and by Bussy in 1828.

Bessemer process (BES-uh-muhr), a method of making steel with controlled carbon content by oxidizing (and thus removing) impurities with a blast of air through the melted pig iron. After reduction of the ore in the *converter,* or furnace, desired amounts of alloying elements are added; named for Sir Henry Bessemer, an English engineer (1813–1898), one of the discoverers.

Beta Centauri (BAY-tuh sen-TAW-ry), a bright double star in constellation Centaurus; tenth brightest star in visual magnitude.

Beta Crucis, a bright star in constellation Crux; 20th brightest star in visual magnitude.

beta particle, a free electron produced by the decay of radioactive atoms.

betatron (BAY-tuh-trahn), *n.* a particle accelerator used to increase the speed and energy of electrons and drive them to a target where they may produce gamma rays.

Betelgeuse (BEE-tuhl-jooz), *n.* a bright, reddish star in the constellation Orion; 11th brightest star in the sky in visual magnitude; diameter about 600 times that of the sun.

bev, BEV, abbreviation for *billion electron volts;* see **electron volt.**

bevatron (BEV-uh-trahn), *n.* a particle accelerator used to increase the speed of protons and send them to a target where reactions can take place and be studied.

Bi, symbol for **bismuth.**

bi-, a word part meaning *two* or *twice;* as *bilateral* (on both sides).

bicarbonate (by-KAHR-buh-nuht), *n.* a carbonic acid salt containing the $HCO_3 =$ radical, such as sodium bicarbonate, $NaHCO_3$.

bichloride (by-KLOH-ryd), *n.* a compound composed of a metallic ion and 2 chloride ions, as mercuric bichloride, $HgCl_2$.

bicuspid (by-KUHS-pid), *adj.* having 2 projections, or *cusps,* as: **1.** a bicuspid tooth; see **tooth. 2.** the *bicuspid valve,* an alternate term for **mitral valve.**

biennial (by-EN-ee-uhl), *n.* a plant that needs 2 growing seasons to complete its life cycle (from seed to seed), such as the beet, carrot, onion, and pansy. Seed formation usually takes place during the second season.

bifocal (BY-foh-kuhl), *n.* an eyeglass lens with 2 focal sections: the upper for distant vision and the lower for near vision. *adj.* **bifocal.**

Big Dipper, a 7-star constellation visible in the northern sky. The 2 stars at the side farthest from the handle point to Polaris, the North Star; the back and tail of the constellation Ursa Major; see **Ursa Major.**

bignonia family (big-NOH-nee-uh), see **Polemoniales.**

bilateral symmetry (by-LAT-uhr-uhl SIM-uh-tree), a characteristic of organisms having similar parts on the right and left sides of their bodies; such parts on one side are often mirror images of those on the other side.

bile (BYL), *n.* an orange or green fluid produced by the liver which flows into the intestine to aid in fat digestion; it is stored in the gall bladder.

bill, an alternate term for **beak.**

bimetallic (by-muh-TAL-ik), *adj.* containing 2 different metals; especially applied to thermocouples and thermostats; see also **thermostat.**

binary (BY-nuh-ree), *adj.* having 2 or double parts: *binary* arithmetic (the basis of most computers) is a number system using only 2 symbols, 0 and 1.

binary decision, in computer engineering, a selection between 2 alternatives; often called a *yes-no* or *go-no go decision.*

binary star, a single-appearing star that is actually a pair of stars that revolve around each other. They can be seen as 2 separate stars only with a fairly powerful telescope.

An *eclipsing binary star* appears from Earth to be variable because the larger, usually less luminous, star interferes with the line of sight from Earth to the brighter, revolving star

binaural (by-NAWR-uhl), *adj.* referring to, or using, both ears, as *binaural* sound reproduction.

binding energy, energy needed to break atomic particle, atom, or molecule into components.

binocular (buh-NAHK-yuh-luhr), **1.** *adj.* using 2 eyes. **2.** *n.* a portable double telescope, or

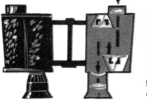

Prism binocular: the viewer's angle of depth perception is widened by reflection of light through a prism system, thus extending the distance and range of sight

any other device with eyepieces for both eyes.

binocular vision, vision from both eyes at the same time but with 2 images perceived as one. An object seen from 2 angles makes judgment of distance and depth perception possible.

bio-, a word part meaning *life.*

biochemistry (by-oh-KEM-is-tree), *n.* the study of the chemistry of living things; includes the changes of substances within the living body, as during digestion.

biocides (by-OH-sidz), *n.* pesticides.

biodegradeable (by-oh-dee-GRADE-a-ble), *adj.* capable of disintegrating in the environment.

biological clock, the idea of an internal clock by which animals time certain life activities independent of environmental factors.

biology (by-AHL-uh-jee), *n.* the science that deals with life of all kinds. Its 2 main divisions are *botany,* the study of plants, and *zoology,* the study of animals. *adj.* **biological.**

bioluminescent (by-oh-loo-mi-NES-uhnt), *adj.* glowing with light produced by living organisms; the firefly's glow is *bioluminescent.*

biomass (by-oh-MAS), *n.* the part of a habitat that is living matter.

biome (by-OHM), *n.* land area made up of a group of living organisms in a particular environment, such as desert or tundra.

biometry (by-AHM-uh-tree), *n.* the use of statistics and other mathematical methods in studying biological problems.

bionics (by-AHN-ix), *n.* the design, construction, and operation of machines that perform the functions of living organisms.

biophysics (by-oh-FIZ-ix), *n.* the investigation of living things in relation to physical laws and properties: the *biophysicist* may study the eye as an optical system. *adj.* **biophysical.**

biopsy (BY-ahp-see), *n.* the study of tissue cells or fluids removed from living organisms, often a surgical procedure.

biosphere (BY-oh-sfeer), *n.* the portions of the earth, water, and atmosphere that support life.

biota (by-OH-tuh), *n.* in ecology, the entire plant and animal life of any region.

biotin (BY-uh-tuhn), *n.* vitamin H, one of the B vitamins probably essential to normal growth. Lack of it in rats produces dermatitis and thickened skin but its value to humans is undetermined; found in yeast, grains, egg yolk, vegetables, and fruit.

biotron (BY-uh-trahn), *n.* an enclosed chamber with rigidly controlled humidity, temperature.

biped (BY-ped), *n.* any animal having 2 feet, such as man. *adj.* **bipedal.**

birch family, see **Fagales.**

bird, *n.* a warm-blooded animal belonging to the vertebrate class *Aves.* Birds lay eggs, have wings, and are the only animals with feathers. Most can fly, but some, such as the ostrich and penguin, cannot; see **Aves.**

bird-hipped dinosaur, see **dinosaur, Ornithischia.**

bird of prey, any bird that kills and eats other animals, including the eagle, vulture, hawk, and owl; they have sharp, powerful beaks and talons and keen eyesight.

birth, *n.* **1.** the appearance of a new individual organism from within the female parent's body, rather than from an egg hatched externally. **2.** more specifically, as in placental mammals, delivery of the formed infant from the mother's uterus, rather than from an egg, whether internally or externally hatched; see also **viviparous, ovoviviparous, oviparous.**

birthmark, *n.* a skin blemish present at birth or developing shortly afterward; sometimes caused by lack of pigment or by impaired blood circulation; most are harmless.

bismuth (BIZ-muth), *n.* a hard, brittle, grayish-white, metallic chemical element; used in stainless steel to make it more workable, and in certain low-melting-point alloys, as in sprinkler systems; symbol Bi; *at. no.,* 83; *at. wt.,* 208.980; known since ancient times.

bison (BY-suhn), see **Artiodactyla.**

bit, *n.* a 0 or a 1 in the binary system of arithmetic, which uses only these 2 digits; in this system, a *bit* is the smallest amount of information that can be recorded or given; short for *binary digit.*

bituminous coal (bi-TOO-mi-nuhs), a soft coal ranging from about 69% to 86% carbon in composition; some coals with less carbon are classed as bituminous if their heat content is over 11,000 Btu.

bivalve (BY-valv), see **Pelecypoda.**

Bk, symbol for **berkelium.**

blackbody, in physics, a body that absorbs all the radiant energy that strikes it, reflecting none, and radiates energy only in proportion to its temperature.

blackdamp, an alternate term for **chokedamp.**

bladder (BLAD-uhr), *n.* **1.** a thin-walled, expandable organ that receives and stores wastes supplied by the kidneys until the wastes are discharged through the urethra; see **excretory system. 2.** any other expandable organ, especially the air bladder in fishes. **3.** the **gall bladder.**

bladderwort family (BLAD-uhr-wuhrt), see **Polemoniales.**

blade, *n.* the more or less broad part of a leaf, not including the petiole, or leaf stem; also called *lamina.*

blastula (BLAS-choo-luh), *n.* an early stage in the embryonic development of many-celled organisms; dividing cells form a hollow sphere.

bleach, *n.* a substance that makes materials white, or whiter than they were; sunlight and many chemicals, especially chlorine compounds, sulfur dioxide, and hydrogen peroxide, are bleaches. *v.* **bleach.**

blight (BLYT), *n.* any of several plant diseases, usually attacking specific parts, such as leaves or stem; caused by bacteria or fungi.

blimp, *n.* a non-rigid dirigible or airship; see **dirigible.**

blindness, *n.* the condition of being unable to see; may be caused by disease in or injury to the eye, optic nerve, or occipital lobe in the brain.

blind spot, the point at which the optic nerve enters the back of the eyeball; at this point there are no nerve endings and light stimuli cannot be received; see **eye.**

blip, *n.* a spot of light on a photoelectronic screen; in radar, indicates a detected object.

blister, *n.* **1.** a swelling on the skin, containing a watery fluid or serum, usually caused by burns. **2.** a transparent hump built into an airplane's fuselage.

blizzard (BLIZ-uhrd), *n.* a weather condition with low temperatures and strong winds carrying much snow; a severe blizzard is defined as having winds greater than 45 mph, temperature about 10° F or less, and visibility nearly zero.

block and tackle, a combination of simple machines in which the load is attached to a movable pulley connected to a fixed pulley by ropes,

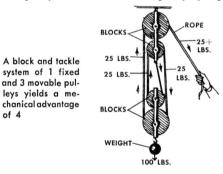

A block and tackle system of 1 fixed and 3 movable pulleys yields a mechanical advantage of 4

chain, or cable; the mechanical advantage obtained depends on the number of ropes joining the movable pulley to the fixed one.

blood, *n.* the fluid that circulates through the body, usually in tubes (veins and arteries); the liquid portion, *plasma,* carries cells of various kinds. In man, these are white blood cells (*leucocytes*), red blood cells (*erythrocytes*), and

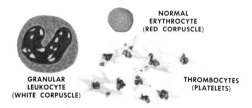

GRANULAR LEUKOCYTE (WHITE CORPUSCLE)

NORMAL ERYTHROCYTE (RED CORPUSCLE)

THROMBOCYTES (PLATELETS)

blood platelets (*thrombocytes*); the blood transports food, oxygen, and hormones to the body cells, and removes waste products from the cells.

blood count, the number, under a microscope, of white and red blood cells in a measured area of a slide. The actual count is important in diagnosis of an illness and the examination may also reveal abnormal conditions other than excess or deficiency of any kind of cell.

blood pressure, the pushing action of the blood against the blood vessel walls (usually measured on arteries); this pressure depends on the pumping action of the heart and on the elasticity of the arterial walls. Blood pressure is at a peak during *systole,* and drops during *diastole;* a pressure of 120/80 means a pressure of 120 millimeters of mercury in systole and of 80mm of mercury in diastole; see also **sphygmomanometer.**

bloodstone, *n.* a greenish type of mineral chalcedony with red specks of jasper.

blood sugar, glucose in the blood; normally present as about one-tenth of 1% of the blood. Excess sugar is stored in the liver as glycogen; see also **diabetes.**

blood type, any of the various combinations of antigens in red blood cells and antibodies in blood serum; in humans, there are 4 basic types, usually called A, B, AB, and O. They are based on 2 kinds of antibodies, *alpha* and *beta* (the serum may contain either of these, both, or neither), and 2 kinds of antigens, *A* and *B* (the red cells may contain either, both, or neither). Many other antigen-antibody relationships exist in blood, including the Rh factor; see **Rh factor.**

blood vessel, any of the arteries, veins, or capillaries that carry blood through the body.

blossom, a common term for **flower.**

blue baby, a baby with some of its venous blood circulating through the arteries; bluish appearance of skin is from dark color of venous blood; caused by a hole connecting chambers of the heart and permitting venous and arterial blood to mix, thus limiting the amount of hemoglobin available to carry oxygen.

blue-green algae, see **Cyanophyta.**

blush, *n.* a reddening color of the skin caused by dilation of blood vessels near the surface, normally due to a stimulus from the sympathetic nervous system. *v.* **blush.**

bog (BAHG, BAWG), *n.* wet, swamp ground, as a filled-in lake, made up mostly of decomposed plants; often a source of peat.

Bohr theory, a theory of the planetary structure of atoms: electrons (negatively charged) revolve in planetlike orbits around a positively charged nucleus; proposed by Niels Bohr, Danish physicist, about 1913.

boiling point, the temperature at which the vapor pressure of a liquid equals atmospheric pressure; for water, 212°F or 100°C.

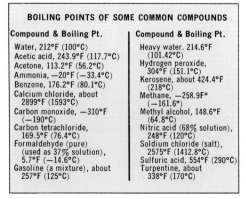

BOILING POINTS OF SOME COMMON COMPOUNDS

Compound & Boiling Pt.	Compound & Boiling Pt.
Water, 212°F (100°C)	Heavy water. 214.6°F (101.42°C)
Acetic acid, 243.9°F (117.7°C)	Hydrogen peroxide, 304°F (151.1°C)
Acetone, 113.2°F (56.2°C)	
Ammonia, −20°F (−33.4°C)	Kerosene, about 424.4°F (218°C)
Benzene, 176.2°F (80.1°C)	Methane, −258.9F° (−161.6°)
Calcium chloride, about 2899°F (1593°C)	Methyl alcohol, 148.6°F (64.8°C)
Carbon monoxide, −310°F (−190°C)	Nitric acid (68% solution), 248°F (120°C)
Carbon tetrachloride, 169.5°F (76.4°C)	Soldium chloride (salt), 2575°F (1413.8°C)
Formaldehyde (pure) (used as 37% solution), 5.7°F (−14.6°C)	Sulfuric acid, 554°F (290°C)
Gasoline (a mixture), about 257°F (125°C)	Turpentine, about 338°F (170°C)

boiling-water reactor, a thermal-neutron reactor in which the temperature and pressure of water are adjusted so that coolant-moderator water can boil into steam within the reactor.

bolometer (boh-LAHM-uh-tuhr), *n.* a sensitive metal resistance thermometer for detecting tiny amounts of radiation; may be used in spectroscopes to detect infrared radiation.

bomb (BAHM), *n.* a container enclosing an explosive; includes explosives dropped from aircraft or self-propelled missiles. Most bombs have a fuse as a *detonator;* this is simply a smaller explosive charge to set off the larger main charge.

bombardment (bahm-BARD-muhnt), *n.* the shooting or aiming of neutrons, alpha particles, and other high-energy particles at atomic nuclei, usually to split the nuclei and, often, to form a new element. *v.* **bombard.**

bombax family (BAHM-bax), see **Malvales.**

bomb calorimeter (kal-uh-RIM-uh-tuhr), a calorimeter consisting of a thick-walled metal container in which a substance is sealed and burned. The rise in temperature of the surrounding liquid, usually water, measures the quantity of heat given off; see also **calorimeter.**

bond, *n.* **1.** in chemistry, the force that joins atoms together to form molecules; *ionic bonds* involve transfer of electrons from one atom to another, as in sodium chloride; *covalent bonds*

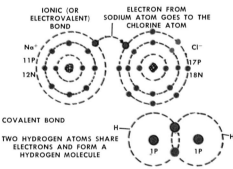

IONIC (OR ELECTROVALENT) BOND

ELECTRON FROM SODIUM ATOM GOES TO THE CHLORINE ATOM

Na⁺ 11P 12N   Cl⁻ 17P 18N

COVALENT BOND

TWO HYDROGEN ATOMS SHARE ELECTRONS AND FORM A HYDROGEN MOLECULE

H 1P 1P H

involve pairs of electrons shared by atoms, as in sulfur trioxide; see also **acceptor atom.** **2.** any substance that binds material together.

bone, *n.* the hardened connective tissue that supports the body of many animals. Bone is about two-thirds mineral matter, chiefly calcium phosphate, and one-third organic matter, mostly gelatin. The center of some bones is composed of a spongy tissue called *marrow,* where red cells are produced. Most bones of birds are hollow.

book lung, one of the respiratory organs in spiders consisting of leaflike air pockets in contact with blood in an anterior chamber and receiving air from the outside through a slit in the body wall; also called *lung book.*

booster rocket, 1. any rocket motor that acts to give additional power to the regular propulsion system of a rocket during some stage of its flight. **2.** the first stage (liftoff) of a multi-stage rocket.

Bootes (boh-OH-teez), *n.* a kite-shaped constellation of the northern sky, most clearly visible in the summer. The huge red star Arcturus marks the tail of the kite.

boracic acid, an alternate term for **boric acid.**

borage family (BOHR-ahj), see **Polemoniales.**

borate (BOHR-ayt), *n.* a salt or ester of any boric acid; specifically, a salt or ester of orthoboric acid, H_3BO_3; see **boric acid.**

borax (BOHR-ax), *n.* a colorless to white crystalline solid; used in cleaning agents, enamels, and in soldering metals; formula, $Na_2B_4O_7 \cdot 10H_2O$; also called *sodium tetraborate.*

borax bead test, a test used to identify certain metallic compounds. An unknown substance is heated with a bead of borax in an oxidizing flame. The bead changes color according to the metal present; cobalt colors the clear bead blue; nickel colors it brown.

boreal (BOHR-ee-uhl), *adj.* northern or arctic, as cold, *boreal* lands.

boric acid (BOHR-ik), any of several acids containing boron; especially, orthoboric acid, a white crystalline solid used in antiseptic solutions, and to make glass, enamel, and glazes; formula, H_3BO_3; also called *boracic acid.*

bornite (BOHR-nyt), *n.* a brown metallic mineral, Cu_5FeS_4, with hardness 3; tarnishes an iridescent purple when exposed to air; an important source of copper.

boron (BOHR-ahn), *n.* a semimetallic chemical element, very hard and brittle; used to harden steel and other alloys, and to absorb neutrons; symbol B; *at. no.,* 5; *at. wt.,* 10.811; isolated independently in 1808 by Davy in England and by Gay-Lussac and Thénard in France.

botany (BAHT-uh-nee), *n.* the study of plant life, one of the 2 major divisions of biological science. *Botanists* are closely identified with agricultural developments of all kinds. The *botanical* sciences include: **cytology**—the study of cells; **histology**—the study of the tissues; **plant physiology**—how the plant functions; **plant pathology**—plant diseases and treatments; **ecology**—relations with the environment; **economic botany**—the uses of plants; see also **genetics, morphology, paleobotany.**

botulism (BAHCH-uh-lizm), *n.* food poisoning due to toxins from *Clostridium* bacteria; usually the result of eating non-acid foods that are improperly canned or preserved.

bovine (BOH-vyn, -veen), *adj.* describing a member of the ox family: cattle are *bovine* animals.

bowel (BOW-uhl), *n.* any part of the digestive canal below the stomach; the intestines.

Bowman's capsule (BOH-muhnz KAP-suhl), see **nephron.**

Boyle's law, one of the basic gas laws: if the temperature of a gas remains the same, the volume decreases as the pressure increases; pressure of a gas is inversely proportional to volume; named for its discoverer, British scientist Robert Boyle.

Br, symbol for **bromine.**

bracket fungus (BRAK-uht), see **Basidiomycetes.**

bract (BRAKT), *n.* a modified leaf that grows around the base of a flower; some tiny flowers have large colorful bracts, often incorrectly called *petals.*

brain, *n.* a nerve-tissue enlargement at the upper end of the spinal cord which serves as the body's control mechanism. In man, the most important region is the *cerebrum;* also includes

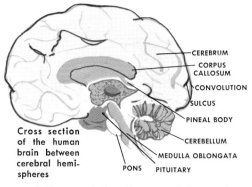

CEREBRUM
CORPUS CALLOSUM
CONVOLUTION
SULCUS
PINEAL BODY
CEREBELLUM
MEDULLA OBLONGATA
PONS   PITUITARY

Cross section of the human brain between cerebral hemispheres

cerebellum, medulla oblongata, thalamus, hypothalamus, pons, and midbrain.

brake, n.   a device that applies friction to halt or slow down anything in motion. Most brakes are applied to rotating wheels or cylinders. A special brake, called a *prony* brake, is used to measure brake horsepower of a power shaft.   v. **brake.**

branched hydrocarbon, a hydrocarbon in which some of the carbon atoms branch off others; contrast with **straight-chain hydrocarbon.**

brass, n.   any alloy of copper and zinc, yellow to red in color; hard, malleable, and ductile; used for electrical mounting parts, screws, and decorative pieces.

breathe (BREETH), v.   **1.** to inhale air into and exhale air from the lungs; the inhaled air is a source of oxygen; the exhaled air rids the system of waste carbon dioxide and water.   **2.** to exchange atmospheric oxygen and carbon dioxide, as do all animals and most plants; to respire.   n. **breath** (BRETH), **breathing.**

breed, n.   a group of animals, all of one species, with some special character that distinguishes the group from others of the species. Herefords are a *breed* of cattle, dachshunds are a dog *breed*. The term is usually applied to domesticated groups, carefully selected and permitted to mate only with chosen animals.   v. **breed.**

breeder reactor, a nuclear reactor that produces energy by fission and also produces more fissionable material than it consumes. If thorium-232 is bombarded by very high-energy neutrons, the fission reaction releases energy. At the same time, fissionable uranium-233 is produced.

Bright's disease, a chronic disease of the kidneys indicated by large accumulations of fluid in the body tissues and by protein and kidney cells in the urine; first described by Richard Bright, British physician (1789-1858).

British thermal unit, the amount of heat needed to raise the temperature of 1 pound of water by 1 degree F; see also **calorie.**   abbr. **Btu.**

bromide (BROH-myd), n.   a salt or ester of hydrobromic acid, such as potassium bromide, KBr, or ethyl bromide, C_2H_5Br; used in medicine for sedatives and in photographic emulsions.

bromine (BROH-meen), n.   a chemical element in the halogen family; a dark-red, poisonous liquid that gives off suffocating fumes; used chiefly in organic compounds, such as ethylene dibromide, important in anti-knock gasolines; symbol Br; at. no., 35; at. wt., 79.909; isolated by Balard in 1826.

bronchial (BRAHN-kee-uhl), adj.   pertaining to a bronchus; the *bronchial* tubes are the bronchi and their branches.

bubble chamber

bronchiole (BRAHN-kee-ohl), n.   any of the small subdivisions of the bronchus, leading to the alveoli; also called *bronchiolus.*

bronchitis (brahn-KY-tis), n.   inflammation of the bronchial tubes of the respiratory system.

bronchus (BRAHN-kuhs), n., pl. **bronchi.** the tube leading from the trachea (windpipe) to each lung. These tubes have branches like trees, which bring air into sacs (alveoli) where gases are exchanged; see **respiratory system.**

brontosaurus (brahn-tuh-SAW-ruhs), see **Saurischia.**

bronze (BRAHNZ), n.   an alloy of copper and tin, reddish-gold in color; hard and corrosion-resistant; used for ornamental work such as statues and bells, and for electrical equipment.

brown algae, see **Phaeophyta.**

Brownian movement, the aimless movement of tiny particles suspended in a fluid; caused by molecules of the fluid bombarding the particles. A speck of powder in water, when seen under the microscope, shows this type of movement; named for Robert Brown, Scottish botanist (1773–1858), who first described it.

bruise (BROOZ), n.   an injury caused by impact or pressure, with no broken skin and no external bleeding; discoloration results from internal bleeding from capillaries.   v. **bruise.**

brush n.   a piece, bundle, or plate of metal or carbon used for conduction of electricity to or from a revolving part, as the armature in a motor.

Bryophyta (bry-AHF-uh-tuh), n.   a division of lower plants; *bryophytes* include hornworts, liverworts, and mosses; they have no true stems, roots,

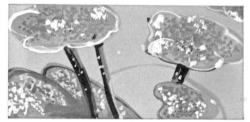

A male liverwort (*Marchantia polymorpha*) during the gametophyte generation, typical of class Hepaticae

leaves, or vascular tissue; reproduce with alternation of generations; and require water for fertilization.

Btu, abbreviation for **British thermal unit.**

bubble, n.   a globe of gas enclosed in a liquid. The liquid may be continuous, or may be a very thin film. A soap bubble in air is usually air surrounded by a soapy water film, which in turn is surrounded by air.

bubble chamber, a device for tracking fast charged particles; in the chamber is (usually)

DIAPHRAGM SUPPORTING PLATE WITH HOLES
BODY OF CHAMBER   WINDOWS   PISTON   MAGNETIC PRESSURE RELEASE VALVE
HIGH ENERGY PI-MESONS ENTERING FROM LEFT IN BUBBLE CHAMBER
RUBBER DIAPHRAGM
MYLAR DIAPHRAGM
TEFLON DIAPHRAGM

superheated liquid hydrogen; passage of the particles through the hydrogen produces a bubble trail that can be photographed and studied; see also **cloud chamber.**

bubonic plague (byoo-BAHN-ik), a highly contagious bacterial disease identified by inflamed swelling of the lymph glands, especially those of the groin and armpit. Fleas that live on rats are the carriers.

buccal (BUK-uhl), *adj.* referring to the mouth or its inside parts (cheeks); a tooth's *buccal* side is the outside—the side next to the cheek.

buckthorn family, see **Rhamnales.**

buckwheat family, see **Polygonales.**

bud, *n.* **1.** in plants, an undeveloped shoot containing tiny leaves, flowers, or both; *terminal* buds occur at the end of a branch or stem;

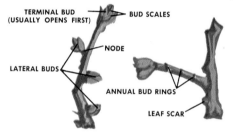

TERMINAL BUD (USUALLY OPENS FIRST) — BUD SCALES
NODE
LATERAL BUDS
ANNUAL BUD RINGS
LEAF SCAR

lateral, or *axillary,* buds along the sides at the nodes. **2.** a bulging growth along the side of an organism that may become a separate organism, as the bud on a hydra; see **budding. 3.** in anatomy, any small part of an organ or tissue that looks like a plant bud, as a *limb bud* on a developing embryo. *v.* **bud.**

budding, *n.* a form of asexual reproduction in which the new organism grows as a bud on the parent. When mature, it breaks off and begins an independent life.

buffalo (BUF-uh-loh), see **Artiodactyla.**

bug, *n.* **1.** any insect in order Hemiptera; see **Hemiptera. 2.** common name for many buglike insects.

bulb, *n.* **1.** a short, underground stem surrounded by a fleshy clump of leaves; stores food for a plant; lilies, hyacinths, and onions grow from bulbs. **2.** an electric lamp.

Bunsen burner (BUHN-suhn), a small gas burner used in laboratories; the air supply can be regulated to control intensity of the flame; designed by R. W. Bunsen, German chemist, in 1855; also spelled **bunsen burner.**

buoy (BOY, BOO-ee), *n.* an anchored floating device used to mark objects for nagivation. Buoys may mark channels, rocks, shallows, or any other important object. Buoys may have lights for nighttime navigation and bells or whistles for use in heavy fog.

buoyancy (BOY-uhn-see), *n.* the force pushing upward on any object in a liquid or gas; it is equal to the weight of fluid displaced; buoyancy keeps ships floating on the water, and makes possible submarine descents beneath the surface; see also **specific gravity.** *adj.* **buoyant.**

burette (byoo-RET), *n.* a narrow glass tube, usually with a stopcock and nozzle; used to pour out and measure liquid; also used to collect liquids or gases.

burmannia family (buhr-MAN-yuh), see **Orchidales.**

burn, *n.* **1.** an injury to tissue caused by heat. First-degree burns cause redness of the area; second-degree burns produce blistering; third-degree burns involve complete destruction of the tissue in the burned area; fourth-degree burns destroy deep-lying tissues and produce considerable charring. *v.* **2.** to injure with heat. **3.** to combust or to cause combustion.

burnout, *n.* the stage in the flight of a rocket at which fuel combustion ends; from this point on, flight depends on previous acceleration and on gravity.

burreed family, see **Pandanales.**

burrow (BUHR-oh), *n.* a hole dug by an animal, usually as a home. Some burrows have many branching tunnels, and are used as storage places, places to hide and escape from enemies, etc. *v.* **burrow.**

bursa (BUHR-suh), *n.* a podlike sac in the body, filled with serous fluid to reduce friction; usually near freely moving joints where tendons slide over ligament or bone.

bursitis (buhr-SY-tis), *n.* painful inflammation of a bursa; *acute* bursitis may follow injuries or infections; *chronic* bursitis is usually accompanied by the deposit of calcium.

butadiene (byoo-tuh-DY-een), *n.* a colorless, gaseous hydrocarbon used to produce rubber, latex paints, ingredients for nylon and other synthetics; formula, C_4H_6.

butane (BYOO-tayn), *n.* a colorless, flammable, gaseous hydrocarbon; used to make compounds and as a fuel; formula, C_4H_{10}.

butanol, an alternate term for **butyl alcohol.**

butte (BYOOT), *n.* an abrupt hill or mountain isolated from others and rising from fairly level land surrounding it.

buttercup family, an alternate term for *crowfoot family;* see **Ranales.**

butterfat, *n.* the fat contained in milk and other dairy products. Whole milk usually contains about 4% butterfat; butter contains 80%; butterfat has a much higher percentage of saturated acids than any other animal fat.

butterfly, see **Lepidoptera.**

buttock (BUHT-uhk), *n.* either of the 2 fleshy prominences at the back of the hips: the buttocks are the rump; in primates, the part on which they sit.

butyl (BYOO-tuhl), *n.* a hydrocarbon radical; formula, C_4H_9.

butyl alcohol, a colorless, poisonous, flammable liquid alcohol; used to make organic chemicals; formula, C_4H_9OH; also called *butanol,* especially when derived from butane.

butyl rubber, a strong, corrosion-resistant, man-made rubber; made from butadiene, isoprene, or isobutene.

butyric acid (byoo-TEER-ik), a colorless liquid with a disagreeable odor; used to make organic compounds; formula, C_3H_7COOH. Butyric esters occur in butter and some oils.

by-product, *n.* a second substance produced in addition to the main product of a chemical reaction or an industrial process: ammonia is a *by-product* in the manufacture of coke.

C, 1. symbol for **carbon. 2.** abbreviation for **Centigrade** or **Celsius.**

Ca, symbol for calcium.

cactus family (KAK-tuhs), see **Opuntiales.**

cadmium (KAD-mee-uhm), *n.* a silvery-white, soft metallic chemical element; used in protective coatings for iron and steel, and in low-melting-point alloys; symbol Cd; *at. no.,* 48; *at. wt.,* 112.40; isolated by Strohmeyer in 1817.

caecilian (si-SIL-yuhn), see **Amphibia.**

caecum (SEE-kuhm), *n., pl.* **-ca.** the pouch at the beginning of the large intestine in some animals from which the appendix opens; also spelled **cecum;** see **digestive system.**

caffeine (KAF-een), *n.* a stimulating alkaloid found in tea, coffee, cocoa, and other plant products; has medicinal uses; formula, $C_8H_{10}N_4O_2$.

caisson (KAY-suhn), *n.* a shell inside which a structural foundation can be built; may be simply a set of walls to hold out water or soft soil while work is going on, but most caissons are used for actual underwater construction. Compressed air is used to force water out.

cal., abbreviation for **calorie.**

Cal., abbreviation for **Calorie.**

calamine (KAL-uh-myn), *n.* **1.** an important zinc ore, zinc silicate; also called *hemimorphite.* **2.** zinc oxide, often used in ointments with a small amount of ferric oxide added.

calcareous (kal-KAIR-ee-uhs), *adj.* chalky; containing calcium carbonate.

calciferol (kal-SIF-uh-rohl), *n.* vitamin D_2, irradiated ergosterol, a crystalline steroid alcohol; important in prevention of rickets; occurs naturally in fish-liver oils.

calcification (kal-si-fuh-KAY-shuhn), *n.* the deposit of calcium in the body. In bone, this results in normal hardening; in other tissues, calcification is abnormal, and is often accompanied by removal of calcium from bone. *v.* **calcify.**

calcine (KAL-syn), *v.* to convert an ore from a carbonate to an oxide by roasting; the roasting decomposes the carbonate, freeing carbon dioxide as a gas. *n.* **calcination.**

calcite (KAL-syt), *n.* a common mineral, composed of calcium carbonate, $CaCO_3$; crystallizes in 6-sided form and occurs in various colors due to impurities; has hardness 3; a chief source of lime; used to make glass and cement; see also **Iceland spar.**

calcium (KAL-see-uhm), *n.* a silvery-white, soft metallic chemical element in the alkaline earth

family; essential for the growth of plants and animals; symbol Ca; *at. no.,* 20; *at. wt.,* 40.08; isolated by Davy in 1808.

calcium carbide, a grayish crystalline solid made by heating lime and coke; reacts with water to form acetylene gas; formula, CaC_2.

calcium carbonate, a solid inorganic compound; occurs in nature as calcite and limestone; used to make lime and cement; formula, $CaCO_3$.

calcium hydroxide, an inorganic base; used to make cement and mortar and in medicines; formula, $Ca(OH)_2$; also called *slaked lime.*

calculator (KAL-kyoo-lay-tuhr), *n.* machine on which mathematical operations are performed.

calf (KAF, KAHF), *n., pl.* **calves. 1.** the young of various kinds of mammals, especially cattle, as well as young elephants, seals, and whales, **2.** the fleshy mass at the back of the lower leg, caused by the large *gastrocnemius* muscle.

calibrate (KAL-uh-brayt), *v.* to determine and verify a scale of values on an instrument, as a thermometer, so that readings can be made and measurements taken. *n.* **calibration.**

californium (kal-ih-FAWR-nee-uhm), *n.* a radioactive chemical element in the actinide series; symbol Cf; *at. no.,* 98; mass number of most stable isotope, 251; first prepared in 1950 by Street, Ghiorso, Thompson, and Seaborg.

caliper (KAL-uh-puhr), *n.* a tool made up of 2

Calipers: (below) external type must be compared with ruler; (right) self-measuring external caliper

legs hinged together at one end, used for measuring lengths of objects not easily measured by a ruler. Most calipers measure inside or outside diameters of round objects.

callus (KAL-uhs), *n.* **1.** a thickening of the outer layers of skin, with excessive growth of the horny layer, usually caused by friction or pressure. **2.** a growth around the joined edges of a fractured bone, which protects the bone while healing is going on. **3.** the healing tissue growing over a plant injury.

calorie (KAL-uh-ree), *n.* a unit of heat energy, the amount of heat needed to raise the temperature of 1 gram of water 1 degree C; see also **British thermal unit.** *abbr.* **cal.**

Calorie, *n.* a unit for measuring the energy value of food: the amount of heat needed to raise the temperature of 1 kilogram of water 1°C; also called *large calorie. abbr.* **Cal.**

calorimeter (kal-uh-RIM-uh-tuhr), *n.* an instrument for measuring the amount of heat in a known quantity of any specific substance, or the amount of heat produced by a chemical reaction. The calorimeter also provides for measurement of heat of fusion and heat of vaporization; see also **bomb calorimeter.**

calyx (KAY-lix), *n.* a group of sepals that forms the outermost portion of flower parts in plants; usually green, but may be colored like petals.

cambium (KAM-bee-uhm), *n.* meristematic or growing tissue in a plant; *vascular* cambium, a

Cambrian

layer of cells separating bark from wood, produces secondary xylem and phloem; *cork* cambium produces layers of cork in the outer bark.

Cambrian (KAM-bree-uhn), *n.* the period of earth history earliest in the Paleozoic Era. Rocks of this period are the earliest that show many animal fossils; began about 600 million years ago and lasted about 80 million years; see also **geologic time table.**

camel (KAM-uhl), see **Artiodactyla.**

Camelopardalis (kah-mel-oh-PAHR-duh-lis), *n.* the *Giraffe,* a northern constellation between Ursa Major and Cassiopeia, visible throughout the year.

camera (KAM-uh-ruh, KAM-ruh), *n.* a device for copying an optical image onto a light-sensitive emulsion. In its simplest form, the camera may be a black box with a pinhole for admission of light. The emulsion may be coated on film or glass. After the image is copied, it is chemically developed and *fixed* (made permanent). Regular cameras use lenses instead of pinholes.

Campanulales (kahm-pan-yoo-LAY-leez), *n.* the largest and most advanced order of dicot herbs, shrubs, trees, and climbers, having a tube- or bell-shaped corolla of 5 petals and with 5 stamens. The 6 families include the tendril-bearing gourd family (*Cucurbitaceae*) of watermelon, cucumber, pumpkin, squash; and 2 families of ornamentals —the bellflower or campanula family (*Campanulaceae*) and the lobelia family (*Lobeliaceae*). The main family is the very large composite family (*Compositae*); see **composite family.**

camphor (KAM-fuhr), *n.* **1.** a solid, white ketone from the camphor tree, but chiefly made by chemical treatment of pinene, a hydrocarbon; used medicinally; formula, $C_{10}H_{16}O$. **2.** the tree of the laurel family that yields camphor.

cancer (KAN-suhr), *n.* any malignant tumor resulting in abnormal cell growth and metabolism; may be fatal; occurs in many kinds of tissues; there is probably no single cause for all types. *adj.* **cancerous.**

Cancer, *n.* the *Crab,* a faintly visible constellation in the zodiac, with no bright stars; best seen in late winter and early spring.

candela (kan-DEE-luh), *n.* a unit of luminous intensity: one-sixtieth the luminance per square centimeter of blackbody radiation at the freezing point of platinum; also called *new candle.*

candle power, the light-producing power, or luminous intensity, of a light source; usually as measured in one direction; see also **candela.**

cane, *n.* **1.** the pithy segmented stem of various plants in the grass family. **2.** any plant having a stem of this type, as sugar cane. **3.** one of the smaller multiple stems from the base of various fruit bushes, such as the raspberry.

canine (KAY-nyn), *adj.* **1.** of, referring to, or like, a dog. **2.** of the family *Canidae,* including dogs, wolves, foxes, etc. **3.** referring to a pointed vertebrate tooth; see **tooth.**

Canis Major (KAY-nis MAY-juhr), the *Greater Dog,* a constellation of the southern sky, containing the brightest star, Sirius, as the dog's nose.

Canis Minor (KAY-nis MY-nuhr), the *Lesser Dog,* a small constellation of the northern sky, whose brightest star is Procyon.

canker (KANG-kuhr), *n,* **1.** an ulcer formed in the mouth or on the lips; common in children; usually the result of a digestive disturbance or cold. **2.** a disease of horses, producing an unpleasant-smelling foot discharge. **3.** a lesion on the bark of a tree. *adj.* **cankerous.**

canna family (KAN-uh), see **Musales.**

Canopus (kuh-NOH-puhs), *n.* a bright star in southern constellation Carina; second brightest star in the sky in visual magnitude.

cantilever (KAN-tuh-lehv-uhr, -lee-vuhr), *n.* a

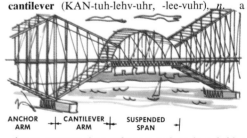

ANCHOR ARM — CANTILEVER ARM — SUSPENDED SPAN

beam supported at only one end, as in a bridge where 2 cantilevers, one on each side, meet in the center to form a *span.*

canyon (KAN-yuhn), *n.* deep valley with steep sides. Often a stream flows through a canyon.

capability (kayp-uh-BIL-uh-tee), *n.* characteristic or potential ability.

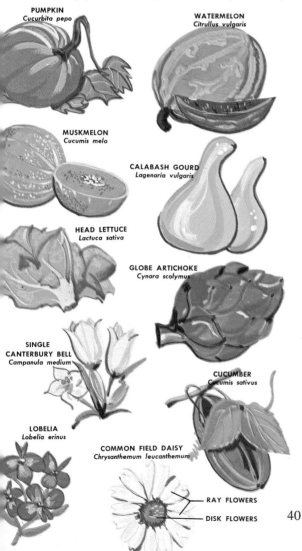

PUMPKIN
Cucurbita pepo

WATERMELON
Citrullus vulgaris

MUSKMELON
Cucumis melo

CALABASH GOURD
Lagenaria vulgaris

HEAD LETTUCE
Lactuca sativa

GLOBE ARTICHOKE
Cynara scolymus

SINGLE CANTERBURY BELL
Campanula medium

CUCUMBER
Cucumis sativus

LOBELIA
Lobelia erinus

COMMON FIELD DAISY
Chrysanthemum leucanthemum

RAY FLOWERS

DISK FLOWERS

40

capacitance (kuh-PAS-uh-tuhns), *n.* the ratio of electric charge on a plate to voltage drop between plates of a capacitor; remains constant regardless of changes in voltage or charge.

capacitor (kuh-PAS-uh-tuhr), *n.* a device made of 2 metallic plates separated by an insulator

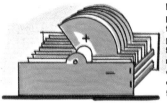

Radio tuning capacitor: capacitance increases as positive section is turned into the negative, thus changing the frequency going into the circuit

(*dielectric*), used to store and deliver electrical charges; also called *condenser.*

capacity (kuh-PAS-uh-tee), *n.* **1.** the volume of a container. **2.** an alternate term for **capacitance.**

Capella (kuh-PEL-uh), *n.* the sixth brightest star in the sky in visual magnitude, in northern constellation Auriga; clearly visible in the winter.

capillarity (kap-uh-LAIR-uh-tee), *n.* the tendency of liquids in very thin tubes to curve upward (capillary *attraction*) or downward (capillary *repulsion*) at the point of contact with the tube wall; also the tendency to rise higher than, or sink lower than the level of the liquid outside the tube; caused by surface tension of the liquid and adhesive or cohesive force between liquid and tube wall; see **surface tension.** *adj.* **capillary.**

capillary (KAP-uh-lair-ee), *n.* a very thin tube, especially the smallest of all blood vessels; the tiny branches which bring arterial blood to the tissues and carry away venous blood. The capillary walls are so thin that food, wastes, and white corpuscles pass through them.

Capricornus (KAP-ruh-kawr-nuhs), *n.* the *Goat,* a faint constellation of the southern zodiac, best seen in autumn.

Caprimulgiformes (kap-ri-muhl-ji-FAWR-meez), *n.* an order of nocturnal birds with weak legs, long wings, short beaks, and wide mouths; includes nighthawks, whippoorwills, and others.

capsule (KAP-suhl), *n.* **1.** a dry dehiscent fruit divided into 2 or more seed-bearing compartments, as in a poppy. **2.** a small medicine-containing tube which is swallowed and dissolves in the stomach, allowing the medicine to act. **3.** a spore-containing receptacle, as in mosses. **4.** see **space capsule.** *adj.* **capsular.**

carapace (KAIR-uh-pays), *n.* a rather hard shell, or exoskeleton, covering the backs of some animals, as turtles, crayfish, and lobsters.

carat (KAIR-uht), *n.* the unit of weight for all precious stones except pearls: equal to exactly 200 milligrams; contrast with **karat.**

carbide (KAHR-byd), *n.* **1.** a metal-carbon compound, or one of carbon with silicon or boron; used for its heat resistance and hardness. **2.** calcium carbide, used in making acetylene gas.

carbohydrate (kahr-boh-HY-drayt), *n.* any of a large number of organic compounds (many occurring in nature), including sugar and starch. A carbohydrate has several carbon atoms, with hydroxyl groups attached to most of them, and at least one carbonyl radical. Only green plants can form carbohydrates naturally, in photosynthesis.

carbolic acid (kahr-BAHL-ik), see **phenol.**

carbon (KAHR-buhn), *n.* a chemical element found in all living tissues; it occurs in various forms such as diamond, coal, and graphite; symbol C; *at. no.,* 6; *at. wt.,* 12.01115; known since ancient times. Carbon compounds are the basis of *organic chemistry;* see also **carbon-12.**

carbon arc, an electric current formed between 2 carbon electrodes; see **arc lamp.**

carbonate (KAHR-buh-nayt), *n.* a salt or ester of carbonic acid, containing the CO_3^- radical, as calcium carbonate.

carbonation (kahr-buh-NAY-shuhn), *n.* the addition of carbonic acid or carbon dioxide gas to substances, as in making *carbonated* beverages.

carbon cycle, the pattern of change of carbon in passing from plants to animals and back again. Plants take in carbon dioxide gas from the atmosphere and convert it to carbohydrates by photosynthesis. Animals eat the plants and obtain energy from the carbohydrates. The release of energy is accompanied by the breakdown of carbohydrates into carbon dioxide and water. The carbon dioxide is exhaled into the atmosphere.

carbon dioxide, a colorless, odorless gas used by plants to make food; given off by plants and animals during respiration; used to make carbonated beverages; formula, CO_2. *Dry ice* (a tradename) is solid carbon dioxide, a refrigerant.

carbon-14, a carbon isotope used in dating prehistoric events; see **radiocarbon dating.**

carbonic acid (kahr-BAHN-ik), an unstable inorganic acid; decomposes readily into carbon dioxide and water; formula, H_2CO_3.

Carboniferous (kahr-buh-NIF-uh-ruhs), *n.* a period of geologic time late in the Paleozoic Era, so named because much of the world's coal was formed during this period; began about 300 million years ago and lasted almost 60 million years; in North America, includes the Mississippian and Pennsylvanian periods.

carbonization (kahr-buh-nuh-ZAY-shuhn), *n.* **1.** the charring of organic matter by heat or chemical treatment to form carbon. **2.** the conversion of coal into coke in coke ovens. **3.** impregnation of a substance, usually a metal, with carbon at high temperatures.

carbon monoxide (mahn-AHKS-eyd), a colorless, odorless, extremely poisonous gas formed by incomplete combustion of carbon compounds; used as a fuel, to extract metals from ores, and to make organic compounds; formula, CO.

carbon star, a star with an unusually high percentage of carbon, as shown by its spectroscopic lines; most are red giants of fairly low temperature.

carbon steel, any steel not containing appreciable amounts of alloying metals. All steels have carbon, usually with a top limit of about 0.85%. Carbon steel is the cheapest steel, most commonly made by the open-hearth process.

carbon tetrachloride (tet-ruh-KLOH-ryd), a colorless, nonflammable liquid with a sweet, aromatic odor; used as a solvent. Its vapors are toxic and thus can be safely used as a fire extinguisher only in ventilated areas; formula, CCl_4.

carbon-12, a carbon isotope adopted in 1961 as the official international standard for all atomic weights of elements; defined as having atomic

carbonyl

weight (or mass) of exactly 12.000; replaced oxygen, formerly defined as the standard with atomic weight of 16.000.

carbonyl (KAHR-buh-neel), *n.* **1.** an organic radical found in ketones, acids, etc.; formula, $>C=O$. **2.** a compound of carbon monoxide and a metal, as $Ni(CO)_4$; used to remove impurities from metals.

carborundum (kahr-buh-RUHN-duhm), *n.* silicon carbide, SiC; used as an abrasive and for electronic resistors.

carboxyl (kahr-BAHKS-uhl), *n.* a radical found in organic acids, ^-COOH.

carbuncle (KAHR-bung-kuhl), *n.* **1.** an infection of the skin and underlying tissue, which become inflamed and filled with pus. **2.** a garnet cut into a rounded form, with no flat faces (facets).

carburetor (KAHR-byoo-ray-tuhr, -ree-tuhr), *n.* a device in any internal-combustion engine for vaporizing the fuel and mixing it in proper proportion with air.

carcinogen (kahr-SIN-uh-juhn), *n.* any substance capable of causing a cancer; certain complex chemicals found in coal tars are examples.

carcinoma (kahr-si-NOH-muh), *n.* a malignant growth originating especially in epithelial tissues, as in the skin; a type of cancer.

cardiac (KAHR-dee-ak), *adj.* pertaining to or near the heart, as the *cardiac* portion of the stomach which food reaches first.

cardiovascular (kahr-dee-oh-VAS-kyuh-luhr), *adj.* pertaining to the heart and blood vessels, as the *cardiovascular* (circulatory) system.

carnallite (KAHR-nuh-lyt), *n.* a granular, milkwhite or reddish mineral: $KMgCl_3 \cdot 6H_2O$, with hardness 1; a main source of pure potassium.

carnelian (kahr-NEEL-yuhn), *n.* a type of chalcedony with bright to deep red markings, used as a gemstone because of its color and hardness.

Carnivora (kahr-NIV-uh-ruh), *n.* an order of flesh-eating mammals with teeth modified for cutting and tearing; often with well-developed canine teeth for killing; one suborder of *carnivores* with toed feet includes hyena, raccoon, mongoose, and the large cat, dog, bear, and weasel families; the second living suborder, with limbs modified for aquatic life, includes seal, sea lion, and walrus.

carnivore (KAHR-nuh-vohr), *n.* **1.** the common name for a mammal in order *Carnivora*. **2.** any flesh-eating member of the animal kingdom. *adj.* **carnivorous.**

carnotite (KAHR-noh-tyt), *n.* a complex yellowish mineral occurring as a powder or a crystal mass; source of uranium, vanadium, and radium.

carotene (KAIR-uh-teen), *n.* a yellow-orange hydrocarbon found in plants; called *pro-vitamin A* because it is converted to vitamin A in the human body; its absence is one cause of night blindness; formula, $C_{40}H_{56}$.

carpal (KAHR-puhl), *adj.* pertaining to the wrist, especially to the joint and the bones involved. *n.* **carpus.**

carpel (KAHR-puhl), *n.* one or more chambers or leaflike organs in a simple or compound pistil of a flower; each carpel bears ovules.

carrier, *n.* **1.** a human or other organism that transmits a disease to others, often without itself suffering the effects of the disease; a *typhoid carrier* may spread typhoid fever to many other people for years, yet be immune to the disease and not show any symptoms. **2.** an aircraft designed to carry loads, especially AAM or ASM missiles.

carrier wave, a high-frequency electromagnetic wave of regular form, which may be modulated (altered) so that it transmits signals; modulation is produced by use of a second wave; see also **amplitude modulation.**

carrot family, see **Umbellales.**

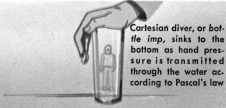

Cartesian diver, or bottle imp, sinks to the bottom as hand pressure is transmitted through the water according to Pascal's law

Cartesian diver (kahr-TEE-zhuhn), an inverted gas-filled tube or figure with one open end; floats submerged in a liquid; when pressure on the liquid surface is increased, the gas compresses and the diver floats below its original position; used as a sensitive device for indicating pressure changes.

STRIPED SKUNK
Mephitis mephitis
FAMILY MUSTELIDAE

EUROPEAN WEASEL, OR STOAT
Mustela erminea
FAMILY MUSTELIDAE

RACCOON
Procyon lotor
FAMILY PROCYONIDAE

GRIZZLY BEAR
Ursus Horribilis
FAMILY URSIDAE

ATLANTIC WALRUS
Odobenus rosmarus
FAMILY ODOBENIDAE

CALIFORNIA SEA LION
Zalophus californianus
FAMILY OTARIIDAE

DOG, *Canis domestica*
FAMILY CANIDAE

STRIPED HYENA
Hyaena hyaena
FAMILY HYAENIDAE

HARBOR SEAL, *Phoca vitulina*
FAMILY PHOCIDAE

cc

cartilage (KAHR-tuh-luhj), n. a strong, elastic type of connective tissue that provides body support much as bone does. In vertebrate development, much cartilage is replaced by bone, but some cartilage remains, even in human adults, especially in the trachea and in the disks between vertebrae. *adj.* **cartilaginous.**

cartography (kahr-TAHG-ruh-fee), n. the technique of making maps and charts. Much cartography depends on aerial photography, and recently, on information from satellites. Formerly confined largely to the earth's surface, *cartographers* now deal also with accurate mapping of the ocean floors and even of the moon and the nearer planets.

Caryophyllales (kair-ee-ohf-uh-LAY-leez), an alternate term for **Centrospermales.**

caryopsis (kair-ee-AHP-sis), n. a small, dry fruit containing one seed whose wall is fused with the ovary wall, as in cereal grains and other grasses.

casein (KAY-see-in), n. the chief protein in milk and its products. Over 80% of milk protein is casein, present as the calcium salt, calcium caseinate; used in industry, especially in paints.

cashew family (KASH-oo, kuh-SHOO), see **Sapindales.**

Cassiopeia (kas-ee-uh-PEE-uh), n. a bright constellation near the North Star, shaped like a crooked letter W. Cassiopeia is on the opposite side of the North Star from the Big Dipper.

cassiterite (kuh-SIT-uh-ryt), n. tin oxide, SnO_2, the chief ore of tin, with hardness 6-7; usually brown because of traces of iron with it.

cassowary (KAS-uh-wair-ee), see **Casuariformes.**

cast iron, one of several iron alloys containing about 2% to 4.5% carbon; very hard and brittle but not usually malleable or ductile; used for construction, machinery, and hardware.

Castor (KAS-tuhr), n. a bright star in the constellation Gemini, the 23rd brightest star in visual brightness. Castor is called *Alpha Gemini,* but is really 6 stars (3 sets of binary stars).

castor oil, a heavy, clear oil obtained from the bean of the castor-oil plant; important in industry as a machine lubricant, and in medicine.

castration (kas-TRAY-shuhn), n. removal of the sex glands from an animal, especially the cutting off of the testicles; important in poultry and livestock raising, since castrated males produce tastier meat than do normal males. A *capon* is a castrated chicken; *steer,* a castrated bull; and *gelding,* a castrated horse.

Casuariformes (kas-yoo-air-i-FAWR-meez), n. an order of large flightless birds of Australia and neighboring lands; each feather has 2 shafts of the same length, one called the *aftershaft;* order includes emu and cassowary.

catabolism (kuh-TAB-uh-lizm), n. the breaking-down part of the process of metabolism; the conversion of complex chemicals into simple chemicals by cells for energy is *catabolism;* contrast with **anabolism.** adj. **catabolic.**

catalyst (KAT-uh-list), n. a substance that increases the speed of a chemical reaction without being used up or changed itself; used in metallurgy, petroleum cracking, and organic synthesis; *enzymes* are catalysts that act in digestion. *adj.* **catalytic.**

cataract (KAT-uh-rakt), n. **1.** an eye disorder in which the lens of the eye, normally transparent, becomes opaque. **2.** a waterfall, especially one involving large volumes of water falling over steep cliffs or rapids in a river.

caterpillar, n. the larval form of a butterfly or moth; see **larva, metamorphosis.**

cat family, cats, lions, tigers, cougars, and others; see **Carnivora.**

cathode (KATH-ohd), n. a negatively charged electrode from which electrons flow, such as the negative terminal of a battery or the filament in a vacuum tube; see also **anode.**

cathode ray, a stream of electrons emitted from cathodes of vacuum tubes, used for a variety of purposes, such as X-rays.

cathode-ray tube, a device for converting the bombardment of electrons against an object into a visible pattern on a screen, as a television receiver tube and screen. The tube consists of an *envelope,* or container under fairly high vacuum; an *electron gun,* the major working part of the tube, which

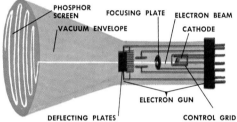

produces, focuses, and deflects the electrons; and the *screen,* a piece of glass coated with fluorescent material. When electrons strike the screen, they produce a visible pattern of the deflection.

cation (KAT-ey-uhn), n. any positively charged atom or ion, such as Na^+ or NH_4^+; especially applied to positive ions in electrolysis, during which cations migrate to the cathode.

catkin (KAT-kin), n. a scaly type of inflorescence with no petals; the birch and the willow have catkins as their blossoms; also called *ament.*

cattail family, see **Pandanales.**

cattle, n. domesticated and useful mammals of the ox family; large, hoofed ruminants; raised mainly for food and classified as *beef, dairy,* or *dual purpose;* the 2 chief types are long horns and short horns. Cows and bulls are most common in North and South America; other peoples commonly use other *Bovidae,* such as goats in Switzerland and camels in Africa.

caudal (KAW-duhl), adj. in animals, pertaining to the tail or the tail area.

cave, n. a hollowed-out area in the earth. Natural caves are usually formed by the action of water, either by the sea hollowing out spaces in cliffs or by rain dissolving away limestone.

cave man, any of various prehistoric groups of men, especially of Paleolithic times, that lived in caves of natural origin.

cavity (KAV-uh-tee), n. a hollowed-out space, especially such a space in a tooth formed by decay; see also **dental caries.**

Cb, symbol for *columbium,* now called **niobium.**

cc, abbreviation for *cubic centimeter,* a small liquid measurement.

43

Cd

Cd, symbol for **cadmium.**

Ce, symbol for **cerium.**

cecum, alternate spelling of **caecum.**

ceiling (SEEL-ing), *n.* **1.** height above ground in aviation: *cloud ceiling* is the distance from the ground to the lowest clouds in an overcast sky or in broken clouds. **2.** the highest distance above ground at which any airplane can operate.

celestial (suh-LES-chuhl), *adj.* referring to objects or conditions in space. *Celestial* bodies include moons, planets, stars, meteorites, and (sometimes) man-made objects.

celestial navigation, navigation by aid of the sun, moon, and stars. Accurate observation of the exact position of a known celestial body at an exact time makes possible accurate calculation of a ship's or plane's position.

celestial sphere, an imaginary sphere with the earth at its center and the stars on the surface of the sphere; based on the ancient belief that Earth was the center of the universe.

celestite (SEL-uhs-tyt), *n.* a white or pale blue crystal mineral, $SrSO_4$, with hardness 3-3½; the chief source of strontium; *strontium sulfate.*

cell, *n.* **1.** the basic unit of living matter. The simplest plants and animals are a single cell. More complex organisms are made up of many cells,

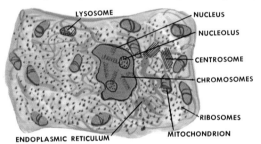

LYSOSOME — NUCLEUS — NUCLEOLUS — CENTROSOME — CHROMOSOMES — RIBOSOMES — MITOCHONDRION — ENDOPLASMIC RETICULUM

General diagram of a living cell: different specialized organelles and surfaces occur in specialized cells; most plant cells have additional cell wall of cellulose

some with highly specialized functions. All cells consist of protoplasm. **2.** a unit for production or storage of electrical energy. Such cells, when wired together, form a *battery.* The common electrical cell is a device for changing chemical to electrical energy. Solar cells and light cells convert radiant energy from sunlight or from other light sources into electrical energy. **3.** any portion of the atmosphere, large or small, that acts as a single unit in motion or change. *adj.* **cellular.**

cell division, either of 2 processes by which body cells reproduce themselves: *mitosis,* or duplication division, in which chromosome number remains unchanged; and *meiosis,* or reduction division, in which chromosome number is halved and gametes formed; see **meiosis, mitosis.**

cell membrane, a delicate, elastic, semipermeable structure surrounding the cytoplasm of all cells; plant cells also have a thick outer wall made of cellulose or lignin or both; see also **cell.**

cellophane (SEL-uh-fayn), *n.* a thin, transparent film of viscose, a substance of the rayon type made by treating cellulose with caustic soda and carbon disulfide; may be colored and imprinted.

cell theory, the view that all plants and animals are made up of cells and cell products. The theory,

first advanced by the Frenchman R. J. H. Dutrochet in 1824, was stated in full form by the German biologists T. Schleiden and M. Schwann in 1838.

cellular (SEL-yoo-luhr), *adj.* of or pertaining to a cell.

celluloid (SEL-yuh-loid), *n.* the first man-made commercial plastic; a form of *cellulose nitrate,* made by treating cellulose with nitric acid; chiefly used as a backing for photographic film, but is highly flammable.

cellulose (SEL-yuh-lohs), *n.* a form of carbohydrate formed from glucose in many plant cells, deposited in cell walls; the starting material for rayon and many other synthetic products.

cellulose acetate, a form of rayon, made from acetic acid, acetate anhydride, and cellulose; has a specific gravity close to that of silk; stronger and wrinkles less than other rayons.

Celsius (SEL-see-uhs), *adj.* an alternate term for *centigrade,* the temperature scale devised by Anders Celsius, a Swedish astronomer; see also **centigrade.** *abbr.* C or **Cels.**

Cenozoic (see-nuh-ZOH-ik), *n.* most recent era in geologic history, includes the present time; often called the *Age of Mammals* and *Age of Man;* includes roughly the last 70 million years of the earth's history; see **geologic time table.**

Centaur (SEN-tawr), *n.* **1.** the common name for **Centaurus.** **2.** a solid-fueled space vehicle, especially the second stage of the launch system; planned with the capability of carrying a 1300-pound vehicle to Mars or Venus.

Centaurus (sen-TAW-ruhs), *n.* the *Centaur,* a bright constellation in the southern sky, containing 2 very bright stars, Alpha Centauri and Beta Centauri.

center of gravity, the point (sometimes outside of the object) at which an object could be suspended so the entire weight would be balanced; decorative mobiles hang from their centers of gravity.

centi-, a word part meaning 100 or 1/100; a *centimeter* is 1/100 of a meter.

Center of gravity in a toy with a weighted bottom remains in the toy, keeping it from turning over

centigrade (SEN-tih-grayd), *adj.* referring to, or based on, a temperature scale dividing into 100 equal parts the range between the freezing point (0°) and boiling point (100°) of water at standard pressure; also called *Celsius. abbr.* **C.**

centimeter-gram-second system, the system of units commonly used for scientific measurements, based on the *centimeter* (1/100 meter) as the unit of length, the *gram* as the unit of mass, and the *second* as the unit of time. *abbr.* **cgs system.**

centipede (SEN-tuh-peed), see **Chilopoda.**

central nervous system, the portion of the nervous system made up of the brain and the spinal cord; controls most voluntary movements in mammals; contrast with **peripheral nervous system.**

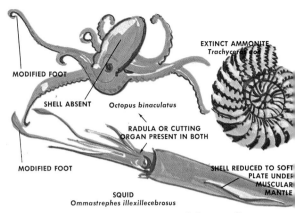

EXTINCT AMMONITE
Trachyceras nodosus

MODIFIED FOOT

SHELL ABSENT   Octopus binaculatus

RADULA OR CUTTING
ORGAN PRESENT IN BOTH

MODIFIED FOOT

SHELL REDUCED TO SOFT
PLATE UNDER
MUSCULAR
MANTLE

SQUID
Ommastrephes illexillecebrosus

centrifugal force (sen-TRIF-yuh-guhl), a force imagined as acting on an object rotating around a central point, tending to throw the object out from the center. If the object stays in its position, the centrifugal force is the reaction to an equal and opposite *centripetal force.*

centrifuge (SEN-tri-fyooj), *n.* a device in which objects can be placed and rotated at high speeds. Centrifuges separate components of liquid mixtures (the cream separator that separates skim milk from butterfat), or liquids from solids (the spin dryer on a washing machine). A special centrifuge is used to test rockets and man's adaptation to high gravitational forces in space.

centriole (SEN-tree-ohl), *n.* either of 2 tiny dark bodies in some cells, located outside the nucleus. The centrioles appear to organize the cellular proteins before mitosis.

centripetal force (sen-TRIP-uh-tuhl), a force acting on an object rotating around a central point, tending to pull the object toward the center; centripetal force is an equal and opposite reaction to *centrifugal force.*

centrosome (SEN-truh-sohm), *n.* the region of cytoplasm in a cell surrounding the centrioles; its significance is still uncertain.

Centrospermales (sehn-truh-spuhr-MAY-leez), *n.* an order of dicot herbs and shrubs, most having ovaries bearing a single ovule and a coiled em-

1. Pokeweed, *Phytolacca americana* (family Phytolacca-
ceae); 2. purslane, *Portulaca grandiflora;* 3. bougain-
villea, *Bougainvillaea globra* (in the four-o'clock family); 4. Indian pink, *Silene laciniate;* 5. spinach, *Spinacia
oleraca*

bryo in the seed. Among its 8 families are the goosefoot family (*Chenopodiaceae*)—beet, sugar beet, spinach; the four-o'clock family (*Nyctagi-naceae*); the fleshy purslane or portulaca family (*Portulaceae*); and the pink family (*Caryophyl-laceae*)—pinks, carnation, sweet William, and chickweed; order is also called *Caryophyllales.*

cephalic index (suh-FAL-ik), a number used by anthropologists in comparing head shapes: 100 times the greatest width of head from side to side divided by the greatest length from front to back.

Cephalochordata (sef-uh-loh-kohr-DAH-tuh), *n.* a subphylum of phylum *Chordata* of animals with notochord extending almost the entire body length, dorsal tubular nerve cord, and slits in the walls of the pharynx; amphioxus (lancelet) is a *cephalochordate.*

Cephalopoda (sef-uh-LAH-poh-duh), *n.* a class in the phylum *Mollusca* of animals with shell often reduced or absent, head well developed,

radula or cutting organ present, and foot modified into arms or tentacles; octopus, squid, nautilus, and cuttlefish are *cephalopods.*

cephalothorax (sef-uh-loh-THOH-raks), *n.* the region at the front of the body formed by a combination of head and thorax; present in many crustaceans and arachnids.

Cepheid variable (SEE-fee-uhd), a type of variable star with regular, alternating periods of light variation; one theory states that the star actually expands and contracts in great pulsations; contrast with **binary star.**

Cepheus (SEE-fee-uhs), *n.* a constellation of the northern sky, near the Pole Star. One of its variable stars, Delta Cephei, is the source of the name *Cepheid variable* for such stars.

ceramic (suhr-AM-ik), *adj.* made of or containing clay or other non-metallic mineral earths.

cereal (SEER-ee-al), *n.* see **grains.**

cerebellum (sair-uh-BEL-uhm), *n.* the portion of the brain in vertebrates which controls muscular coordination. In man, it has 2 hemispheres around a central section; the core has a branching structure often called "tree of life"; see **brain.**

cerebral palsy (SAIR-uh-bruhl PAWL-zee), a brain defect due either to injury at birth or to abnormal brain cell development during embryonic growth; both motor and sensory systems may be affected.

cerebrospinal fluid (sair-uh-broh-SPY-nuhl), the serous fluid contained in cavities of the brain, in the central canal of the spinal cord, and between the meninges.

cerebrum (SAIR-uh-bruhm, suhr-EE-bruhm), *n.* in vertebrates, the major portion of the brain, divided into 2 large hemispheres; composed of *white matter* (nerve fibers and processes) and *gray matter* (cell bodies) which is mostly on the surface. The whole surface is marked with indentations called *convolutions* or *gyri.* The cerebrum controls most voluntary actions; see **brain, nervous system.** *adj.* **cerebral.**

Ceres (SEER-eez), *n.* the largest known asteroid, about 485 miles in diameter.

cerium (SEE-ree-uhm), *n.* a gray, metallic chemical element in the lanthanide series; used to make alloys and to remove fission products from molten uranium; symbol Ce; *at. no.* 58; *at. wt.,* 140.12; isolated independently in 1803 by Klaproth, and by Berzelius and Hisinger.

cesium (SEE-zee-uhm), *n.* a silvery-white, soft metallic chemical element; the heaviest of the alkali metals; used in electronic equipment to absorb excess oxygen; symbol Cs; *at. no.,* 55; *at. wt.,* 132.905; isolated in 1860 by Bunsen.

45

(Top) Killer whale, *Grampus orca,* a toothed cetacean about 25 feet long; (bottom) blue, or sulphur-bottom, whale, *Sibbaldus musculus,* a baleen whale, the largest living mammal, about 80 feet long

Cetacea (suh-TAY-shee-uh), *n.* an order of mammals adapted for aquatic life, with front limbs modified into flippers, hind limbs absent, and fleshy flukes on the tail. *Cetaceans* are divided into 2 major groups: *toothed* (dolphins, porpoises, and many whales, including the largest) and *baleen,* or *whalebone,* whales. Toothed whales may be carnivorous; baleen whales strain plankton from the water.

Cf, symbol for **californium.**

cgs system, abbreviation for **centimeter-gram-second system.**

chain reaction, a chemical or nuclear reaction in which the products formed are themselves active in carrying the reaction further. In nuclear re-

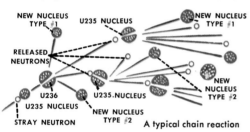

NEW NUCLEUS TYPE #1   U235 NUCLEUS   NEW NUCLEUS TYPE #1

RELEASED NEUTRONS

U236   U235 NUCLEUS   NEW NUCLEUS TYPE #2

U235 NUCLEUS

STRAY NEUTRON   NEW NUCLEUS TYPE #2   A typical chain reaction

actions, neutrons produce fissions that produce other neutrons, in turn producing further fissions; see also **proton-proton reaction.**

chalcedony (kal-SED-uh-nee), *n.* a translucent fibrous type of quartz, occurring in varied colors depending on impurities present. Its appearance makes it valuable as a semiprecious stone. *Sard, carnelian,* and *chrysoprase* are varieties.

chalcopyrite (kal-kuh-PY-ryt), *n.* a metallic yellow ore of copper, $CuFeS_2$, with hardness $3\frac{1}{2}$-4; resembles pyrite, but is softer.

chalk (CHAWK), *n.* a white mineral of calcium carbonate, composed largely of the shells of ancient microorganisms; a form of calcite.

chameleon (kuh-MEE-lee-uhn), see **lizard.**

channel (CHAN-uhl), *n.* **1.** the bed in which a stream of liquid flows; it may be natural, as in a river channel, or man-made, as in sewers. **2.** in navigation, that part of a stream deep enough for travel. **3.** a frequency band allotted for radio or television transmission.

characteristic (kahr-ahk-tuhr-IS-tik), *n.* a definite, describable quality, action, or structural feature of a thing, especially of an organism; a *trait;* a *property. adj.* **characteristic.**

Charadriiformes (kuh-rahd-ree-uh-FAWR-meez), *n.* an order of birds inhabiting the shores of lakes and seas; includes auks, gulls, plovers, terns, and others—the *shore birds.*

charcoal, *n.* a black, amorphous carbon, made by heating wood or bone in a closed vessel with the air excluded; being porous, it can absorb large quantities of gas; used to filter gases and liquids, and as a fuel.

charge, *n.* the electrical characteristic of an atomic particle. A particle with an electrical charge (a *charged* particle) is either positive or negative; protons have *positive* charges; electrons, *negative* ones.

charged particle, any of the fundamental units of matter that carries an electrical charge. The most common units are those that compose the typical atom: positive *protons* and negative *electrons.* The *neutron* is uncharged, electrically neutral.

Charles' law, a basic law of gases: the volume of a gas increases in direct proportion to the increase in absolute temperature, if the pressure is kept constant; named for French physicist Jacques A. Charles.

chasm (KAZM), *n.* a very deep crevice in a surface; on the surface of the earth, a narrow gorge; on glaciers, a very deep pit; on sea bottom, a sharp drop to a much greater depth.

chassis (SHAS-ee), *n.* the frame on which a moving part or vehicle or other device rests or is built: the *chassis* of a car or airplane is the frame on which the other parts are built.

chela (KEE-luh), *n., pl.* **-lae.** the claw of the lobster or other arthropod.

Chellean (SHEL-ee-uhn), *adj.* describing man's development at the earliest part of the Paleolithic period in earth history, nearly 500,000 years ago. For many years Chellean man was known only by the axes and other artifacts he left behind; recent discoveries indicate that man of this period has been found; he is intermediate between Australopithecus and Java man.

chemical (KEM-ih-kuhl), **1.** *n.* an element or compound, found in nature or man-made. **2.** *adj.* pertaining to chemistry, as in *chemical* bond.

chemical change, any of various processes involving energy in which one substance is converted into another, such as rusting of metal, burning of fuel, and photosynthesis; contrast with **physical change.**

chemical energy, the energy existing in the bonds holding atoms and molecules together; evolved or produced during all chemical reactions.

chemical equation (ee-KWAY-shuhn), a symbolic form for expressing a chemical reaction, as in $Zn + 2HCl \rightarrow ZnCl_2 + H_2$ (one atom of zinc combines with 2 molecules of hydrochloric acid to produce one molecule of zinc chloride and one molecule of hydrogen).

chemical reaction, the rearrangement of atoms or electrons in compounds or molecules to form different substances, consuming or releasing light, chemical, thermal, or electrical energy. In chemical reactions, weight of the final products equals combined weights of the starting products.

chemiluminescence (kem-i-loo-muh-NES-uhnts), *n.* luminescence of a material obtained by transforming chemical energy directly into light, especially with little heat.

chemistry (KEM-is-tree), *n.* the science concerned with the composition of matter and with other than purely physical changes in the state of

46

matter. *Chemists* work in laboratories and factories in several major specialties: **analytical chemistry**–kinds and quantities of substances; **physical chemistry**–physical properties of chemical processes; **inorganic chemistry**–chemical reactions excluding those of carbon compounds; **organic chemistry**–the chemistry of carbon compounds.

chemosynthesis (KEE-moh-sen-the-sis), *n.* the synthesis of organic substances by any organism that manufactures its own food using energy from chemical reactions, as in certain bacteria; contrast with **photosynthesis.**

chemotherapy (kem-oh-THAIR-uh-pee), *n.* the use of chemicals, such as drugs, to treat or control diseases without injuring the patient; see **pharmacology.**

chemotropism (kuh-MAHT-roh-pizm), *n.* a tropism (reaction) in which the direction of a plant's growth or movement is determined by chemicals.

chert (CHUHRT), *n.* a flinty quartz, usually dull in appearance, often found in limestone.

chiasma (ky-AS-muh), *n., pl.* **-mata, -mas. 1.** a point of crossing, as the *optic chiasma* or the crossing of the optic nerves in the midbrain. **2.** the points of contact between members of a pair of chromosomes in the prophase of meiosis; genes on one chromosome may cross over onto the other chromosome at these points, allowing new combinations of genes to appear in future generations; see **meiosis.**

chicken pox, a highly contagious disease, usually occurring in children, and giving future immunity; shows as a red rash on the skin; caused by the same virus that produces shingles; known medically as *varicella.*

chicle (CHIK-uhl), *n.* the milky latex recovered from the bark of the sapodilla tree; used in making chewing gum.

Chilopoda (ky-LAH-puh-duh), *n.* a class of phylum *Arthropoda* of animals with long segmented bodies and a pair of legs on each segment; the front legs may excrete a poison used in defense and food-getting; centipedes are the only *chilopods.*

Chiroptera (ky-RAHP-tuh-ruh), *n.* an order of mammals with front limbs modified for flying by a lengthening of the second to fifth digits to support a membranous wing; hind limbs have

Hoary bat, *Lasiurus cirereus*

clawed digits for hanging upside down for sleeping; insect or fruit eating, with one species a blood sucker; *chiropterans* include all bats.

chitin (KY-tin), *n.* the hard outer shell of insects, crabs, and similar animals. Chitin is chemically a carbohydrate very similar to cellulose; used industrially. *adj.* **chitinous.**

chiton (KY-tuhn), see **Amphineura, Mollusca.**

chloral (KLAWR-uhl), *n.* a colorless, oily, liquid aldehyde used in insecticides; formula, CCl_3CHO. *Chloral hydrate* ($CCl_3CHO \cdot H_2O$) is used as a sedative.

chlorella (klawr-EL-uh), see **Chlorophyta.**

chloride (KLOH-ryd), *n.* **1.** a salt of hydrochloric acid, generally soluble in water. **2.** an anion formed from chlorine, Cl^-.

chlorination (kloh-ruh-NAY-shuhn), *n.* **1.** a process that uses chlorine, such as bleaching or water and sewage purification. **2.** the addition or substitution of chlorine in a compound.

chlorine (KLOH-reen), *n.* a chemical element in the halogen family; a very poisonous, yellowish-green gas that attacks the respiratory system; used in bleaches and disinfectants and for chlorination of organic compounds; symbol Cl; *at. no.,* 17; *at. wt.,* 35.453; isolated by Scheele in 1774.

chloroform (KLOH-ruh-fawrm), *n.* a heavy, nonflammable, colorless liquid with a sweet odor; used as a solvent, to make other chemicals, and, originally, as a general anesthetic; formula, $CHCl_3$.

chlorophyll (KLAWR-uh-fil), *n.* a complex substance responsible for the green coloring in plants, often present with color concealed by other pigments; located within chloroplasts; consists of 2 very complex esters: $C_{55}H_{72}MgN_4O_5$ and $C_{55}H_{70}MgN_4O_6$; see **photosynthesis.**

Chlorophyta (klawr-AHF-uh-tuh), *n.* a plant division including the true green algae; *chlorophytes* may be unicellular, multicellular, or colonial; reproduce asexually and sexually; includes spirogyra, pleurococcus, and chlorella; see **alga.**

chloroplast (KLAWR-uh-plast), *n.* any of the specialized bodies outside the nucleus of a plant cell (typically in the leaves) that contain chlorophyll confined in structures called *lamellae.*

chloroprene (KLAWR-uh-preen), *n.* a colorless, liquid organic compound; used to make synthetic rubber and plastics; formula, C_4H_5Cl.

chlorpromazine (klawr-PRAH-muh-zeen), *n.* a synthetic drug related to the antihistamines; used as a sedative, especially in nervous disorders; formula, $C_{17}H_{19}N_2SCl$.

chokedamp, *n.* a gas, primarily carbon dioxide, often found at the bottom of mines, pits, or wells; formed by slow decay of organic material; dangerous only because it replaces oxygen; also called *blackdamp.*

cholera (KAHL-uh-ruh), *n.* **1.** a highly infectious, usually fatal, disease of the digestive tract; more correctly, *asiatic cholera.* **2.** *cholera morbus,* a rarely fatal, noninfectious disease, occurring usually in summer or fall, probably due to tainted food.

cholesterol (kuh-LES-tuh-rohl), *n.* a fatty sterol found in the nerve tissue, brain, and spinal cord of all animals, as well as in blood and all animal fats. The relation between cholesterol and hardening of the arteries and heart attacks is being studied. Plant cholesterol is not used by animals, even herbivorous ones.

cholic acid (KOH-lik), one of the steroids found in liver bile; formula, $C_{24}H_{40}O_5$.

Chondrichthyes (kahn-DRIK-thi-eez), *n.* a class in the chordate subphylum *Vertebrata,* including fishes with cartilaginous skeletons and usually

Chordata

leathery skins with imbedded scales; examples are sharks, rays, skates, and chimeras, represented by a few deep-sea species.

1. Stingray, Dasyatis ruy; 2. ratfish, Hydrolagus colliei (in a separate subclass); 3. tiger shark, Galeocerdo cuvieri; 4. barndoor skate, Raja laevis

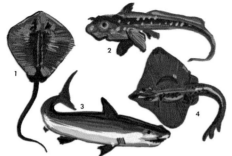

Chordata (kawr-DAH-tuh), *n.* a phylum of animals having a notochord and slits in the wall of the pharynx at some stage of the life cycle, a long, hollow nerve cord the length of the back, and a ventral heart; *chordates* include the protochordates and vertebrates, including man.

chorea, an alternate term for **Saint Vitus' dance.**

chorion (KAWR-ee-ahn), *n.* the outermost membrane surrounding the embryo in most vertebrates. In many mammals, the chorion comes in contact with the uterine wall to form much of the placenta; see also **amnion.**

choroid (KAWR-oyd), *n.* a dark, middle membrane of the eye containing many blood vessels; also called *choroid coat;* see **eye.**

chrom-, a word part meaning *pigment* or *color,* as in *chromatin;* or meaning *chromium.*

chromate (KROH-mayt), *n.* a salt of chromic acid containing a CrO_4^- or a $Cr_2O_7^-$ radical; used as oxidizing agents and for paint pigments.

chromatic aberration (kroh-MAT-ik ab-uh-RAY-shuhn), optical distortion caused by the different distances light of various wavelengths must travel through a medium. Special shapes of lenses or special combinations of lenses may eliminate the problem; see also **aberration.**

chromatid (KROH-muh-tid), *n.* one of a pair of strands making up a chromosome; called *daughter chromosome* after the metaphase of mitosis; see **mitosis.**

chromatin (KROH-muh-tin), *n.* protoplasm in the cell nucleus that can be stained a dark color for microscopic examination; especially, the particles that form the chromosome and carry genes; a source of DNA.

chromatophore (kroh-MAT-uh-fawr), *n.* any pigment-bearing cell in a plant or animal. In some organisms, as in the chameleon, the changing shapes of chromatophores cause change in skin color.

chrome, *n.* **1.** a common term for **chromium.** **2.** chromium steel, a strong, hard alloy used for machine parts. **3.** any of the chromium compounds used as pigments.

chromite (KROH-myt), *n.* a brownish-black granular mineral, $FeCr_2O_4$, with hardness 5½; the chief source of chromium metal.

chromium (KROH-mee-uhm), *n.* an extremely hard, bluish-white metallic element with a high melting point; used in alloys and in electroplating to increase strength and prevent corrosion; symbol Cr; *at. no.,* 24; *at. wt.,* 51.996; isolated by Vauquelin in 1798.

chromoplast (KROH-muh-plast), *n.* any of the bodies in the cytoplasm of plant cells containing pigments of various colors other than green.

chromosome (KROH-muh-sohm), *n.* a long, threadlike object in a living cell nucleus. Chromosomes occur in pairs, and there is a characteristic number for each kind of organism: man has 23 pairs. The chromosomes are believed to carry genes, the combination of which determines hereditary characteristics. *adj.* **chromosomal.**

chromosphere (KROH-muh-sfeer), *n.* a layer of transparent gas, chiefly hydrogen, in the sun's atmosphere, as much as 15,000 miles thick, between the photosphere and the corona.

chronic (KRAHN-ik), *adj.* lasting for a considerable time; describing abnormal conditions that do not appear and disappear rapidly, as a disease; contrast with **acute.**

chronology (krahn-AHL-uh-jee), *n.* the arrangement of time and past events into periods marked by distinctly different characteristics; see **geologic time table.**

chronometer (kruh-NAHM-uh-tuhr), *n.* **1.** a large and accurate watch used especially for timekeeping on long sea voyages, now largely replaced by radio broadcasts of time signals. **2.** any very accurate timepiece.

chrysalis (KRIS-uh-lis), *n., pl.* **-salides.** the stage of an insect's metamorphosis when a caterpillar forms a smooth, hard case; the *pupa,* intermediate between *larva* and adult or *imago;* see **pupa.**

chrysoberyl (KRIS-uh-bair-uhl), *n.* a mineral oxide of beryllium and aluminum, $BeAl_2O_4$, with hardness 8½; found in various shades of green, brown, yellow; 2 types, alexandrite and cat's-eye, are valued as gemstones; see **gem.**

Chrysophyta (kri-SAHF-uh-tuh), *n.* a plant division including the yellow-green and golden-brown algae and the diatoms; *chrysophytes* have chlorophyll masked by other pigments and food usually stored as oil; plant may be unicellular, multicellular, or colonial; silica often found in cell walls; reproduces asexually and sexually; see **alga, Thallophyta.**

chuffing, *n.* irregular burning of rocket engine fuel after normal burnout; adds unplanned thrust to the flight of the rocket.

chugging, *n.* uneven combustion in a chemical propulsion device; may cause destruction.

chyme (KYM), *n.* the semifluid, often homogeneous, material produced during digestion in the stomach; passed on to the small intestine.

cicada (si-KAY-duh), see **Homoptera.**

Ciconiiformes (si-koh-nee-uh-FAWR-meez), *n.* an order of birds that are usually long-legged waders, with long necks and beaks; includes flamingo, ibis, stork, and heron.

cilia (SIL-ee-uh), plural of **cilium.**

ciliary (SIL-ee-air-ee), *adj.* **1.** referring to, or bearing, cilia. **2.** referring to certain threadlike muscles and other structures in the eye.

Ciliata (sil-ee-AY-tuh), *n.* a class in phylum *Protozoa* of animals having cilia for locomotion at some stage of development. *Ciliates* usually have

2 nuclei, a *micronucleus* which undergoes mitosis, and a *macronucleus* which does not; includes paramecium, volvox, vorticella, and stentor; also called *Infusoria;* see **paramecium.**

cilium (SIL-ee-uhm), *n.* *pl.* **cilia.** a hairlike thread on the surface of some protoplasmic cells. Motion of the cilia causes movement of fluids in the body. Some protozoans use cilia for locomotion. *adj.* **ciliary.**

cinnabar (SIN-uh-bahr), *n.* mercury sulfide, HgS, the ore from which mercury is obtained, with hardness 2½; a red mineral found mostly in Spain, Italy, and China.

cion (SY-uhn), *n.* a plant bud or shoot grafted onto another plant, called the *stock;* also spelled **scion.**

circadian cycle (suhr-KAY-dee-uhn), the inherited daily rhythm of physiological functions and patterns of behavior in animals.

circinate (SEER-suh-nayt), *adj.* coiled up on the axis with the tip in the center, as *circinate vernation* in the fern plant, also called *fiddlehead.*

circuit (SUHR-kuht), *n.* an electrical system for the passage of current; may include a number of elements, as batteries, transformers, generators, capacitors, and the wires connecting them.

Series circuit: if one element burns out, the current stops and all lights go out

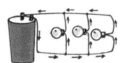
Parallel circuit: consists of circuits within a circuit. If one element burns out, current bypasses it and lights continue burning

circuit breaker, a device for breaking an electric circuit, either to prevent overload or on a time program as part of a normal operation. The circuit breaker throws a switch when an overload occurs; accomplishes what a fuse does, but there is no part to replace as with a burned-out fuse.

circuitry (SUHR-kuh-tree), *n.* the components of an electrical or electronic circuit in detail.

circulation (suhr-kyoo-LAY-shuhn), *n.* the movement of a fluid through a system; especially, the movement of the blood in a system from an originating point, through the body and back to the origin. *adj.* **circulatory.**

circulatory system (SUHR-kyoo-luh-taw-ree), *n.* the system by which blood circulates through the body. In vertebrates and some other animals, the system is closed, with blood confined to vessels which return the blood to its origin; includes heart, arteries, capillaries, and veins. In simpler animals, where all cells are close together, materials pass from one cell to the next.

circumcision (SUHR-kuhm-sizh-uhn), *n.* the removal of the foreskin of the glans.

circumnavigation (suhr-kuhm-nav-uh-GAY-shuhn), *n.* travel completely around a globe. A rocket that goes completely around the moon or any other space object will *circumnavigate* it.

circumpolar (suhr-kuhm-POH-luhr), *adj.* **1.** near one of the earth's poles. **2.** in the neighborhood of a polar star: the Big Dipper, always visible above the horizon, is a *circumpolar* constellation.

cirrhosis (si-ROH-sis), *n.* any of several liver diseases that result in the formation of large amounts of connective tissue: **1.** *nutritional* cirrhosis, or *portal* cirrhosis, usually caused by poor diet. **2.** *biliary* cirrhosis, caused by failure of bile to pass from the liver to the intestines; usually congenital.

cirrocumulus (sir-oh-CYOO-myuh-luhs), *n.* fleecy white clouds in rows; about 25,000 feet high; known as *mackerel sky;* indicate that a storm is near.

cirrostratus (sir-oh-STRAY-tuhs), *n.* thin white clouds, like a web; about 28,000 feet high; indicate a storm is approaching when follow cirrus.

cirrus (SIR-uhs), *n.* **1.** whitish filmy clouds, made up of tiny ice crystals; about 30,000 feet high; may mean storm is approaching. **2.** a flexible appendage, as on an animal antenna.

cis-, a word part originally meaning *on the same side.* In organic chemistry, some compounds occur in pairs identical in formula but having different properties because of the geometrical relation of the atoms. Those with the atoms concerned on the same side, or close to each other, are *cis*-isomers; those with the atoms on opposite sides, or far from each other, are *trans*-isomers.

cislunar space (sis-LOO-nuhr), space between Earth and the moon—the nearer portions of space.

citric acid (SIT-rik), an organic acid found in citrus fruits; used in drugs and flavorings, and for printing textiles; occurs as colorless crystals; formula, $C_3H_4(OH)(COOH)_3$.

citrus family (SIT-ruhs), see **Geraniales.**

Cl, symbol for **chlorine.**

clam, see **Pelecypoda.**

class, *n.* a biological grouping of plants or animals with some common structures; next below a phylum or subphylum in systematic ranking: *Aves* and *Mammalia* are classes of phylum *Chordata.*

classification (klas-i-fi-KAY-shuhn), *n.* a system for arranging objects: **1.** the system for grouping plants and animals into various ranks of re-

Major parts of the human circulatory system

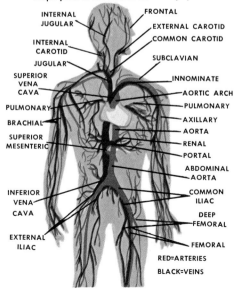

INTERNAL JUGULAR
FRONTAL
EXTERNAL CAROTID
COMMON CAROTID
INTERNAL CAROTID
SUBCLAVIAN
JUGULAR
SUPERIOR VENA CAVA
INNOMINATE
AORTIC ARCH
PULMONARY
PULMONARY
BRACHIAL
AXILLARY
SUPERIOR MESENTERIC
AORTA
RENAL
PORTAL
ABDOMINAL AORTA
INFERIOR VENA CAVA
COMMON ILIAC
DEEP FEMORAL
EXTERNAL ILIAC
FEMORAL
RED=ARTERIES
BLACK=VEINS

49

classify

lationship; originated by the Swedish naturalist Carolus Linnaeus. **2.** the sorting of ores and other fragments by screening into size ranges; much used in mining and metallurgy. *v.* **classify.**

clastic (KLAS-tik), *adj.* composed of pieces or fragments, as sedimentary rock formed of cemented bits of earlier rocks.

clavicle (KLAV-i-kuhl), *n.* the collarbone; see **skeletal system.**

claw, *n.* **1.** a sharp nail on a foot, especially on birds or mammals. **2.** the chela of a lobster or similar animal.

clay, *n.* a rock substance made chiefly of alumina, silica, mica, and water, broken by erosion into fine particles. Clay mixed with the proper amount of water can be molded and oven-fired.

cleavage (KLEEV-uhj), *n.* the way an object splits: **1.** many rocks split along definite parallel planes that are characteristic for each kind. **2.** the series of cell divisions by which an egg develops into an embryo. *v.* **cleave.**

cleft palate (PAL-uht), a defect caused by failure of the 2 sides of the roof of the mouth to join completely during embryonic development; may be corrected by surgery.

cliff (klif), *n.* a steep face of rock overlooking a lower place.

climate (KLY-muht), *n.* the general weather pattern for any region, including all the changes that occur. Climate is affected by many factors, including latitude, altitude, relation of land and water areas, presence of mountain ranges, and prevailing winds. *adj.* **climatic.**

climatology (kly-muh-TAHL-uh-jee), *n.* the study of climate and the weather conditions that make up the climate; a branch of meteorology.

climax community, in ecology, the final community in a succession; maintains itself indefinitely unless the environment changes; see **community.**

clinometer (kly-NAHM-uh-tuhr), *n.* a small surveying instrument held in the hand to measure vertical angles; can also be used as a level; one type is important in aiming guns.

cloaca (kloh-AY-kuh), *n.* the opening into which the intestinal, reproductive, and urinary tracts empty; found in birds, reptiles, amphibians, and fishes but only in the embryo of mammals.

clockwise, *adv.* in the same direction as that in which the hands of a clock move.

clone (KLOHN), *n.* offspring or organism reproduced from an individual asexually.

closed circulatory system, a type of blood circulation in animals in which blood is confined in vessels or tubes and pumped through them by means of a muscular heart; found in the higher animals; contrast with **open circulatory system.**

closed loop, in automation, a feedback system of control; one in which the difference between actual and desired values is measured, with the information causing a controller to change the operation so that the desired value is achieved, as in a thermostat-controlled heating system.

clot (KLAHT), *n.* a clump or coagulated mass, especially a blood clot. The ability of blood to form a clot prevents excessive loss of blood from wounds. The clot is formed of fibrin, a blood protein. *v.* **clot.**

cloud, *n.* **1.** any visible suspension of particles in a gas. **2.** an accumulation of condensed water vapor, either as tiny droplets of water or as ice crystals. The condensation takes place because of a drop in temperature, often as a result of the vapor moving to higher levels in the air.

cloud chamber, a device for photographing the track of a charged particle by the condensation of liquid on ions; these ions are created by the particle as it passes through a gas; invented by British physicist C.T.R. Wilson.

cloud seeding, the discharge of substances into clouds for the purpose of either inducing rain or avoiding rain. Most experiments have involved use of tiny silver iodide crystals as "seeds," on which water vapor will begin condensing.

cloven-hoofed (KLOH-vuhn-huhft), *adj.* having hoofs with a cleft, usually dividing the 2 middle toes, as in pigs, goats, and cattle.

clubfoot, *n.* a usually congenital deformity in which the toes point in a direction other than normal; there are 4 kinds: up or down, and in or out. Braces and surgery are corrective measures.

club moss, see **Lycopsida.**

Cm, symbol for **curium.**

Co, symbol for **cobalt.**

coagulate (koh-AG-yuh-layt), *v.* to thicken, said usually of a liquid in which solid material clumps together, either separating from the liquid or turning the mass to a solid; blood *coagulates* when it forms a clot. *n.* **coagulation.**

coal, *n.* the rocky substance formed from decomposed plant life millions of years ago; black or dark brown and very high in carbon content. Coal is a major fuel for power. The chief kinds are *anthracite* and *bituminous.*

coal gas, 1. any gas given off in the burning of coal. **2.** combustible gas, largely hydrogen, methane, and carbon monoxide, formed by the coking of coal in absence of air.

Coalsack, *n.* a dark patch seen in the southern Milky Way near Crux; once thought to be a

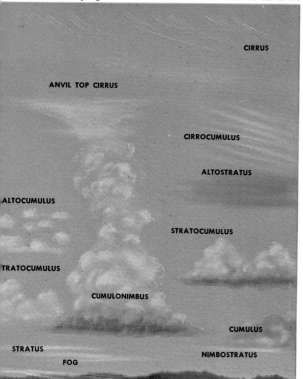

CIRRUS

ANVIL TOP CIRRUS

CIRROCUMULUS

ALTOSTRATUS

ALTOCUMULUS

STRATOCUMULUS

TRATOCUMULUS

CUMULONIMBUS

CUMULUS

STRATUS

NIMBOSTRATUS

FOG

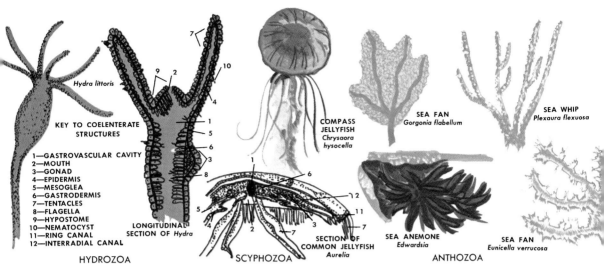

Hydra littoris

KEY TO COELENTERATE STRUCTURES

1—GASTROVASCULAR CAVITY
2—MOUTH
3—GONAD
4—EPIDERMIS
5—MESOGLEA
6—GASTRODERMIS
7—TENTACLES
8—FLAGELLA
9—HYPOSTOME
10—NEMATOCYST
11—RING CANAL
12—INTERRADIAL CANAL

LONGITUDINAL SECTION OF *Hydra*

COMPASS JELLYFISH
Chrysaora hysocella

SEA FAN
Gorgonia flabellum

SEA WHIP
Plexaura flexuosa

SECTION OF COMMON JELLYFISH
Aurelia

SEA ANEMONE
Edwardsia

SEA FAN
Eunicella verrucosa

HYDROZOA   SCYPHOZOA   ANTHOZOA

nebula, now believed to be caused by clouds of cosmic dust obscuring the stars.

coal tar, a heavy, dark-colored mixture of hydrocarbons obtained in the coking of bituminous coal; used to make organic compounds.

cobalt (KOH-bawlt), *n.* a gray metallic chemical element; used to harden alloys and color paints and ceramics and as a radioisotope source; symbol Co; *at. no.,* 27; *at. wt.,* 58.9332; isolated by Brandt in 1737.

cobaltite (KOH-bawl-tyt), *n.* a pinkish-silver crystalline mineral, (Co,Fe)AsS, with hardness 5½; a chief source of cobalt metal.

coca family (KOH-kuh), see **Geraniales.**

cocaine (koh-KAYN), *n.* an alkaloid often used as a local anesthetic; a narcotic obtained from the leaves of the coca plant; formula, $C_{17}H_{21}NO_4$.

coccus (KAHK-uhs), *n., pl.* **cocci** (KAHK-see). any round or almost round bacterium. Some occur singly, but many appear in clusters; *staphylococci* usually appear in clusters.

coccyx (KAHK-six), *n.* a group of joined vertebrae at the bottom of the spinal column of primates; see **skeletal system, vertebra.**

cochlea (KAHK-lee-uh), *n., pl.* **-ae, -as.** a spiral tube in the inner ear; contains the hearing organ, or *organ of Corti.* In birds and a few mammals, it is a fairly straight tube. Sound waves stimulate nerve endings in this organ and the stimulus is transmitted to the brain; see **ear.**

cockpit, *n.* a small space in an aircraft usually occupied by the pilot and one or 2 other persons; contains most of the flight instruments.

cockroach, see **Orthoptera.**

cocoon (kuh-KOON), *n.* the case of silk thread made by a caterpillar for its pupal stage of metamorphosis. The silkworm makes a cocoon that is the source of all natural silk; see **pupa.**

code, *n.* **1.** a group of signals for sending messages. **2.** the system for indicating computer information.

codeine (KOH-deen, -dee-uhn), *n.* an alkaloid in opium, less habit-forming and much milder in action than morphine; used to relieve pain and induce sleep; formula, $C_{18}H_{21}NO_3 \cdot H_2O$.

cod-liver oil, oil made from the liver of codfish; a major former source of vitamins A and D for infants, generally replaced by synthetic vitamin sources today.

coefficient (koh-ee-FISH-uhnt), *n.* any factor modifying some other factor, as *coefficient of friction;* may be either a constant or variable.

Coelenterata (suh-len-tuh-RAY-tuh), *n.* a phylum of sea animals and some fresh-water animals such as hydras. All *coelenterates* have stinging cells called *nematocysts;* most have a large central body cavity, called the *gastrovascular cavity;* see also **Anthozoa, Hydrozoa, Scyphozoa.**

coelom (SEE-lohm), *n.* the body cavity present either in adult or in embryo stages of most animals higher than the flatworms in development. Many organs of the body are covered by the mesoderm of the coelom.

coenzyme (koh-EN-zym), *n.* **1.** any of several organic molecules in plant and animal cells which are often necessary for enzymes to act. **2.** the part of an enzyme molecule that is not protein; usually a metallic or vitamin molecule; see **enzyme.**

cogwheel, *n.* a wheel with teeth notched into its rim, used for transmitting motion by meshing of the teeth with those of another cogwheel. Many machine gears are cogwheels.

coherent radiation (koh-HEER-uhnt), radiation of waves that shows a relatively high degree of similarity of phase, direction, and amplitude over a considerable portion of space for a considerable length of time, produced by a *laser.*

cohesion (koh-HEE-zhuhn), *n.* the tendency for identical molecules to cling together; the force of cohesion results in the round shape of a water drop; see also **adhesion.** *adj.* **cohesive.**

coil, *n.* **1.** a spirally wound wire used for electrical purposes, especially for induction of direct current when an iron core is inside the coil. **2.** any device of spiral shape.

coke, 1. *n.* the solid product of coal heated in the absence of air; almost entirely carbon. **2.** *v.* to make coke from coal. *n.* **coking.**

cold, *n.* **1.** a series of symptoms associated with an infection of the respiratory organs, especially the nose and throat. Most colds are caused by viruses. **2.** absence of heat. *adj.* **3.** having less heat than some comparable object.

cold-blooded, *adj.* having a body temperature about the same as that of the environment and changing with the environment; characteristic of all animals except birds, mammals, and a few fishes; also called *poikilothermal;* contrast with **warm-blooded.**

cold front, the boundary between 2 air masses of different temperatures. The colder mass usually moves toward and under the warmer mass; heavy showers are frequent in cold fronts.

cold neutron, a neutron having average kinetic energy much less than that of air molecules at room temperature; contrast with **thermal neutron.**

cold sore, an eruption on the lower part of the face, usually close to the mouth, and often accompanying symptoms of a cold; result of a virus infection; known medically as *herpes simplex.*

Coleoptera (koh-lee-AHP-tuh-ruh), *n.* an order of insects including all beetles and certain other insects, usually with hard, protective outer wings covering a second pair of membranous wings; with chewing mouth parts and showing complete metamorphosis; largest order in the animal kingdom; see **Insecta.**

colitis (koh-LY-tis), *n.* an inflammation of the wall of the colon due to a variety of causes, such as infection, parasites, nervous tension and others.

collagen (KAHL-uh-juhn), *n.* a protein that forms the basic supportive tissue of tendons, bones, cartilage, and other connective tissues.

collenchyma (kohl-EN-kuh-muh), *n.* living plant cells having primary walls with regular or irregular thickenings of cellulose; used for support and strength; contrast with **sclerenchyma.**

collision (kuh-LIZH-uhn), *n.* **1.** a crash, or violent meeting. **2.** in physics, electrical or mechanical interaction of one object with another, producing a relative, usually rapid, deceleration; see **chain reaction, proton collision.** *v.* **collide.**

collodion (kuh-LOH-dee-uhn), *n.* a solution of pyroxylin (cellulose dinitrate) in either alcohol or ether; formerly used in making artificial fibers; certain forms are used to protect wounds.

colloid (KAHL-oyd), *n.* a system in which tiny particles of a substance are dispersed in another substance, as solid in a gas (smoke), gas in a liquid (whipped cream), and liquid in a liquid (milk); see also **emulsion.** *adj.* **colloidal.**

colon (KOH-luhn), *n.* the large intestine, especially the last, descending portion; see **digestive system.** *adj.* **colonic.**

colony (KAHL-uh-nee), *n.* **1.** any group of animals or plants of the same kind living in close association. **2.** a mass of bacteria on a culture medium. *adj.* **colonial.**

color, *n.* the visual effect of the different wavelengths into which light can be resolved; color is produced when light waves strike the cones in the retina of the eye. An object is seen as red only because the object absorbs light of most wavelengths and reflects light in the red wavelengths.

color blindness, a hereditary condition in which a person sees different colors only as different shades of gray; most common in males; see also **Daltonism.**

colorimeter (kuhl-uh-RIM-uh-tuhr), *n.* an instrument for distinguishing between colors, usually by comparison with a standard; used in chemical analysis and blood classification.

Columbiformes (koh-luhm-bi-FAWR-meez), *n.* an order of birds with compact bodies, short legs, and fanlike tails; includes pigeons and doves.

columbite-tantalite (KAHL-uhm-byt-TANT-uh-lyt), *n.* a dark gray, crystalline mineral, $(Fe,Mn)(Nb,Ta)_2O_6$; chief source of niobium.

columbium, former name of **niobium.**

columnar cell (kuh-LUM-nuhr), *n.* an epithelial cell, longer than it is wide, usually found lining the intestines, and generally having cilia that move fluid; see **epithelium.**

coma (KOH-muh), *n.* **1.** an unconscious state, shown by inability to respond to normal stimuli; produced by some diseases, injury, or drugs. *adj.* **comatose. 2.** the head of a comet.

comb jelly, see **Ctenophora.**

combustible (kuhm-BUHS-tuh-buhl), **1.** *adj.* capable of burning. **2.** *n.* any material that can burn.

combustion (kuhm-BUHS-chuhn), *n.* the burning of a substance, ordinarily with oxygen present; always produces heat. *v.* **combust.**

combustion chamber, the space at the head end of a cylinder where combustion produces the propulsive power in internal-combustion engines.

comet (KAHM-it), *n.* a heavenly body moving around the sun in a rather irregular orbit; consists of a bright glowing head, or *coma,* surrounding a starlike *nucleus;* a long *tail* streams out behind the body of the comet.

command destruct, a system for missile destruction, brought into operation when a missile becomes a threat to safety.

commensalism (kuh-MEN-suh-lizm), *n.* in ecology, a form of symbiosis in which an organism living on a host neither benefits nor harms the host but does itself benefit; some barnacles attach themselves to whales. *adj.* **commensal.**

common cold, see **cold.**

communicable disease (kuh-MYOO-nuh-kuh-buhl), a disease that may be transmitted from one individual to another.

communication (kuh-myoo-nuh-KAY-shuhn), *n.* **1.** transmission or relay, especially of messages. *v.* **communicate. 2.** *pl.* **-s.** collectively, the science or techniques of means of communication, as telephony, telegraphy, etc.

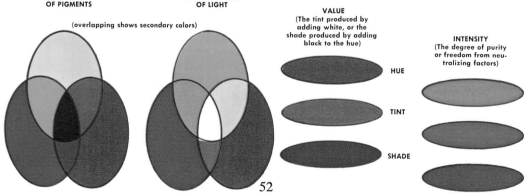

PRIMARY COLORS OF PIGMENTS   PRIMARY COLORS OF LIGHT

(overlapping shows secondary colors)

VALUE
(The tint produced by adding white, or the shade produced by adding black to the hue)

INTENSITY
(The degree of purity or freedom from neutralizing factors)

HUE

TINT

SHADE

communication satellite, a satellite used for the transmission of messages; *passive* communication satellites reflect messages, as in *Echo; active* satellites use repeaters to amplify the messages, as in *Telstar* and *Relay.* A third type is *synchronous* satellites; see **active repeater satellite, synchronous orbit.**

community (kuh-MYOO-ni-tee), *n.* all of the organisms of a given area related by environmental needs.

commutator (KAHM-yuh-tay-tuhr), *n.* a split metal ring used to reverse the DC current to the coils of the armature of a DC motor. Separately

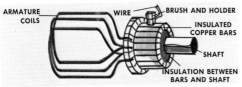

ARMATURE COILS — WIRE — BRUSH AND HOLDER — INSULATED COPPER BARS — SHAFT — INSULATION BETWEEN BARS AND SHAFT

insulated, the split ring halves on the rotating armature make contact with metal brushes which conduct the current.

companion cell, a long, narrow plant cell which accompanies a sieve tube element in plant phloem; see **phloem, sieve tube.**

comparative anatomy, the science of comparison of similar and related structures in different species of plants and animals.

comparator (KAHM-puh-ray-tuhr, kuhm-PAIR-uh-), *n.* **1.** a device for comparing linear measurements; a gauge set to a standard with which it compares the sample being checked; may show variations as small as 1/20,000 inch. **2.** an optical color standard used in chemical analysis to determine hydrogen-ion concentration by color of an acid-base indicator. **3.** an optical color standard for determining percentage composition of substances by depth of color.

compass (KUHM-puhs), *n.* **1.** an instrument, either magnetic or gyroscopic, for indicating direction with respect to north; see also **gyrocompass, magnetic compass. 2.** an adjustable instrument for drawing circles or arcs of circles; the tracing point is rotated about the fixed point, or center.

complementary color (kahm-pluh-MEN-tuh-ree), a color that will add its light waves to those of another color to produce white (or gray): certain shades of yellow and blue, added together, produce white. Direct light waves produce complementary effects by adding to each other; pigments produce complementary effects by subtraction, due to selective absorption; see **color.**

complete flower, a flower with all typical parts: sepals, petals, pistils, and stamens.

composite family (kuhm-PAHZ-it), any of a large family (*Compositae*) of ornamental plants with many small flowers, or *florets,* tightly packed into a single head, called an *inflorescence* (often mistaken for a single flower). The head may be made of tiny central *disk* flowers surrounded by *ray* flowers, as in a daisy. The flower head grows from a group of green bracts called an *involucre.* Aster, sunflower, and dandelion are typical of the 20,000 composites; see **Campanulales.**

compost (KAHM-pohst), *n.* a mixture of decaying organic material, such as dead leaves and grass cuttings, used as fertilizer.

compound (KAHM-pownd), **1.** *n.* a chemical substance containing atoms of 2 or more elements, always present in the same proportion by weight, and whose chemical and physical properties are different from those of the elements themselves: sodium chloride, an edible salt, is a *compound* of sodium, a metal, and chlorine, a poisonous gas. **2.** *adj.* made up of several parts or elements.

compound bar, a bimetallic bar; see **bimetallic.**

compound eye, a group of small simple eyes clustered together, characteristic of arthropods; each

Section of a compound eye (ommateum) of an insect: each ommatidium consists of (1) corneal facet, (2) crystalline lens, (3) retinal cells, and (4) nerve fibers

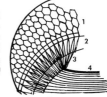

simple eye (*ommatidium*) contributes to a mosaic image of the whole; also called *ommateum.*

compound flower, the head, or inflorescence, of any composite plant, composed of many small flowers; see **composite family.**

compound fracture (FRAK-chuhr), a bone break in which part of the bone penetrates the flesh and causes a surface wound.

compound leaf, a series of leaflets on a common stalk, all formed from a single bud; the entire structure is one leaf; black walnut trees have compound leaves; see **leaf** picture.

compress, 1. *v.* (kuhm-PRES), to apply or increase pressure in or on any system or part: *compressing* a gas makes a given amount occupy less space or makes possible the inclusion of a greater amount in a given space. **2.** *n.* (KAHM-pres), a soft pad of material such as linen, applying pressure, heat, cold, or moisture to any part of the body.

compression (kuhm-PRESH-uhn), *n.* **1.** generally, any result of increasing pressure, particularly in gases. **2.** the increased pressure of vapor inside the cylinder head of an internal-combustion engine, produced by a piston stroke.

compression ratio (RAY-sho), in an internal-combustion engine, total cylinder volume after explosion divided by clearance volume (the small space between cylinder head and piston at full compression). The higher the compression ratio, the more power is produced.

compressor (kuhm-PRES-uhr), *n.* any device that forces a gas to occupy a smaller volume.

computer (kuhm-PYOO-tuhr), *n.* a complex machine for rapid performance of recurring calculations; computers usually consist of input devices, storage or memory devices, arithmetic-logic units, output devices, and controls; see also **analog computer, digital computer.**

concave (KAHN-kayv), *adj.* curving inward; having a curve similar to that of a spherical surface viewed from inside a sphere; see **lens.**

concentrated (KAHN-suhn-tray-tuhd), *adj.* **1.** containing a relatively high proportion of solute to solvent, said of a solution. **2.** brought to a focus, said of light rays. **3.** having a higher proportion of metal ore after a process of partial purification. *n.* **concentration.**

concentric (kuhn-SEN-trik), *adj.* arranged in a series of circles with a common center, as the ridges in fingerprints or a tree's annual rings.

conception (kuhn-SEP-shuhn), *n.* **1.** the beginning of pregnancy; fertilization of an ovum by a sperm. **2.** an idea or theory. *v.* **conceive.**

conchology (kahnk-AHL-uh-jee), *n.* **1.** the study of mollusk shells. **2.** the study of mollusks in general; also called *malacology.*

concussion (kuhn-KUHSH-uhn), *n.* **1.** violent mechanical shock or shock wave, especially to a part of the body. **2.** the symptoms following such a blow to the brain and spinal cord.

condensation (kahn-den-SAY-shuhn), *n.* **1.** change from the gaseous to the liquid state, produced by removal of heat from the gas. **2.** combination of 2 molecules, either identical or different, to form a different kind of molecule. *v.* **condense.**

condenser (kuhn-DEN-suhr), *n.* **1.** a device in which gases are converted into liquids (occasionally to solids), usually consisting of a device for permitting contact of a *coolant* with the gas or with a heat-conductive surface enclosing the gas. **2.** an alternate term for **capacitor.**

conditioned response, in psychology, a learned, specific response to a stimulus; learned by reinforcement; see also **reflex.**

conduction, *n.* **1.** the transmission of energy through successive particles, as in the conduction of heat or electric current through a wire. **2.** transmission of water, foods, etc., through the cells of a plant. **3.** transmission of nerve impulses through tissues. *adj.* **conductive.** *v.* **conduct.**

conductivity (kahn-duhk-TIV-i-tee), *n.* a measurement of any substance's quality as an electric current conductor; at temperatures well above absolute zero, conductivity is inversely proportional to temperature.

conductor (kuhn-DUHK-tuhr), *n.* **1.** a substance (usually a metal) that will carry electric current. **2.** a substance that will transfer heat.

conduit (KAHN-dit, KAHN-doo-it), *n.* **1.** an open or closed channel (trench, pipe, etc.) for transporting liquids. **2.** a channel or pipe containing cables, electric wiring, etc.

cone, *n.* **1.** any of the sensory bodies with a conical shape situated in the retina of the eye, and containing visual purple. The cones function in bright light and are sensitive to both colored and white light. **2.** a seed-bearing structure in gymnosperm plants consisting of a central axis with series of scale-like plates arranged on it; there are male, or pollen, cones and female, or seed, cones.

coney (KOH-nee), see **Hyracoidea.**

configuration (kuhn-fig-yuh-RAY-shuhn), *n.* relative position, as: **1.** in chemistry, the relative positions of electrons in the atom, of atoms in the molecule, of monomeric molecules in a polymer, etc. **2.** in astronomy, the positions of stars, planets, etc., in relation to each other. **3.** in electronics, the arrangement of circuit elements.

congenital (kuhn-JEN-uh-tuhl), *adj.* present at the time of birth or dating from birth; describing a condition resulting from an error in development which usually may not be inherited.

conglomerate (kuhn-GLAHM-uhr-uht), *n.* a clastic rock consisting of hard, rounded pebbles embedded in a fine, natural, sedimentary cement, the *matrix.* *adj.* **conglomerate.**

conidium (koh-NID-ee-uhm), *n., pl.* **conidia.** an asexual spore of certain fungi, not contained in a sporangium and often produced in chains, as in penicillium and others.

conifer (KOH-ni-fuhr, KAH-ni-fuhr), *n.* any tree or shrub of a group of gymnosperms (order *Coniferales*) usually bearing woody cones, lance-

TYPICAL CONIFER FEATURES

WINGED SEED

CONE FRUIT

NEEDLE-LIKE LEAVES

shaped, needle-like leaves, and sperm carried in a pollen tube, as pines and redwoods. *adj.* **coniferous.**

conjugation (kahn-juh-GAY-shuhn), *n.* **1.** a reproductive process characteristic of some protozoans: either permanent fusion or temporary linking of 2 cells; in the latter case, with exchange of nuclear material; the earliest form of *sexual reproduction.* **2.** in plants, the fusion of like gametes (*isogametes*).

conjunctiva (kahn-junk-TYV-uh), *n.* the inner mucous membrane lining the eyelid and forming the white, front part of the eyeball; see **eye.**

conjunctivitis (kuhn-junk-ti-VY-tis), *n.* inflammation of the conjunctiva, caused by microbial infection or by smoke, dust, or other particles.

connective tissue (kuh-NEK-tiv), body tissue which binds together and supports other structures; composed of scattered cells, fibers, and ground substance; varying proportions of these parts produce different kinds of connective tissue: fibrous tissue, ligaments, and tendons have mostly fibers—white, yellow, or reticular; bone and cartilage have mostly ground substance (*matrix*); and fatty tissues have mostly cells for storage.

conscious (KAHN-shuhs), *adj.* aware of, or mentally responsive to, sensory stimuli. *n.* **consciousness.**

conservation (kahn-suhr-VAY-shuhn), *n.* careful, planned use of natural resources to keep them flourishing and prevent their depletion or destruction. *v.* **conserve.**

conservation of energy, a basic phenomenon and law of non-nuclear physics: in any system, energy may be converted from one form into another, or into several others, but it cannot be created or destroyed.

constellation (kahn-stuh-LAY-shuhn), *n.* any of nearly 100 arbitrary groupings of stars into real or fancied shapes; convenient for locating and identifying stars and other celestial objects.

MAJOR CONSTELLATIONS
and important stars

(* = Zodiac group)

NORTHERN SKY

Andromeda (23)
Aquila, *Eagle* (31)—Altair (V)
*Aries, *Ram* (5)—Hamel (F)
Auriga, *Charioteer* (10)—Capella (K)
Boötes, *Bear Driver* (15)—Arcturus (N)
Big Dipper (12)—Pointers (1)
Camelopardalis, *Giraffe* (16)
*Cancer, *Crab* (2)
Canes Venatici, *Hunting Dogs* (13)
Canis Minor, *Lesser Dog* (7)—
    Procyon (G)
Cassiopeia (24)
Cepheus (25)—Cepheids (R)
Coma Berenices, *Berenice's Hair* (14)
Corona Borealis, *Northern Crown* (21)
Cygnus, *Swan or Northern Cross* (29)—
    Deneb (S); Albireo (T)
Draco, *Dragon* (20)
*Gemini, *Twins* (3)—Castor (B); Pollux (C)
Hercules (26)
*Leo, *Lion* (1)—Regulus (A)
Little Dipper = Ursa Minor
Lyra, *Lyre* (3)—Vega (U)
Ophiuchus, *Serpent Bearer* (27)
Orion, *Warrior* (8)—
    Betelgeuse (H); Bellatrix (I)
Pegasus, *Winged Horse* (28)
Perseus (18)—Algol (W)
*Pisces, *Fishes* (6)
Serpens, *Serpent* (22)
*Taurus, *Bull* (4)—
    Aldebaran (D); Pleides (E)
Triangulum, *Triangle* (17)
Ursa Major, *Great Bear* (11)—Mizar (M)
*Virgo, *Maiden* (9)

SOUTHERN SKY

*Aquarius, *Water Bearer* (36)
Ara, *Altar* (42)
Canis Major, *Greater Dog* (46)—Sirius (H)
*Capricornus, *Sea Goat* (35)
Carina, *Keel* (44)—Canopus (G)
Centaurus, *Centaur* (39)—
    Alpha Centauri (C); Beta Centauri (D)
Cetus, *Whale* (58)
Columba, *Dove* (51)
Corona Australis, *Southern Crown* (48)
Corvus, *Crow* (37)
Crux, *Southern Cross* (40)—
    Alpha Crucis (E); Beta Crucis (F)
Dorado, *Swordfish* (50)
Eridanus (56)—Achernar (K)
Grus, *Crane* (54)
Hydra, *Water Serpent* (38)
Lepus, *Hare* (52)
*Libra, *Balance or Scales* (32)
Monoceros, *Unicorn* (47)
Ophiuchus, *Serpent Bearer* (27)
Orion, *Warrior* (8)—Rigel (J)
Pavo, *Peacock* (49)
Phoenix (55)
Pisces Austrinus, *Southern Fish* (57)—
    Fomalhaut (L)
Puppis, *Poop* (45)
*Sagittarius, *Archer* (34)
*Scorpius, *Scorpion* (33)—Antares (B)
Triangulum Australe, *Southern Triangle* (43)
Tucana, *Toucan* (53)
Vela, *Sails* (41)
*Virgo, *Maiden* (9)—Spica (A)

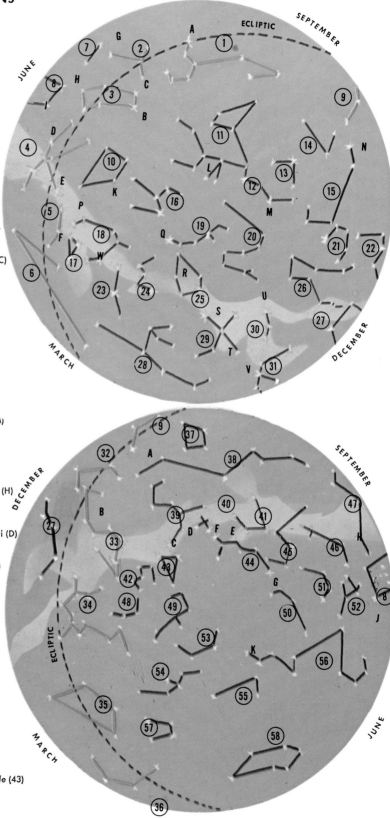

55

constrictor (kuhn-STRIK-tuhr), *n.* **1.** a snake that squeezes prey in its coils until suffocated. **2.** any muscle that narrows a passage of the body; see **sphincter.**

contact (KAHN-takt), *n.* **1.** the physical touching of 2 objects, as 2 wires, etc. In propeller-driven airplanes, *contact* is the turning on of the ignition key so that starting is possible. **2.** exposure to a substance or condition, especially to contagious diseases. *adj.* **3.** in aerial navigation, referring to flight with surface objects in sight instead of relying on instruments.

contact lens, a transparent lens, usually of plastic, fitting over a portion of the cornea of the eye; used instead of eyeglasses to correct vision.

contagious (kuhn-TAY-juhs), *adj.* spread by physical contact, said especially of certain communicable diseases. *n.* **contagion.**

contaminant (kahn-TAM-uh-nuhnt), *n.* anything that makes impure (*contaminates*) something else; especially, waste material escaping into the air.

continental divide, elevation separating river systems that flow to opposite parts of a continent; the Great Divide in the Rocky Mountains separates streams flowing to the Gulf of Mexico from those flowing to the Pacific Ocean; see also **drainage system.**

continental drift, supposed tendency of continents to move on the earth's surface because of "plates" that shift with volcano-like activity.

continental shelf, a shallow, ocean-bottom plain,

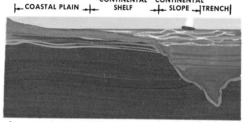

|⊢ COASTAL PLAIN ⊣|⊢ CONTINENTAL SHELF ⊣|⊢ CONTINENTAL SLOPE ⊣|TRENCH|

between land and the slope to the deep basins of the ocean.

continuous-wave radar, radar transmitting a steady signal capable of long-distance operation with much less power than pulse radar.

contour (KAHN-toor), *n.* external outline or shape; the boundary of a figure, as the contour of a dog's head; see also **configuration.**

contour feather, any of the vaned feathers making up the surface covering and streamlined form of a bird's body; *flight* feathers are strong contour feathers; see also **feather.**

contour map, a map on which land elevations are indicated by lines; each line is a closed curve representing the name elevation; successive lines represent a uniform change.

contract (kuhn-TRAKT), *v.* **1.** to shrink or reduce in size. **2.** to acquire, or "catch," a disease.

contractile vacuole (kahn-TRAK-tahl VAK-yuh-wohl), a membrane-lined space in a cell, usually containing fluid, that discharges its contents to the outside of the cell by sudden contraction; expels wastes, maintains water balance, and may perform other functions; see **ameba.**

contraction (kahn-TRAK-shuhn), *n.* **1.** decrease in length, area, or volume; a metal usually undergoes contraction as it is cooled. **2.** in physiology, the shortening of myofibril tissue in muscles in response to a stimulus. *v.* **contract.**

control experiment, a scientific test to check the results of other tests. It usually requires keeping the same conditions as for the earlier experiments except for one condition, changed in such a way that any important difference in the new results can be detected.

control panel, a convenient arrangement for regulating electrical current, containing switches and circuit breakers or fuses, as well as wiring for branch circuits; found in computers, guidance systems, and all complex engineering installations.

control rod, a rod containing elements able to absorb neutrons, thus controlling the power of a nuclear reactor.

control surface, any adjustable airfoil that regulates the attitude of an airplane; see **airfoil.**

convection (kuhn-VEK-shuhn), *n.* the flow of heat from one place to another, caused by *convection currents* (mass movements of heated particles) in liquids and gases.

convergent (kuhn-VUHR-juhnt), *adj.* **1.** evolving along similar lines, especially 2 unrelated and perhaps isolated groups of animals or plants. **2.** turned inward, as the eye when focusing upon a near central point. *n.* **convergence.**

converter (kuhn-VUHR-tuhr), *n.* any device for changing matter or energy into another form: **1.** a *Bessemer converter* that blasts air through pig iron to make steel. **2.** any device for changing the form of electric current; especially, a *synchronous converter* to change alternating current to direct current; it combines a synchronous motor and DC generator in one machine. **3.** in electronics, a circuit that converts a signal at one frequency to another.

convertiplane (kuhn-VUHR-tuh-playn), *n.* an aircraft adapted for vertical takeoff and landing as well as for forward travel at high speeds; some operate by rotating propeller, wings, and other parts from a horizontal to vertical position; others have helicopter-type rotor blades as well as jet propulsion equipment or propellers.

convex (kahn-VEKS), *adj.* curving outward, as the surface of a sphere viewed from outside the sphere; applies especially to lenses and mirrors.

convoluted tubule (KAHN-vuh-loot-uhd TOOB-yuhl), either of 2 looped portions of a uriniferous tubule; the *proximal* starts in the cortex of the kidney; the *distal* leads to the main collecting tubule; functions to reabsorb about 99% of the fluid; the remaining 1% is excreted as waste.

convolution (kahn-vuh-LOO-shuhn), *n.* an infolding or coiling structure, especially the foldlike ridges on the surface of the cerebrum; also called *gyrus;* see **brain.**

convulsion (kuhn-VUHL-shuhn), *n.* a sudden, violent, involuntary contraction of voluntary muscle, often occurring in a series of spasms.

coolant, *n.* any fluid that conducts heat; in nuclear reactors, used to carry heat so that it may do useful work; may or may not act as a neutron moderator.

coordination (koh-ohr-di-NAY-shuhn), *n.* **1.** combined action of a group of muscles, usually voluntary, to produce complex movements. *v.* **coordinate. 2.** in chemistry, a theory to explain *coordination compounds,* complex molecules, such as chlorophyll, in which metallic atoms form an unusual bond to the rest of the molecule.

Copernican system (koh-PUHR-ni-kuhn), a description of the universe with the sun at the center of the solar system and all planets, including Earth, in circular orbit around the sun; planets rotate on their axes, producing night and day; named for Nicolaus Copernicus, Polish astronomer; contrast with **Ptolemaic system.**

copper (KAHP-uhr), *n.* a reddish, soft, metallic chemical element; a good electrical conductor; used for wire and strong, corrosion-resistant alloys such as brass and bronze; symbol Cu; *at. no.,* 29; *at. wt.,* 63.54; known since ancient times.

copperhead, *n.* any of several poisonous pit viper snakes found in central and eastern United States; colored with red and copper cross stripes; may grow to 4½ feet long; see **snake.**

copulation (kahp-yuh-LAY-shuhn), *n.* the temporary union of 2 animals, usually resulting in the transfer of sperm cells from the male so that one may fertilize the ovum of the female.

Coraciiformes (koh-rah-see-uh-FAWR-meez), *n.* an order of birds common along waterways; usually feed on aquatic animals; may nest in burrows made in cliffs; includes kingfishers, hornbills, and others.

coral (KAWR-uhl), see **Anthozoa, coral reef.**

coral reef, a solid mass in the ocean, usually lying on bedrock or volcanic base; composed of limy deposits ($CaCO_3$) from the bodies of marine animal skeletons, algae, and corals, firmly cemented. Reefs lie at or just below the sea surface.

coral snake, any of several poisonous snakes, ranging from southern United States to South America; grows 2 to 4 feet long; see **snake.**

cordillera (kawr-DIL-uh-ruh), *n.* a long chain of mountain ranges, forming a single mountain system, such as all the Rocky Mountain ranges.

cordite (KAWR-dyt), *n.* a smokeless, explosive powder, basically a mixture of nitroglycerin and nitrocellulose.

core, *n.* the inner or central part of something: **1.** the innermost region of Earth of solid but hot nickel and iron, surrounded by molten nickel and iron. **2.** any material in the center of a coil or electromagnet that provides a path for magnetic lines of force. **3.** the center of a fruit containing seeds. **4.** the fuel and moderator elements in a nuclear reactor.

corium (KOH-ree-uhm), *n.* the sensitive vascular layer of the skin just under the epidermis; contains nerve endings and sense organ receptors.

cork, *n.* **1.** the spongy, air-filled outer bark of the *cork oak* tree, used as insulation and in objects needing buoyancy in water. **2.** a similar tissue found in varying amounts in the bark of most woody plants.

corm (KAWRM), *n.* an erect, fleshy, short, underground stem for storage with scale-like leaves; forms buds which may propagate. Crocus and gladiolus grow from corms.

cormorant (KAWR-muh-ruhnt), see **Pelicaniformes.**

cornea (KAWR-nee-uh), *n.* a transparent layer of tissue at the surface in front of the eyeball; see **eye.** *adj.* **corneal.**

cotyledon

corolla (kuh-RAHL-uh), *n.* the ring of petals surrounding a flower just inside the calyx; the petals as a group.

corona (kuh-ROH-nuh), *n.* **1.** the light area surrounding the sun's chromosphere, clearly visible during total solar eclipse. **2.** a series of colored rings caused by light diffraction apparent when looking at the sun or moon through water vapor. **3.** a visible area of electrical discharge from a conductor, due to ionization of atmospheric gases.

coronagraph (kuh-ROH-nuh-graf), *n.* a telescope specially constructed for accurate observations of the sun's corona, with exceptionally clear lenses and freedom from dust.

coronary (KAWR-uh-nair-ee), *adj.* circling an object, as a crown around a head; in medicine, refers to the arteries supplying the heart itself with blood. They arise from the aorta and provide all heart muscle with nutrition. A clot in one of these arteries is a *coronary thrombosis.*

corpuscle (KAWR-puh-suhl), *n.* **1.** any extremely small body. **2.** any of several kinds of cells in the blood, lymph, etc. (as white and red corpuscles). **3.** a minute particle, of the smallest unit conceivable, as in the *corpuscular* theory of light.

corpuscular radiation (kawr-PUHS-kyoo-luhr), radiation in the form of atomic particles (electrons, protons, and alpha particles); such radiation as is observed on earth and in the atmosphere originates as *solar* or *cosmic radiation,* and travels at tremendous speeds.

corrosion (kuh-ROH-zhuhn), *n.* the slow destruction of materials by chemical reactions: rust is metallic *corrosion* caused by slow oxidation. *v.* **corrode.** *adj.* **corrosive.**

cortex (KAWR-teks), *n.* **1.** in plants, the layer of young herbaceous stem or root tissue between the epidermis and the sap-carrying tissues. **2.** in animals, the outer layer of an organ, as the *adrenal cortex. adj.* **cortical.**

corticosterone (kawr-ti-KAHS-tuhr-rohn), *n.* a steroid present in the adrenal cortex; it and related steroids are essential to body metabolism; formula, $C_{21}H_{30}O_4$.

cortisone (KAWR-tuh-sohn), *n.* a steroid present in the adrenal cortex, important to food metabolism and of medicinal value in rheumatoid arthritis and some other disorders; formula, $C_{21}H_{28}O_5$.

corundum (koh-RUN-duhm), *n.* an extremely hard (hardness 9) mineral found in crystalline or amorphous form, Al_2O_3; also occurs as gemstones such as ruby and sapphire.

cosmic ray (KAHZ-mik), radiation originating beyond Earth's atmosphere, detected when it reaches the atmosphere by the high-speed particles produced in colliding with gases; these are chiefly electrons, protons, and alpha particles. Some of the rays originate in the sun, others in the region of the stars; many appear to come from the Milky Way.

cosmonaut (KAHZ-muh-nawt), *n.* the Russian term for **astronaut.**

cottonmouth, see **water moccasin.**

cotyledon (kaht-uh-LEE-duhn), *n.* the seed leaf in angiosperm plants, ranging in size from a thin, leaflike structure to a large fleshy mass with much food stored in it. The cotyledon serves as the *primitive leaf,* usually turning green and manufacturing food for the plant until regular leaves develop; see **dicotyledon, monocotyledon.** adj. **cotyledonous.**

coulomb (KOO-lahm, -lohm), *n.* a unit of electrical quantity: that quantity of current that in one second flows past a point in a conductor carrying one ampere; named for C. A. Coulomb, French physicist (1736-1806).

countdown, *n.* a step-by-step procedure in preparation for missile launching or for other complex operations with a decisive stage (t = 0). All steps are planned in advance and the count proceeds backward with no step performed until the previous step has been taken.

counterclockwise, *adv.* opposite to the direction in which the hands of a clock move.

countershading, *n.* a form of protective coloration in some animals in which lighter color tones

The darker back of the bluefin tuna *(Thunnus thynnus)* blends with dark water when seen by a predator from above; the lighter belly blends with sunlight when seen from below

occur on parts usually in shadow and darker tones on parts usually exposed to light.

couple ((KUHP-uhl), *v.* **1.** to join together. **2.** in electricity, to join by a magnetic or electric field that links 2 objects not physically touching or joined. *n.* **coupling.**

covalent bond (koh-VAY-luhnt), a chemical bond in which the atoms share pairs of electrons, common in organic compounds; see **bond.**

cover slip, any circular or square piece of uniformly thin glass or plastic used to cover a microscopic slide preparation.

cow, *n.* **1.** any adult female bovine, especially one bred to give milk. **2.** the female of certain other mammals, including the elephant, moose, seal, and walrus.

Cowper's gland (KOW-puhrz, KOO-puhrz), *n.* either of 2 small glands in male mammals, located near the base of the penis, which supply a mucous secretion to the semen.

cowpox (KOW-pahks), *n.* a disease of cattle, with eruptions on udders; cowpox virus is used as vaccine against human smallpox.

Cr, symbol for **chromium.**

crab, see **Crustacea, horseshoe crab.**

cracking, *n.* a method for breaking down complex hydrocarbons of high molecular weight in petroleum to yield a high percentage of low molecular weight hydrocarbons suitable for gasoline; involves catalysts and high temperatures.

cramp, *n.* any painful spasmodic muscle contraction; may be a single muscle or a group involved; either with a single spasm or with a series of spasms.

cranial nerve (KRAY-nee-uhl), in man, any of the 12 pairs of nerves leading from the brain to anterior parts of the body; 10 of the 12 are found in all reptiles, birds, and mammals; contrast with **spinal nerve.**

cranium (KRAY-nee-uhm), *n.* that part of the skull enclosing and protecting the brain; consists of cartilage in a few kinds of fish, bone in all other adult vertebrates; see **skull.**

crater (KRAY-tuhr), *n.* **1.** a cupped pit at the mouth of a volcano, geyser, or other surface opening in the ground. **2.** the depression in the earth made by the impact of meteorites, bombs, land mines, etc.

crayfish, see **Crustacea.**

creek (CREEK, CRIK), *n.* any small water stream, especially a small river branch; often called a *branch* in the southern United States.

creep, *n.* **1.** in metals, slow plastic deformation under stress, often greatly accelerated at higher temperatures. **2.** in geology, the slow downhill motion of soil, rocks, etc., which increases soil erosion; also used in oceanography for slow downhill flow of the ocean bottom.

creosote (KREE-uh-soht), *n.* either of 2 oils made by destructive distillation: **1.** *wood* creosote, a light-colored oil made from wood; used as a disinfectant and preservative. **2.** *coal-tar* creosote, a dark oil, largely phenol and related compounds, used to preserve wood and in ore-flotation; see **destructive distillation.**

cresol (KREE-sohl), *n.* one of 3 isomeric phenols found in coal tar; used as disinfectants and for organic synthesis; formula, $CH_3C_6H_4OH$.

crest, *n.* **1.** the highest point in a wave, between 2 troughs; see **wave.** **2.** a high point of land, as the *crest* of a hill.

Cretaceous (kruh-TAY-shuhs), *n.* a period in the Mesozoic era characterized by formation of large chalk beds; during this period early mammals were developing and dinosaurs dying out; began more than 100 million years ago and lasted about 50 million years; see also **geologic time table.**

cretin (KREE-tin), *n.* a person in whom thyroxine supply is inadequate or absent. This condition (*cretinism*) is congenital, and leads to development of an enlarged head but small extremities, and other defects.

crevasse (kruh-VAS), *n.* a deep crack (fissure), usually in a glacier or rock formation.

cricket, see **Orthoptera.**

Crinoidea (kri-NOY-dee-uh), *n.* a class of echinoderms with stalked, attached bodies, fine, featherlike arms and tentacle-like tube feet modified for food getting. Parts of stalks from extinct *crinoids* are often found as fossils; also called *sea lilies;* see **Echinodermata** picture.

critical mass, the minimum mass necessary to start a self-sustaining chain fission reaction, assuming uniform distribution of fissionable material in a particular geometric shape (sphere, rod, etc.).

crocodilian (krah-kuh-DIL-ee-uhn), *n.* any of several large, tropical, flesh-eating reptiles of the order *Crocodilia;* with long jaws, protruding eyes and nostrils, a body covered with thick scaly skin, short legs with webbed feet, and a long tail; includes alligator and crocodile, distinguished mainly by the crocodile's more pointed snout and tail that is flatter on the sides; see **Reptilia.**

Cro-Magnon man (kroh-MAG-nuhn), one of a prehistoric race of humans who inhabited Europe; noted for erect stature, height (about 6 feet in males), and large brain; lived about 25,000 years ago, following Neanderthal man; he was the earliest *Homo sapiens,* and is regarded as the immediate ancestor of modern Caucasoids.

crop, *n.* **1.** an enlarged section of the alimentary canal in birds, insects, and some other animals; serves as a pre-digestive storage place. **2.** the product of plants grown by man for his own purposes, as a corn crop, tomato crop. etc.

cross breeding, **1.** the mating of plants or animals of different varieties or races. **2.** matings between distantly related or unrelated individuals. *adj.* **cross-bred.**

cross-eye, see **strabismus.**

cross-fertilization (fuhr-tuh-luh-ZAY-shuhn), *n.* fertilization of an ovum by a sperm from another individual of the species, as in flowers and most animals; contrast with **self-fertilization.**

crossing-over, see **chiasma.**

crossopterygian (krah-sahp-tuh-RIJ-ee-uhn), *n.* any member of a group of lobe-finned fishes, extinct except for one species recently discovered, believed to be ancestral to amphibian animals.

cross-pollinate (pahl-uh-NAYT), *v.* to transfer pollen from one plant to the stigma of another plant, preventing self-fertilization and insuring production of hybrid seed.

cross section, a slice cut across any substance, usually at right angles to the long axis of the substance: a *cross section* of a tree trunk will reveal annual rings; see **section.**

croup (KROOP), *n.* inflammation of the larynx or trachea, frequent in children and characterized by noisy inhalation of breath and a harsh cough.

crowfoot family, see **Ranales.**

crucible (KROO-suh-buhl), *n.* any container of heat-resistant material designed for use at high temperatures or to hold very hot substances, as molten steel.

crude oil, petroleum as it comes from the oil well, with no impurities removed or components separated by fractional distillation.

cruising speed (KROOZ-ing), the normal operating speed for a vehicle, especially an airplane; the speed considered most efficient in terms of economical fuel consumption, altitude, and weather.

crust, *n.* **1.** the outer portion of Earth, as contrasted with the underlying portions composed of denser matter; usually crystalline in nature; varying in thickness. **2.** the horny outer coat or covering of something, as the outer wall of a hoof, or a scab over a wound.

Crustacea (krus-TAY-shuh), *n.* a class of largely aquatic arthropods with segmented bodies covered by a hard substance called *chitin,* and numerous segmented appendages; vary from microscopic organisms to the 12-foot-wide giant crab; included among *crustaceans* are crayfish, lobsters, shrimps, crabs, barnacles, and various water fleas such as *Daphnia.*

Crux (KRUHKS), *n.* the *Southern Cross,* an important southern, cross-shaped constellation; contains Alpha Crucis and Beta Crucis, among the brightest stars in the sky. A line from Gamma Crucis, the star at the top of the cross, through Alpha Crucis, at the foot, points approximately to the south celestial pole.

crymotherapy (kry-moh-THER-a-pee), *n.* medical treatment using cold temperatures.

cryogenesis (kry-uh-JEN-uh-sis), *n.* in medicine, the production of cold to achieve a lowered body temperature; used in some surgery or therapy.

cryogenics (kry-uh-JEN-iks), *n.* the study of the properties of matter at extremely low temperatures; liquid helium is much used in such work because it liquefies at a lower temperature than any other substance, $-269°$ C. The properties of most substances are quite different at such *cryogenic* temperatures; see also **helium.**

cryolite (KRY-uh-lyt), *n.* a fine crystalline mineral, Na_3AlR_6, with hardness 2½; usually white; used as a flux in extracting aluminum.

CONTROL WINDING   CENTRAL WIRE

Cryotron switch (greatly enlarged); current through the control winding halts the passage of current through the superconducting central wire

cryotron (KRY-uh-trahn), *n,* a device operated near absolute zero, consisting of a wire with another coil of wire around it; at very low temperatures the wire is a superconductor and large changes in current are thus produced by small changes in magnetic field; the *thin-film* cryotron substitutes a thin film for the coil; the device serves much the same function as tubes or transistors.

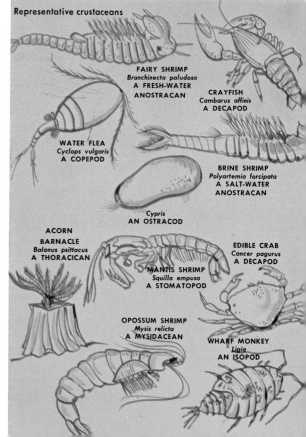

Representative crustaceans

FAIRY SHRIMP
Branchinecta paludosa
A FRESH-WATER
ANOSTRACAN

CRAYFISH
Cambarus affinis
A DECAPOD

WATER FLEA
Cyclops vulgaris
A COPEPOD

BRINE SHRIMP
Polyartemia forcipata
A SALT-WATER
ANOSTRACAN

Cypris
AN OSTRACOD

ACORN
BARNACLE
Balanus psittacus
A THORACICAN

EDIBLE CRAB
Cancer pagurus
A DECAPOD

MANTIS SHRIMP
Squilla empusa
A STOMATOPOD

OPOSSUM SHRIMP
Mysis relicta
A MYSIDACEAN

WHARF MONKEY
Ligia
AN ISOPOD

crystal

crystal (KRIS-tuhl), *n.* **1.** a solid substance with naturally formed flat surfaces, sharp edges, and a definite angle between pairs of surfaces; produced by the regular pattern of atoms or molecules in the solid; classified by the axes of the geometric solid, and the angles between faces; see **crystal system.** **2.** a substance exhibiting piezoelectricity, such as galena, used in radios.

crystal defect, any imperfection in the structure or composition of a crystal; especially trace impurities which affect the crystal.

crystalline (KRIS-tuh-lin), *adj.* pertaining to crystals; having a definite geometric structure.

crystallize (KRIS-tuh-lyz), *v.* to change from liquid state to solid crystalline state (as water to ice), or to precipitate, as crystals from solution.

crystallography *n.* science of the systems of crystals, their aggregation forms and structure.

crystal set, a radio receiver that makes use of a crystalline rectifier, as galena, instead of vacuum tubes or transistors.

crystal system, any of the 6 types of geometric atomic structures in crystals: **cubic** (also called

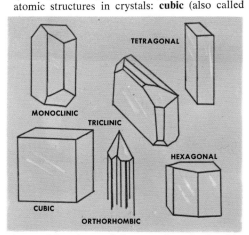

isometric), **tetragonal, hexagonal, orthorhombic, monoclinic,** or **triclinic.**

Cs, symbol for **cesium.**

Ctenophora (tee-NAHF-uh-ruh), *n.* the phylum of marine animals called *comb jellies,* mainly characterized by comb plates (rows of stiff cilia), which function in locomotion; *Pleurobrachia* is

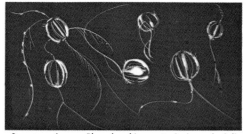

Sea gooseberry, *Pleurobrachia,* a typical comb jelly

¾ inch long, while the *Venus's-girdle* may be over 3 feet long; most have tentacles, but a few do not; some are like long ribbons in appearance.

Cu, symbol for **copper.**

cubic (KYOO-bik), *adj.* **1.** of or pertaining to any space measure with 3 dimensions, as a *cubic* centimeter. **2.** of or pertaining to any crystal

having 3 equal perpendicular axes; also called *isometric;* see **crystal system.**

cuboidal cell (KYOO-boi-duhl), a roughly cube-shaped epithelial cell, found characteristically in the kidney and the thyroid gland; see **epithelium.**

cuckoo (KOO-koo), see **Cuculiformes.**

Cuculiformes (kyoo-kyoo-li-FAWR-meez), *n.* an order of road-running birds; with slightly curved beaks, slender bodies, and long tails; some species use the nests of other birds; includes cuckoos.

cud, *n.* a small ball of food mixed with saliva from the first stomach of any ruminant animal, brought back to the mouth where it is chewed and swallowed again before complete digestion takes place; see **ruminant.**

culture (KUHL-chuhr), *n.* the growth of cells or other organisms (especially bacteria and viruses) under carefully regulated conditions to avoid contamination.

cumulonimbus (kyoo-myuh-loh-NIM-buhs), *n.* a heavy rain cloud, with a dark base about 2,000 feet above the ground, and towering high above its base; usually with violent air currents moving in many directions.

cumulostratus (kyoo-myuh-loh-STRAY-tuhs), *n.* any cloud of the cumulus type, but with a stratus-type base; may bring showers.

cumulus (KYOOM-yuh-luhs), *n.* clouds piled into high stacks, somewhat cauliflower-shaped. They have low bases (about 2,000 feet) and may extend as high as 25,000 feet; usually found at a cold front of an unstable air system; tend to bring heavy showers.

cupric (KOO-prik), *adj.* pertaining to the copper ion with a valence of 2, Cu^{++}, or to compounds containing this ion.

cuprite (KYOO-pryt), *n.* a reddish-brown mineral occurring in crystalline or amorphous form, Cu_2O, with hardness 3½-4; an ore of copper.

cuprous (KYOO-pruhs), *adj.* pertaining to the copper ion with a valence of one, Cu^+, or to compounds containing this ion.

curare (kyoor-AHR-ee), *n.* any of several organic poisonous compounds that relax or paralyze the muscles; especially, one prepared from plants of genus *Strychnos* in the logania family.

curator (kyuh-RAY-tuhr, KYUHR-uh-), *n.* a person responsible for the overall planning concerned with the care, preparation, and exhibitions of museum collections, or research and exhibition within a specific department, as the *curator* of fishes.

curd (KUHRD), *n.* the solid product obtained by the coagulation of milk, consisting largely of casein; made into cheeses.

curie (KYOO-ree, kyoo-REE), *n.* the unit for expressing radioactivity: equal to 37 billion nuclear transformations per second; about the radiation of one gram of radium; the practical unit is the micromicrocurie.

curium (KYOO-ree-uhm), *n.* a transuranium radioactive element in the actinide series; metallic form is silvery-white; symbol Cm; at. no., 96; mass number of most stable isotope, 247; first made in 1944 by Seaborg, Ghiorso, and James, and named by Seaborg for Marie and Pierre Curie.

current, *n.* **1.** the flow of a fluid, as a stream within a larger body of water. **2.** the flow of

Cycad, *Strangeria paradoxa,* a living fossil

electricity caused by movement of electrons. **3.** the rate of electrical flow, measured in amperes. *adj.* **4.** existing at the present time.

curvature of the spine (KUHR-vuh-chuhr), a movement of the spine from its normal position; associated with several disorders, as *Pott's disease,* the decay of the central portion of the vertebrae; see also **lordosis.**

cusp (KUHSP), *n.* a projection or tapered point; see **bicuspid, tooth.**

custard-apple family, see **Ranales.**

cuticle (KYOO-ti-kuhl), *n.* **1.** the dry, horny cells forming the outer layer of the human epidermis. **2.** a waxy layer secreted by the epidermis of a leaf, serving to reduce water evaporation. **3.** a secretion of cells that covers the outer surface of many animals.

cutin (KYOO-tin), *n.* a waxy, resinous, "waterproof" substance in many plant cell walls; when secreted by surface cells of leaves and stem, forms the cuticle.

cuttlebone (KUHT-uhl-bohn), *n.* the shell or *pen* of a squid, the *cuttlefish,* given to canaries as a source of calcium; see **Cephalopoda.**

cyanamide (sy-AN-uh-mid, sy-uh-NAM-id), *n.* **1.** a solid, crystalline organic compound used for organic synthesis; formula, $CNNH_2$. **2.** calcium cyanamide, used for fertilizers, pecticides, and to make melamine for plastics; formula, $CaCN_2$.

cyanate (SY-uh-nayt), *n.* a compound containing a cyanate radical, ^-OCN, such as potassium cyanate (KOCN); used in organic chemicals.

cyanide (SY-uh-nyd), *n.* a compound containing a CN^- radical; used in electroplating and metallurgy; most cyanides are extremely toxic. Organic cyanides are also called *nitriles.*

cyanogen (sy-AN-uh-juhn), *n.* an extremely poisonous, colorless gas with a burning odor; used to make organic compounds; formula, C_2N_2.

Cyanophyta (sy-uh-NOF-uh-tuh), *n.* a division of plants, the *blue-green algae; cyanophytes* grow as single cells or in colonies; cells have no plastids and nuclei may not be apparent; chlorophyll is masked by red and blue pigments; reproduces almost entirely by fission; includes nostoc and oscillatoria; see **alga, Thallophyta.**

cyanosis (sy-uh-NOH-sis), *n.* a bluish cast to the skin occurring when the blood lacks oxygen which colors it red. *adj.* **cyanotic.**

cybernetics (sy-buhr-NET-iks), *n.* the study of the relationship between communication and control in machines and in biological processes; particularly applied to the action of data-processing machines as compared with nervous and mental activities; see the study of decision-making machines that "remember" errors. *adj.* **cybernetic.**

cycad (SY-kuhd), *n.* any of a group of tropical, cone-bearing gymnosperms in order *Cycadales,* with thick stems topped by fernlike leaves and cones; most are extinct and found only as fossils; a few species survive.

cycle (SY-kuhl), *n.* **1.** a series of events ending at the same point as, or a point identical with, its beginning. **2.** in electricity, such a series of events in alternating current. **3.** in biology, any chemical or biological process that produces end products identical with the starting products; see also **life cycle, carbon cycle.**

cyclone (SY-klohn), *n.* the circular motion of masses of air around a low-pressure center, counterclockwise in the Northern Hemisphere, clockwise in the Southern. In tropical areas, cyclones generate hurricanes and typhoons; in nontropical areas, they produce tornadoes and other milder weather changes.

cyclopropane (sy-kloh-PROH-payn), *n.* a colorless, flammable, gaseous hydrocarbon with a characteristic odor; used as an anesthetic and for making organic compounds; formula, C_3H_6.

Cyclostomata (sy-kloh-stoh-MAH-tuh), *n.* a class in subphylum *Chordata* of fishes without

SUCKING MOUTH

Parasitic sea lamprey, *Petromyzon marinus;* sucking mouth has horny-toothed tongue that cuts into prey

jaws; often shaped like eels. Living groups of *cyclostomes* include lampreys and hagfish.

cyclotron (SY-kluh-trahn), *n.* a particle accelerator with 2 hollow, metallic semicircles; the particles travel through these when high-frequency alternating current is applied. A strong magnetic field acts perpendicular to the plane of the semicircles; proper phase adjustment causes acceleration of the particles at each revolution they make; when their speed and energy are high enough, they are released to strike a target.

Cygnus (SIG-nuhs), *n.* the *Swan* or *Northern Cross,* a northern constellation; its tail star, Deneb, is 19th brightest star in visual magnitude.

cylinder (SIL-in-duhr), *n.* **1.** any round-sided, can-shaped object such as a drum. **2.** a metal chamber having this shape, into the open head of which a moving piston compresses a gas, as in an internal-combustion engine.

cyst (SIST), *n.* **1.** a closed, fluid-filled sac on or in the body, often abnormal. **2.** a spore-like dormant animal, often protozoan, encased in a protective cover. *adj.* **cystic.**

cytology (sy-TAHL-uh-jee), *n.* the study of cells, including structure, development, function, biochemical composition, and specialization.

cytoplasm (SY-tuh-plazm), *n.* all protoplasm outside the nucleus of a cell. It may contain vacuoles, plastids, and other organelles.

cytosine (SY-tuh-seen), *n.* a pyrimidine-type base occurring as one of the 4 fundamental units in DNA and RNA; always pairs with guanine.

61

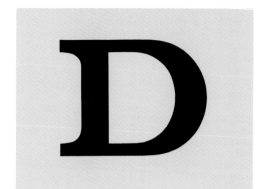

d., abbreviation for **density.**

D, symbol for **deuterium.**

dactyl-, dactylo- (DAK-tuh-loh), a word part meaning *digit,* as a finger or toe: a *dactylogram* is a fingerprint.

daddy longlegs, see **Arachnida.**

daltonism (DAWL-tuh-nizm), *n.* a form of color blindness in which a person cannot distinguish between red and green; named for the British scientist John Dalton, who had the condition and studied it.

dam, *n.* **1.** any structure to slow or alter the flow of water. **2.** a mother, a term used in discussing the ancestry of livestock.

damp, *v.* **1.** to reduce a vibration or other action. **2.** to use friction, a coil, or a vane to reduce the swinging of the indicator needle on an electric meter and make the needle come to rest more quickly. *n.* **damping.** *n.* **3.** vapor or fumes, such as *chokedamp.*

Daphnia, a water flea; see **Crustacea.**

D'Arsonval galvanometer (DAHR-suhn-vuhl), see **galvanometer.**

Darwinism (DAHR-win-izm), *n.* the theory of natural selection and origin of species as proposed by Charles Darwin in 1859.

data (DAY-tuh, DAT-uh), *pl. n.* (*sing.* **datum**) a set of facts; information.

data processing, the handling of data, usually in numerical form, by automatic methods, especially by electronic devices using magnetic tapes for input and computers for operation and control.

daylight-saving time, a time system in which clocks are set one hour ahead of the standard time for any given time zone; often adopted in periods of long daylight to allow for daytime recreation at the end of the day; see also **standard time.**

DC, d-c, d.c., abbreviation for **direct current.**

DDT, *n.* a poisonous organic compound, occurring as colorless crystals or white powder; used as an insecticide; formula, $(ClC_6H_4)_2CHCCl_3$; short for *dichloro-*d*iphenyl-*t*richloroethane.*

dead reckoning, a system of navigation in which position is calculated entirely from known starting point, speed, and direction of travel, action of wind and water currents, etc., instead of radio fixes or observations on the sun and stars.

death (deth), *n.* the end of life.

debriefing. *n.* the systematic procedure in which a person reports all details and answers all questions after a task. It may include complete physical examination.

decay (dee-KAY), *n.* **1.** the slow process by which a biological substance decomposes, generally by action of oxidizing bacteria or molds. **2.** a gradual decrease or deterioration, as that due to aging. **3.** the process by which a radioactive substance undergoes nuclear disintegration. *v.* **decay.**

deceleration (dee-sel-uh-RAY-shuhn), *n.* any decrease of velocity; the opposite of *acceleration. v.* **decelerate.**

deci- a word part meaning *one-tenth.*

decibel (DES-uh-bel), *n.* an energy ratio used especially in the study of loudness of sound; equal to one-tenth of a bel; see **bel.**

deciduous (di-SIJ-oo-uhs), *adj.* falling off at a certain time of year or time of life. Deer antlers, milk teeth, and the leaves of many plants are *deciduous.*

declination (dek-luh-NAY-shuhn), *n.* **1.** any deviation from a standard. **2.** the angle between true north and magnetic north, measured from any point. **3.** in astronomy, the latitude north or south of the celestial equator, stated in degrees.

decompose (dee-kuhm-POHZ), *v.* **1.** to break down into simpler substances. **2.** in chemistry, to convert a substance into simple substances, as to convert a complex molecule into simpler molecules, or into atoms of the elements. **3.** in biology, to decay. *n.* **decomposition.** *adj.* **decomposed.**

decompression (dee-kuhm-PRESH-uhn), *n.* reduction of pressure; especially, a reduction of compressed air to atmospheric pressure; must be performed slowly where animal life is involved, usually in *decompression chambers.*

decontaminate (dee-kuhn-TAM-i-nayt), *v.* to rid clothing, the body, or any other region of toxic chemicals, or bacteria; in recent usage, to rid such a region of radioactive hazards.

deductive reasoning (dee-DUK-tiv), reasoning from a general principle to a specific application of it: if all who read this definition have functioning eyes, and if John is reading this definition, then John has functioning eyes. Almost every statement in mathematics, without which science would be impossible, depends on a deductive process of reasoning; contrast with **inductive reasoning.**

deer, see **Artiodactyla.**

defecation (def-uh-KAY-shuhn,) *n.* the discharge of waste or usually solid fecal material (*feces*) after digestion. *v.* **defecate.**

deficiency disease (dee-FISH-uhn-see), any disease chiefly due to lack of essential nutrients, such as iron, calcium, or vitamins; see **vitamin.**

deflection (dee-FLEK-shuhn), *n.* **1.** the swinging of an indicator on a scale from the zero position due to the action of some force. **2.** a change in the direction of a wave or a beam of particles.

deformation (DEF-uhr-may-shuhn, dee-fawr-MAY-) *n.* **1.** any disturbance in structure, especially by external forces. **2.** any change in original size (volume) or shape of rocks produced by gravitational or heat-expansion and heat-flow forces, called *tectonic forces.*

deformity (dee-FAWR-mi-tee), *n.* any part of the body not developed into its normal shape.

degeneration (dee-jen-uh-RAY-shuhn), *n.* change to a lower or less highly organized form; especially, breaking down of a tissue so that it does not function normally. *v.* **degenerate.** *adj.* **degenerative.**

degree (duh-GREE), *n.* **1.** a unit of measurement on temperature and other scales. **2.** a unit of measurement for arcs and angles; 1/360th of the angular measure of any circle, especially the circumference of the earth.

dehiscent (dee-HIS-uhnt), *adj.* opening up at maturity: when a *dehiscent* fruit splits open, seeds are released; see **fruit** picture.

dehydrate (dee-HY-drayt), *v.* **1.** to remove water from a substance, as drying hydrochloric acid to get anhydrous hydrogen chloride. **2.** to lose water from a substance, as loss from body tissues during fever. *n.* **dehydration.**

deionization (dee-ey-uh-nuh-ZAY-shuhn), *n.* the purification of a substance, especially of water, by removal of salt ions, as through ion-exchange processes; see also **ion exchange.**

deliquescent (del-uh-KWES-uhnt), *adj.* **1.** absorbing water vapor from the air to such an extent that a saturated solution is produced, said of certain solids. **2.** in botany, branching into many small subdivisions, used especially of the veins in leaves and trees. **3.** gradually wasting away or softening, as portions of a fungus during decay.

delta (DEL-tuh), *n.* **1.** the fourth letter of the Greek alphabet, used to indicate that something is fourth in a series: *Delta* Cephei is the fourth brightest star in the constellation Cepheus. **2.** anything roughly triangular in shape, especially the alluvial deposit of soil or gravel by a large stream at the point of entry into a sea, usually resulting in numerous channels between the sea and the main stream.

denatured alcohol, alcohol to which a substance such as acetone or methane has been added so that the alcohol cannot be used as a medicine or for drinking, but still can be used as an industrial solvent.

dendrite (DEN-dryt), *n.* any of a number of nerve fibers along which impulses travel toward the body of the nerve cell. They receive impulses across the synapse from the axon processes of the preceding cell; see **neuron.**

Deneb (DEN-eb), *n.* a star in the tail of Cygnus; 19th brightest star in visual magnitude.

denitrifying bacteria (dee-NY-truh-fy-ing), anaerobic bacteria that obtain oxygen for respiration by breaking down nitrogen compounds (usually nitrates into nitrites or free nitrogen) from decaying organisms in the soil.

density (DEN-si-tee), *n.* **1.** the mass of a substance per unit volume; commonly given as grams/cm^3 or pounds/ft^3. *adj.* **dense.** *abbr.* **d.** **2.** the amount of blackening on developed film.

dental caries (KAIR-eez), gradual decay and breakdown of hard tooth tissue by the action of microorganisms on carbohydrates; if not treated, may reach the pulp; *tooth decay.*

dentine (DEN-teen), see **tooth.**

dentition (den-TISH-uhn), *n.* **1.** the teeth. **2.** the arrangement of teeth in the mouth, including number of each kind and their order; used in physical anthropology.

deoxyribonucleic acid (dee-AHK-see-ry-boh-noo-KLEE-ik), any of several complex organic acids found in combination with protein in the chromosomes and genes of living cells; carries genetic traits in heredity and is essential for cell division; a typical formula is $C_{39}H_{51}O_{25}N_{15}P_4$; also spelled **desoxy-.** *abbr.* **DNA.**

DNA molecule—differences occur through the many possible combinations and positions of adenine and thymine pairs and guanine and cytosine pairs along the double-helix "ladder" of sugar and phosphates

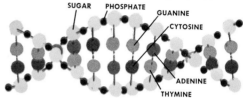

deposit (dee-PAHZ-it), *n.* **1.** anything that is laid down, as soil laid down by water. **2.** a thin layer placed on a surface, as an electrolytic *deposit* of nickel on steel. *v.* **deposit.**

depressant (duh-PRES-uhnt), *n.* a substance that lowers (*depresses*) the activity of metabolic or vital processes, such as tranquilizers, digitalis, alcohol, and others.

depth perception, the ability to judge the distance to an object or the distance between objects; occurs because our eyes are set a certain distance apart; see also **binocular vision.**

depth sounding, determination of the amount of water between a ship and the bottom of a body of water; may use a lead attached to a line, sonar, or other techniques.

derivative (duh-RIV-uh-tiv), *n.* **1.** generally, anything *derived* (obtained) from something else, frequently by modification. **2.** in chemistry, a compound derived from another, often with characteristics different from the original.

dermatology (duhr-muh-TAHL-uh-jee), *n.* the study of the skin and its disorders.

dermis (DUHR-mis), *n.* the skin, especially the *corium,* or actively growing layers; see **skin.**

Dermoptera (duhr-MAHP-tuh-ruh), *n.* an order of mammals related to bats with limbs modified for gliding; common name *flying lemur,* but they are not lemurs and do not fly.

desert, *n.* an arid barren region that can support little or no vegetation.

desiccate (DES-uh-kayt), **1.** *v.* to dry out or remove water from something; to dehydrate; chemicals can be *desiccated* in a device (*desiccator*) containing a water-absorbing compound. Tissues being prepared for microscopic study are desiccated by treatment with a graded series of alcohols, ranging from 10% to 100% in concentration. *n.* **desiccation.** **2.** *n.* a chemical compound, a residue, formed by desiccating.

desoxyribonucleic acid (des-ahk-), an alternate spelling for **deoxyribonucleic acid.**

destructive distillation, the heating of an element or compound until a nonreversible chemical change has set in; contrast with **distillation.**

detergent (dee-TUHR-juhnt), *n.* a substance that cleanses, especially used of chemicals other than soaps; replacements for soaps.

deuterium (doo-TEER-ee-uhm), *n.* an isotope of hydrogen, one proton and one neutron in its nucleus; symbol D or H^2; *at. wt.,* 2.0159; also called *heavy hydrogen.*

deuteron (DOO-tuhr-ahn), *n.* the nucleus of the deuterium atom; mass, 2; charge, 1$^+$.

Devonian (duh-VOH-nee-uhn), *n.* fourth geologic period of the Paleozic era, between the Silurian and Mississippian periods; lasted about 50 million years and ended about 290 million years ago. Seed-bearing plants first appeared and modern fishes were common; see also **geologic time table.**

dew, *n.* water condensed from the water vapor in the atmosphere, usually onto cool surfaces, forming chiefly at night.

Dewar flask (DOO-uhr, DYOO-), a glass vessel with 2 walls from between which air has been removed so that temperature of the contents is

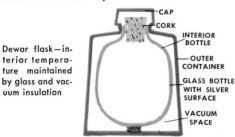

Dewar flask—interior temperature maintained by glass and vacuum insulation

CAP
CORK
INTERIOR BOTTLE
OUTER CONTAINER
GLASS BOTTLE WITH SILVER SURFACE
VACUUM SPACE

kept constant; based on the fact that glass is a poor conductor of heat and a vacuum is a nonconductor; first devised by James Dewar, a Scotish scientist, for transporting liquid air (temperature of −190°C); a vacuum bottle.

dew point, the temperature at which a given mass of air is saturated with water vapor; any cooling of the air below this point results in dew, or sometimes fog or frost.

dextral (DEKS-truhl), *adj.* at or toward the right side; most machine screws have a *dextral* thread; contrast with **sinistral.**

dextrose (DEKS-trohs), see **glucose.**

di-, a word particle meaning *2;* in chemistry, it denotes 2 atoms, as carbon *di*oxide (CO_2).

Di, symbol for **didymium.**

diabetes (dy-uh-BEE-teez, -tuhs), *n.* one of the disorders in which excessive amounts of urine are discharged, particularly *diabetes mellitus,* caused by insulin deficiency, in which carbohydrates (sugar or starch) are not oxidized properly and appreciable sugar appears in the urine. *adj.* **diabetic.**

diagnosis (dy-uhg-NOH-sis), *n.* **1.** determination of the character of a disease or disorder. **2.** the procedure by which a physician determines the character of a disease; can include physical examination, patient's description of symptoms, X-rays, blood tests, biopsy, urinalysis, etc. *adj.* **diagnostic.**

diamond (DY-muhnd, DY-uh-), *n.* an allotropic form of carbon; occurs as brilliant, colorless, flawless crystals when pure; the hardest known substance, with hardness 10; used for jewelry, drill bits, glass cutting, and polishing gemstones; see **gem** picture.

diaphragm (DY-uh-fram), *n.* **1.** in anatomy, a wall of muscle or other tissue separating 2

cavities or forming a cavity; especially, the muscular wall between the thorax and abdomen in mammals; see **respiratory system. 2.** any thin disk or membrane, often movable, especially one that controls amount of light, as in a camera.

diarrhea (dy-uh-REE-uh), *n.* a condition in which feces are discharged much more frequently than normally and are usually watery; often a symptom of intestinal disease.

diastole (dy-AS-tuh-lee), *n.* the period of expansion of the heart muscle, alternated with the period of contraction (*systole*); see also **blood pressure.**

diastrophism (dy-AS-truh-fizm), *n.* any deformation of the earth's crust, or the processes causing it; usually divided into *orogeny,* the major deformations shaping mountain chains, and *epirogeny,* the less violent but longer lasting deformations affecting wider areas in continent-making. *adj.* **diastrophic.**

diatom (DY-uh-tohm), see **Chrysophyta.**

diatomaceous earth (dy-uh-tuh-MAY-shuhs), a whitish, crumbly clay composed of the silica shells of diatoms, used as a filter and heat insulator.

diatomic (dy-uh-TAHM-ik), *adj.* **1.** having 2 atoms (often of the same kind) in a molecule: molecular hydrogen is *diatomic.* **2.** having 2 radicals or atoms capable of reacting; bivalent.

dichromatic (dy-kroh-MAT-ik), *adj.* **1.** having a color under transmitted light that may appear different depending on thickness of the slice of material. **2.** in zoology, belonging to a group with 2 different color patterns in the species. **3.** color blind, used of those who can distinguish only 2 of the 3 primary colors.

Dick test, the injection of scarlet fever toxin into the skin in order to detect immunity or susceptibility to scarlet fever.

dicot (DY-kaht), short term for **dicotyledon.**

dicotyledon (dy-kaht-uh-LEE-duhn), *n.* any flowering plant (angiosperm) of subclass *Dicotyledoneae* with 2 cotyledons or seed leaves

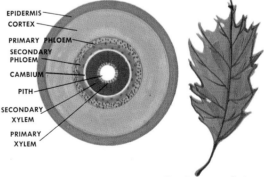

EPIDERMIS
CORTEX
PRIMARY PHLOEM
SECONDARY PHLOEM
CAMBIUM
PITH
SECONDARY XYLEM
PRIMARY XYLEM

Typical leaf and woody stem of a dicotyledonous plant

in the seed embryo, flower parts in 4s and 5s, leaves with netted venation, and, frequently, woody stems; includes petunia, rose, and maple. *adj.* **dicotyledonous.**

didymium (dy-DIM-ee-uhm), *n.* **1.** a mixture of certain elements in the lanthanide rare-earth series; the salts are used for coloring glass and as an antiseptic; once considered an element, with symbol Di; now known to be primarily a mixture of praseodymium and neodymium.

die, 1. *n.* any device for giving a specific shape to materials under pressure, including stamping dies, cutting and threading dies, and wire-drawing dies. **2.** *v.* to stop functioning as a living unit, either as a cell or as a complete organism.

dielectric (dy-uh-LEK-trik), *n.* a substance that does not conduct electricity; an insulator.

diesel engine (DEE-zuhl), a form of internal-combustion engine in which a piston suddenly compresses air in the cylinder, heating air enough so that fuel injected directly into the cylinder will ignite; differs from the conventional gasoline engine, which requires a spark to ignite a pre-mixed combination of fuel and air; named for Rudolf Diesel (1858–1913), German engineer.

diet (DY-uht), *n.* **1.** food, especially in relation to its nutritious quality. **2.** a special course of feeding designed to achieve some effect, as improvement of health or reduction of weight. *v.* **diet.**

dietetics (dy-uh-TET-iks), *n.* the study of diet as related to health and nutrition.

differential (dif-uh-REN-shuhl), **1.** *n.* an assembly of gears allowing 2 shafts to rotate at different speeds: the *differential* in the rear end of conventional automobiles allows the outer rear wheel to turn faster than the inner rear wheel in rounding a curve. **2.** *adj.* referring to a different rate of occurrence of a trait in individuals.

differentiation (dif-uh-ren-shee-AY-shuhn), *n.* **1.** in psychology, the process of learning to respond to a specific stimulus but not to one slightly different in some way; see also **conditioned response, generalization. 2.** in embryology, the development, usually by cells within a group of cells, of different (specialized) characteristics. *v.* **differentiate.**

diffraction (di-FRACK-shuhn), *n.* the effect produced when a limited section of a wave front meets a surface; sometimes considered as the bending of light waves around an object, resulting in a change in amplitude or phase of the waves. Light diffraction patterns are used in spectroscopic analysis. X-ray and electron diffraction patterns are used in nondestructive material testing in industry. *v.* **diffract.** *adj.* **diffractive.**

diffusion (di-FYOO-zhuhn, *n.* **1.** the movement of molecules of one substance into another substance; takes place rapidly in gases, more slowly in liquids, and extremely slowly in solids. **2.** in biology, the movement of molecules through a cell membrane or through a semipermeable membrane. *v.* **diffuse.**

digestion (di-JES-chuhn, dy-), *n.* the conversion of food into a form that an organism can assimilate; may take place in the organism as a whole or in specific digestive areas, such as the well-defined digestive system of a vertebrate. *v.* **digest.** *adj.* **digestive.**

digestive system, the complete set of organs in any given animal that function to digest food into simpler chemicals which the cells can assimilate; the system varies greatly in different animals. In man, the main parts of the system are: esophagus, stomach, small intestine, and large intestine.

digit (DIJ-uht), *n.* **1.** a toe or a finger. **2.** any numeral in a number system, such as 0, 1 in the binary system or 0 through 9 in the decimal.

digital computer (DIJ-uh-tuhl), any computer that performs mathematical operations upon numbers in digit form; used in data-processing for high speed; see also **computer.**

digitalis (dij-i-TAL-uhs), *n.* **1.** a heart medicine made by drying and powdering leaves from the purple foxglove, a common garden plant; increases blood pressure and contracts arterioles. **2.** a foxglove plant.

digitigrade (di-JIT-uh-grayd), *adj.* using only the toes to walk upon, as the cow and horse.

dike (DYK), *n.* **1.** in geology, an intrusion cutting across the base plane of the rock into which it thrusts; see **intrusion. 2.** a structure that holds back waters of a river or the sea.

dilation (dy-LAY-shuhn), *n.* a process of expansion, as the pupil of the eye in darkness; also called *dilatation.* *v.* **dilate.**

dilute (dy-LOOT), *adj.* reduced in concentration; usually applied to solutions in liquids: *dilute* hydrochloric acid, as defined for medical supplies, is 10% hydrogen chloride and 90% water. *n.* **dilution.** *v.* **dilute.**

dimension (duh-MEN-shuhn), *n.* extent in one direction. Ordinary space is regarded as 3 *dimensional:* length, breadth, and thickness (height) are the dimensions that describe any solid in ordinary space. Time is sometimes regarded as a fourth dimension.

Dinornithiformes (dyn-ohr-nith-i-FAWR-meez), *n.* an order of extinct, flightless, running birds, including the moas of New Zealand.

dinosaur (DY-nuh-sawr), *n.* any of a number of prehistoric reptiles of the Mesozoic era, divided into 2 types: the lizard-hipped (*Saurischia*) and the bird-hipped (*Ornithischia*). Fossil remains

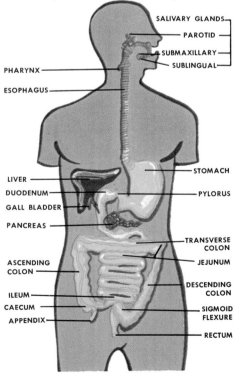

Organs of the human digestive system

SALIVARY GLANDS
PAROTID
SUBMAXILLARY
SUBLINGUAL
PHARYNX
ESOPHAGUS
STOMACH
LIVER
DUODENUM
PYLORUS
GALL BLADDER
PANCREAS
TRANSVERSE COLON
JEJUNUM
ASCENDING COLON
DESCENDING COLON
ILEUM
CAECUM
SIGMOID FLEXURE
APPENDIX
RECTUM

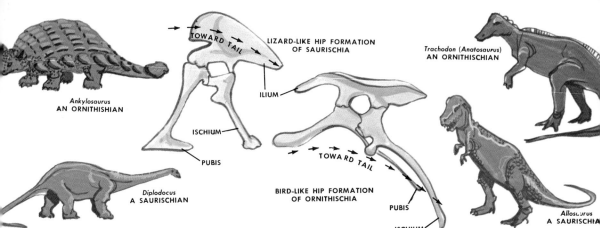

Ankylosaurus
AN ORNITHISHIAN

ISCHIUM

PUBIS

ILIUM

TOWARD TAIL

LIZARD-LIKE HIP FORMATION
OF SAURISCHIA

Trachodon (Anatosaurus)
AN ORNITHISCHIAN

TOWARD TAIL

BIRD-LIKE HIP FORMATION
OF ORNITHISCHIA

PUBIS

ISCHIUM

Diplodocus
A SAURISCHIAN

Allosaurus
A SAURISCHIA

show that dinosaurs ranged from species the size of a chicken to those almost 100 feet long; see **Ornithischia, Saurischia.**

diode (DY-ohd), *n.* **1.** a vacuum tube with only 2 elements: cathode and anode. **2.** a semi-

CATHODE ANODE

B BATTERY

A BATTERY

conductor with 2 terminals, functioning like a vacuum tube diode in rectifying current.

dioecious (dy-EE-shuhs), *adj.* with male and female reproductive organs in separate plant individuals; contrast with **monoecious.**

diphtheria (dif-THEER-ee-uh), *n.* a highly infectious disease caused by a bacterium; characterized by swelling of the throat and, often, the formation of a false membrane; toxins from the bacteria are absorbed at the membrane.

dipleurula larva (dy-PLOOR-yuh-luh), the hypothetical ancestral larva of echinoderms, having bilateral symmetry and looped, ciliated bands.

diplodocus (duh-PLAHD-uh-kuhs), see **Saurischia.**

diploid (DIP-loyd), *adj.* having the full number (2n) of chromosomes for a given species, as all animal and sporophyte plant body cells, and all germ cells before meiosis; see **meiosis.**

Diplopoda (di-PLAHP-uh-duh), *n.* a class of wormlike arthropods; the *millipedes,* with a cylindrical body covered with chitin and with many segments, each bearing 2 pairs of legs.

dipole (DY-pohl), *n.* **1.** an object having 2 equal but oppositely charged points (poles), as a magnet or a molecule. **2.** an antenna with 2 equal arms, used in FM and TV transmission and reception. *adj.* **dipolar.**

Diptera (DIP-tuh-ruh), *n.* an order of insects, comprising all *true flies,* with only one pair of wings and 2 rodlike organs called *halteres* which replace the second pair of wings and are used for balance in flight; see **Insecta.**

direct current, electrical current of fairly steady value flowing in only one direction; contrast with **alternating current.** *abbr.* **DC, d-c, d.c.**

direction finder, a radio navigation aid, previously used on ships and planes to find location and direction of travel; based on use of loop antenna which gives its strongest signal when in line with waves from a transmitter; also called *aircraft* direction finder or *ADF.*

dirigible (DIR-i-juh-buhl), *n.* an *airship;* a lighter-than-air vessel that can be steered and has an engine; may be rigid, as a zeppelin, or nonrigid, as a blimp.

disaccharide (dy-SAK-uh-ryd), *n.* any sugar that can be converted into 2 simpler sugars *(monosaccharides)* by hydrolysis or enzyme action; common examples are sucrose, lactose, and maltose.

discrimination (duh-skrim-uh-NAY-shuhn), *n.* in psychology, the ability to recognize and respond only to a certain stimulus, learned through reinforcement; generally, the ability to distinguish between similar objects or other stimuli.

disease (di-ZEEZ), *n.* a condition of an organism that interferes with normal functioning.

disinfectant (dis-in-FEK-tuhnt), *n.* any substance that will eliminate infection; especially, any chemical that will kill the active microorganisms on objects outside the body. *v.* **disinfect.**

disintegrate (dis-IN-tuh-grayt), *v.* **1.** to break into parts or into the simplest components. **2.** to disrupt an atom or its nucleus, producing simpler atoms or nuclei. *n.* **disintegration.**

disk flower, see **composite family.**

dislocation (dis-loh-KAY-shuhn), *n.* **1.** in medicine, a condition in which a bone has slipped out of place at a joint. **2.** in crystals, a defect caused by atoms of one place slipping past those in another. **3.** in geology, alternate term for **fault.** *v.* **dislocate.**

dispersion (dis-PUHR-zhuhn), *n.* **1.** in physics, the separation of a complex electromagnetic wave into its components; especially, the separation of light into its component colors. **2.** in chemistry, the scattering of particles in a solution; see also **colloid.** *v.* **disperse.**

displacement, *n.* **1.** a change in position from that previously occupied by a body; especially, in physics, a change in position of a body relative to its surroundings, as a representation of the path taken by a particle as it moves from one point to another. *v.* **displace.**

dissect (di-SEKT), *v.* to cut into pieces; especially, in anatomy, to cut an organism into parts which can be carefully studied. *n.* **dissection.**

dissociation di-soh-see-AY-shuhn), *n.* the breaking up of a chemical substance into simpler components (usually ions), as the ionization of a strong acid when in solution; such formation of ions takes place normally.

dissonance (DIS-uh-nuhnts), *n.* a combination of tones in music, usually unpleasant, obtained when the frequencies (or some harmonic) of the tones are too close together. *adj.* **dissonant.**

distal (DIS-tuhl), *adj.* at a distance away from any named point; with relation to the hip, the knee is at the *distal* end of the femur (thighbone); contrast with **proximal.**

distemper (dis-TEM-puhr), *n.* any of several infectious diseases of dogs, cats, and other animals, caused by virus or bacterial invasion. Canine distemper, in dogs, is first characterized by fever and a discharge from nose and eyes.

distillation (dis-tuh-LAY-shuhn), *n.* evaporation of a liquid and condensation of the vapors back to a liquid state, a physical change done especially to remove impurities; mixtures of several liquids can also be separated by distillation, usually accomplished by heat or by reduced pressure; contrast with **destructive distillation.** *v.* **distill.**

distortion (di-STOHR-shuhn), *n.* a change in an image or sound from the way it originated; especially, in electronics, undesired changes in the wave form of a signal. *v.* **distort.**

distributor (dis-TRIB-yoo-tohr), *n.* a device used for distributing electric current to spark plugs, as in an internal-combustion gasoline engine.

diurnal (dy-UHR-nuhl), *adj.* taking place during daylight or every day; contrast with **nocturnal.**

divergent (dy-VUHR-juhnt), *adj.* progressing in different directions from a common point, as in *divergent* evolution: animals or plants arising from a common ancestor become increasingly different from one another; contrast with **convergent.** *n.* **divergence.** *v.* **diverge.**

diverticulum (dy-vuhr-TIK-yuh-luhm), *n., pl.* **-cula.** a closed, saclike structure leading off a main canal or cavity; may be abnormal or normal, such as the appendix in man or branches of the digestive system in flatworms.

DNA, abbreviation for **deoxyribonucleic acid.**

dogbane family, see **Gentianales.**

dog family, dogs, foxes, wolves, jackals, and others; see **Carnivora.**

dogwood family, see **Umbellales.**

doldrums (DOHL-druhmz), *pl. n.* a belt of low atmospheric pressure surrounding Earth near the equator, noted for little wind and high humidity.

dolomite (DAHL-uh-myt, DOH-luh-), *n.* **1.** a mineral, calcium-magnesium carbonate, $CaCO_3 \cdot MgCO_3$, commonly grayish; a source of magnesium and a building material. **2.** a sedimentary rock composed of dolomite mineral.

dolphin (DAHL-fin), see **Cetacea.**

domesticated (duh-MES-ti-kay-tuhd), *adj.* adapted by man to life in association with humans or to satisfy human wants; tame.

dominant (DAHM-uh-nuhnt), *adj.* of a gene, expressing itself physically in preference to its allele; if a physical trait (for example, brown eyes) is expressed when an individual has genes (alleles) for both brown and blue eyes, the gene for brown eyes is said to be *dominant;* contrast with **recessive.** *n.* **dominance.**

donor (DOH-nuhr), *n.* **1.** a person who supplies blood for transfusion purposes. **2.** an atom that can give up an electron and become positively charged; contrast with **acceptor atom.**

dope, *n.* **1.** any thick paste or liquid, especially one applied as a protective coating, as in airplanes. **2.** in common usage, any narcotic drug or even any stimulant used to affect behavior.

Doppler effect (DAHP-luhr), a change in observed frequency of wave motion, especially familiar in sound and light waves, due to changing distance between the wave-generating object and the observer; the whistle or horn of a rapidly

Doppler effect in sound—as a whistle nears and moves away, its apparent pitch changes because of variation in wave frequency reaching the observer's ear

approaching train has an increasing pitch to the ear of the observer; named for C. J. Doppler, Austrian physicist; see also **red shift.**

dormant (DAWR-muhnt), *adj.* inactive; having a metabolic rate much lower than that in the normally active organisms. Some cells are dormant for long periods of time and then become active under the proper stimulus.

dorsal (DAWR-suhl), *adj.* at the back or rear, used in biological description, as a *dorsal* fin; contrast with **ventral.**

dosimeter (doh-SIM-uh-tuhr), *n.* a device used for measuring the amount of radiation (*dose*) a person is receiving.

double bond, bonding between the atoms of a molecule in which the atoms share 2 electron pairs, rather than one as in single covalent bonding; important in organic synthesis, such as from ethylene, $CH_2=CH_2$.

double refraction, a property of certain clear crystalline minerals, such that a single light beam, in passing through the crystal (such as calcite), is bent into 2 beams, each at a definite angle.

double star, 2 stars that appear as a single point of light to the naked eye, but can be seen as 2 with binoculars, telescope, or spectroscope; see also **binary star.**

down, *n.* a type of feather consisting of a fluffy mass of barbs bearing barbules, without a shaft or vane; found under contour feathers of adult birds and covering birds just hatched; see **feather.**

Draco (DRAY-koh), *n.* the *Dragon,* a constellation near the northern Pole Star, with its head between Ursa Major and Cepheus.

drag, *n.* the force on a plane or other object traveling through air that produces resistance to forward motion; much of the drag on a plane is due to actual pressure of air on the wing surfaces, but the lift that keeps a plane aloft also contributes drag; see also **thrust.**

dragonfly, see **Odonata.**

drainage system, a system including a large river and all its tributaries, flowing through a basin into a large body of water such as a sea or ocean; the Mississippi-Missouri is the drainage system for most of the United States between the Appalachian Divide and the Rocky Mountain Divide.

dram, *n.* **1.** in apothecaries' weight, 60 grains, or ⅛ ounce. **2.** in measures of liquid volume, ⅛ fluid ounce.

drift, *n.* **1.** in oceanography, a sluggish current. **2.** in navigation, the part of a ship's or airplane's direction due to water currents, wind, or similar factors. **3.** in geology, the total mass of material deposited by glacial movement or melting.

drone (DROHN), *n.* **1.** a male bee, which does none of the work in the colony, and whose only known function is fertilization of the queen. **2.** an aircraft without pilot, under remote control.

Drosophila (druh-SAH-fuh-luh), *n.* a small fly belonging to the order *Diptera;* found on fruit; bred and studied extensively by geneticists.

drug, *n.* **1.** a chemical used to improve or maintain the health of an organism or to relieve pain. **2.** a narcotic.

drumlin, *n.* a low, oval-shaped hill made chiefly of rock and soil deposits left by the motion of ice sheets or glaciers.

drupe (DROOP), *n.* any fruit with a thin exocarp (skin), fleshy mesocarp, and hard endocarp (pit), as peach and olive; see **fruit** picture.

dry cell, an electric battery in which the electrolyte is present as a deposit in a porous medium rather than as a free-flowing liquid. Most such electrolytes are a solution absorbed into starch or other powder to make a heavy paste.

dry fruit, any simple fruit with a dry pericarp; see **dehiscent, indehiscent.**

dry ice, solid carbon dioxide (CO_2), which sublimes (goes directly from a solid to a gas) at about $-78.5°C$; used as a refrigerant. The term was originally a tradename.

duck, see **Anseriformes.**

duckbill, see **Monotremata.**

duckweed family, see **Arales.**

duct, *n.* **1.** any passageway for fluids that has definite walls; especially, such a passage for secretions or excretions. **2.** a vessel carrying secretions from glands. **3.** in botany, a cavity formed by cells. **4.** in electricity, a single channel carrying a conducting cable or wire.

ductile (DUK-tuhl), *adj.* capable of being shaped, as by hammering, drawing, or rolling; a term used chiefly of metals. *n.* **ductility.**

ductless gland, an alternate term for **endocrine gland.**

dugong (DOO-gahng), see **Sirenia.**

dune (DOON), *n.* a ridge of wind-drifted sand, usually piled up around some obstruction.

duodenum (doo-uh-DEE-nuhm), *n.* a section of the small intestine, from the pylorus to the jejunum; in man, about 12 inches long; see **digestive system.** *adj.* **duodenal.**

dura mater (DOO-ruh MAY-tuhr), see **meninges.**

duramen (doo-RAY-muhn), an alternate term for **heartwood.**

Dutch elm disease, a fungus disease of elm trees, carried by a black beetle; causes yellowed leaves and eventual death of the trees.

dwarf, *n.* any organism that is somewhat smaller than the ordinary size for its stage of growth. *Dwarfism* occurs in plants and in other animals, as well as in man. Human dwarfs may be of several types: *midgets* with normal proportions, due to pituitary gland inactivity; *cretins* with physical deformities and mental deficiency, due to thyroid gland deficiency; or *achondroplastics* with large heads, small legs, and normal body, due to hereditary endocrine defects.

dwarf star, a star in the last stage of stellar evolution; extremely dense but with very small radius, about equal to that of planet Saturn; very low in luminosity; also called *white dwarf.*

Dy, symbol for **dysprosium.**

dyad (DY-ad), *n.* **1.** any pair of like individuals, especially one of the double synapsed chromosomes that form half of a tetrad during meiosis. **2.** any radical or element equivalent to 2 hydrogen atoms.

dyna-, a word part meaning *power.*

dynamics (dy-NAM-iks), *n.* the study of forces that produce or tend to produce motion in objects or in matter-energy systems; a branch of mechanics. *adj.* **dynamic.**

dynamite (DY-nuh-myt), *n.* a high explosive rendered stable by absorbing of the nitroglycerin (the explosive substance) onto *kieselguhr* (a porous diatomaceous earth); the powder, manufactured into sticks, is much used for blasting.

dynamo (DY-nuh-moh), *n.* a rotating machine that converts either mechanical energy to electrical (a *generator*) or electrical energy to me-

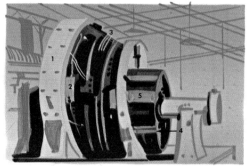

Commercial dynamo, a DC generator: (1) field magnet, or *stator;* (2) magnetic poles; (3) armature, or *rotor;* (4) commutator; (5) one of several brushes

chanical (a *motor*); has 2 basic units: *armature* and *field;* either may be the rotating part *(rotor)* and the other the stationary part *(stator);* see also **generator, motor.**

dynamometer (dy-nuh-MAHM-uh-tuhr), *n.* a device that measures force; especially, one that measures mechanical power, generally in terms of horsepower of rotating engines or motors. The force causing rotation (torque) is measured and is multiplied by the speed of rotation.

dyne (DYN), *n.* the basic unit of force in the cgs system: the amount of force on an object of one gram mass that will produce an increased velocity of one centimeter per second during every second it continues to act.

dysentery (DIS-uhn-ter-ee), *n.* a disease attacking the intestine, and especially the colon; involves painful inflammation and frequent, watery, blood-containing bowel discharges; 2 common types are *amebic* and *bacillary dysentery.*

dysprosium (dis-PROH-see-uhm), *n.* a metallic chemical element in the lanthanide series; symbol Dy; *at. no.,* 66; *at. wt.,* 162.50; isolated in 1886 by Boisbaudran.

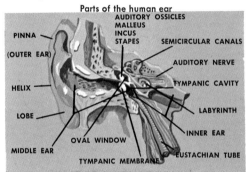

eagle, see **Falconiformes.**

ear, *n.* **1.** a sensory organ that detects sound waves and transmits impulses to the nervous system; the impulses are then heard as sound; in many animals, occurs as an eardrum (tympanum) on the skin, with no external ear as on mammals. **2.** the outer ear. **3.** the portion of a cereal plant that bears flowers and fruit.

Parts of the human ear

AUDITORY OSSICLES
MALLEUS
INCUS
STAPES
PINNA
SEMICIRCULAR CANALS
(OUTER EAR)
AUDITORY NERVE
HELIX
TYMPANIC CAVITY
LOBE
LABYRINTH
INNER EAR
OVAL WINDOW
MIDDLE EAR
EUSTACHIAN TUBE
TYMPANIC MEMBRANE

earth, *n.* **1.** land; soil. **2.** the British term for an electrical ground; see **ground wire.**

Earth, *n.* the only planet positively known to be inhabited by living organisms; has an average diameter of 7,927 miles; nearly spherical, but flattened slightly at the poles and slightly pear-shaped; has an elliptical orbit about the sun, with an average distance of nearly 93 million miles; it is the third planet from the sun, and the only one known to have an atmosphere containing oxygen; it has plentiful water on its surface.

earthquake, *n.* the tremor caused by a sudden fracture in the earth's crust, or lithosphere; such fractures usually occur by slipping along fault lines, or as a result of volcanic activity.

earth science, a general term for any of the sciences dealing with Earth, as geology, meteorology, geophysics, etc.

earth-to-orbit system, a system for travel, supply, and communication between the earth and a satellite in permanent orbit which serves as a space station. *abbr.* **ETO.**

earthworm, see **Annelida.**

Ebenales (ebb-uh-NAY-leez), *n.* an order of dicot shrubs and trees having simple alternate leaves and flowers with petals joined at least at the base, an indefinite number of stamens, and a seed with a hard covering. The order includes the sapodilla family (*Sapotaceae*) which yields trop-

ical fruits and chicle for chewing gum, and the ebony family (*Ebenaceae*) which provides hard ebony wood and persimmon, a large, edible berry.

ebony family (EBB-uh-nee), see **Ebenales.**

ecdysis (EK-duh-suhs), a technical term for **molt.**

echidna (ih-KID-nuh), see **Monotremata.**

Echinodermata (ee-kyn-uh-DUHR-mah-tuh), *n.* a phylum of marine invertebrates with almost perfect radial symmetry in the adult, but with bilateral symmetry in the larva. *Echinoderms*

Representative echinoderms: (1) common starfish, *Henricia sanguinolenta,* class Asteroidea; (2) sea urchin, *Arbacia punctulata,* class Echinoidea; (3) sea cucumber, *Cucumaria frondosa,* class Holothuroidea; (4) sea lily, *Myzostoma,* class Crinoidea

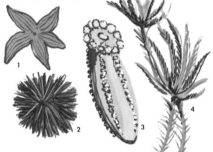

have hard, calcium-containing body walls; include starfish, sea urchins, sea cucumbers, and sea lilies; see also **dipleurula larva.**

echo (EK-oh), *n.* a wave produced by reflection of a primary wave from some object, and directed back toward the source of the primary wave; especially applied to sound waves and radio waves. *v.* **echo.**

eclipse (ee-KLIPS, ih-), *n.* in astronomy, the temporary cutting off of light from a satellite, a portion of a planet or other celestial body because some other object comes between the observer and the body. In a *solar* eclipse, the moon comes between Earth and the sun; in a *lunar* eclipse, Earth comes between the sun and moon, putting the moon into shadow.

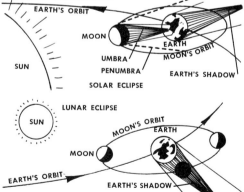

ecliptic (ee-KLIP-tik), *n.* **1.** the apparent, yearly path of the sun. **2.** the great circle formed by the plane of the earth's orbit intersecting the apparent path of the sun.

ecology (ee-KAHL-uh-jee), *n.* the study of the relationships between living organisms and their environments, including their interrelationships with other living plants and animals.

ecosystem (EE-koh-sis-tuhm), *n.* the living organisms of any specific habitat together with their nonliving environment; a pond, including all its plant and animal life, its water supply, and the atmosphere around it, forms an ecosystem.

ectone (ek-tohn), *n.* area in transition between two different plant communities, as the zone between forest and prairie.

ecto, a word part meaning *on the outside.*

ectoderm (EK-tuh-duhrm), *n.* the outermost layer of germ cells in the embryo of many-celled animals; forms nervous system, skin, and other structures; contrast with **endoderm, mesoderm.**

ectoplasm (EK-tuh-plazm), *n.* the outer, sometimes stiff, portion of the cytoplasm in a cell, just under the cell surface.

eczema (Ek-suh-muh, eg-ZEE-muh), *n.* any of various skin disorders accompanied by scale or crust formation, redness, and serous ooze from blistery surfaces, usually with much itching.

eddy (ED-ee), *n.* **1.** any current in a liquid stream traveling in a different direction from the main current; often a spiral or circular current. **2.** in electricity, an *eddy current,* a small, circular, unwanted current in an electromagnet, traveling at right angles to the path of the magnetic field.

edema (ee-DEE-muh), *n.* the accumulation of abnormal amounts of serous fluid in body cavities, usually resulting in swelling; a symptom in many different diseases.

Edentata (ee-duhn-TAH-tuh), *n.* an order of mammals in which teeth are either absent or degenerate and without enamel; *edentates* include armadillo, sloth, and anteater.

edible (ED-uh-buhl), *adj.* can be safely eaten, said of materials and organisms.

EEG, abbreviation for **electroencephalogram.**

eel, *n.* **1.** any of a group of snake-like fishes; see **Osteichthyes. 2.** a lamprey; see **Cyclostomata.**

eel-grass family, see **Naiadales.**

efferent (EF-uhr-uhnt), *adj.* carrying anything away from an organ; *efferent nerves* carry impulses away from the central nervous system; *efferent tubes* (arteries) carry blood from the glomeruli in the kidney.

effervescent (ef-uhr-VES-uhnt), *adj.* bubbly with trapped gas, as a carbonated beverage. *n.* **effervescence.**

efficiency (ee-FISH-uhnt-see), *n.* in machines, the ratio of energy output to energy input, stated as a percentage; always less than 100% because of friction and other factors. *adj.* **efficient.**

efflorescent (ef-loh-RES-uhnt), *adj.* **1.** pertaining to loss of water of crystallization, resulting in powder formation on the crystal surface. **2.** in botany, flowering. *n.* **efflorescence.**

effort, *n.* the effective force: if 10 lbs. of force are required to lift a 100-lb. weight by means of a pulley, the *effort* is said to be 10 lbs.

eft, see **newt.**

egest (ee-JEST), *v.* to eliminate digestive waste from the body. *n.* **egestion.**

egg. *n.* a female gamete; see **ovum.**

einsteinium (eyn-STY-nee-uhm), *n.* a man-made, radioactive, metallic chemical element in the actinide series; symbol Es; *at no.,* 99, mass number of most stable isotope, 254; identified in 1952 after a thermonuclear blast at Los Alamos.

EKG, abbreviation for **electrocardiogram.**

elastic (ee-LAS-tik), *adj.* changing size and shape when force is applied, but returning to original condition when force is removed. *n.* **elasticity.**

electret (ee-LEK-tret), *n.* a dielectric (nonconducting solid) that has a permanent electric charge on its surface; made from carnauba wax from the wax palm.

electric (ee-LEK-trik), *adj.* pertaining to, making use of, or produced by, electricity; also termed **electrical.**

electrical energy, energy in electrical form, produced by transformation of mechanical energy (as in generators) or chemical energy (as in batteries), etc.; measured in kilowatt-hours.

electric eye, see **photoelectric cell.**

electricity (ee-lek-TRIS-uh-tee), *n.* the energy properties of electrical charges in motion (current) and at rest, including magnetic phenomena. Most properties of electrical currents can best be understood in terms of the motion of electrons.

electro-, a word part meaning *electrical.*

electrocardiogram (ee-lek-troh-KAHR-dee-uh-gram), *n.* a recording of the action of the heart muscle by means of changes in a low-voltage, direct-current charge through the body. The apparatus (*electrocardiograph*) reveals heart conditions that are hard to detect. *abbr.* **EKG.**

electrochemistry (ee-lek-troh-KEM-uh-stree), *n.* the study and use of electricity in chemical reactions; electrolytic extraction of pure metals from compounds is an example.

electrode (ee-LEK-trohd), *n.* any conductor through which an electrical current enters or leaves any medium, such as electrolytic solutions, solids, gases, molten masses, or vacuums; see also **anode, cathode.**

electrodynamics (ee-lek-troh-dy-NAM-iks), *n.* the study of the interaction of magnets and electric currents. In an *electrodynamic* rocket-propulsion system, a very hot gas is ionized by electric and magnetic fields; see **plasma.**

electroencephalogram (ee-lek-troh-en-SEF-uh-luh-gram), *n.* a recording of electrical currents in the brain, made by tracing the skin surface currents onto charts using an *electroencephalograph.* The delicate voltages are electronically magnified and are of diagnostic use; the normal currents can be distinguished from abnormal. *abbr.* **EEG.**

electrohydrodynamics (-hy-droh-dy-NAM-iks), *n.* that branch of science dealing with the properties of a plasma in a magnetic field; also called *magnetohydrodynamics.*

electroluminescence (ee-lek-troh-loo-mi-NES-uhnts), *n.* the production of light by applying alternating electric current to a phosphor, not involving an intermediate step of ionizing mercury vapor particles (as in fluorescence); possible efficiency is higher than with other lighting sources.

electrolysis (ee-lek-TRAHL-uh-sis), *n.* the process of decomposing a chemical substance (*electrolyte*) into positive and negative ions using electricity. *adj.* **electrolytic.**

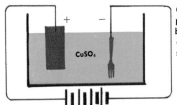

Copper-plating utensils by electrolysis of a copper solution

CuSO₄

electrolyte (ee-LEK-troh-lyt), *n.* a chemical substance that dissociates into ions when fused or in solution and conducts an electric current.

electromagnet, *n.* a device consisting of a soft iron core with a coil of fine wire around it; a magnet only when current flows through the coil; used in relays, basic operation of many electric meters, and industrial equipment work.

electromagnetic spectrum, the total spectrum (range) of electromagnetic radiation, comprising all wavelengths from the long radio waves (10^{16} millimicrons) to the short gamma rays (10^{-5} mm); visible light waves have wavelengths about 10^3 millimicrons (1 micron).

electroscope, *n.* a device for indicating the presence of small amounts of electric charge; often in the form of gold leaves that move a small but measurable amount when charge is present.

electrostatic (ee-lek-troh-STAT-ik), *adj.* pertaining to characteristics of electrical attraction or repulsion (as of positive and negative charges), but not involving motion of electrons.

electrovalent bond (ee-lek-troh-VAY-luhnt), an ionic bond, in which electrons are moved from one element to another.

coated with a thin layer of metal; the object is made the cathode (negatively charged electrode), and positive metal ions are deposited.

Full range of the electromagnetic spectrum (wavelength given in centimeters)

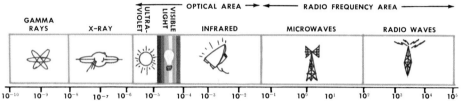

electromotive force (ee-lek-troh-MOH-tiv), the difference in electrical potential between the terminals of any source of electrical energy; usually measured in volts and referred to as *voltage. abbr.* **emf, e.m.f.**

electromotive series, the chemical elements as they are ranked in order of decreasing oxidizing potential; specifically, the order in which each element is able to displace those below it from their compounds, or can displace ions of lower-order elements from solution.

electron (ee-LEK-trahn), *n.* a negatively charged particle; electrons surround the nuclei of atoms in definite orbits or energy levels; see **atom.**

electron gun, the cathode of an electron tube, which produces a stream of electrons, together with equipment that controls and focuses the electrons on to a target; used in TV tubes and oscilloscope tubes; see **cathode-ray tube.**

electronic (ee-lek-TRAHN-ik), *adj.* **1.** pertaining to an electron. **2.** based on the principles of electronics.

electronics (ee-lek-TRAHN-iks), *n.* the branch of physics that includes the conduction of electricity without wires, as in a vacuum tube or through a gas; sometimes, the study and application of electron behavior and movement.

electron microscope, a very powerful microscope in which streams of electrons rather than light rays are used to magnify an object; see also **microscope.**

electron tube, any tube, either evacuated or gas-filled, through which electrons flow in the absence of conducting wires; vacuum tubes and fluorescent tubes are examples.

electron volt, the amount of energy gained by a particle with a single charge (such as an electron) in going through a potential difference of one volt. *abbr.* **ev.**

electrophoresis (ee-lek-troh-fuh-REE-sis), *n.* the motion of charged particles in any solution or suspension under the influence of an electric field.

electroplating (ee-LEK-truh-play-ting), *n.* the process in which an object is electrolytically

element (EL-uh-muhnt), *n.* **1.** a pure substance that cannot be broken down into simpler substances by any chemical means; contains atoms of only one kind. There are 105 known chemical elements; see also **periodic table.** **2.** an individual part or component of something, as an *element* (dry cell, switch, lamp, etc.) in an electric circuit.

elementary particle, in nuclear physics, any particle regarded as basic in nuclear matter in any of its energy states; see **nuclear particle.**

elephant, see **Proboscidia.**

elephantiasis (el-uh-fuhn-TY-uh-sis), *n.* a disease caused by infestation of filariae (roundworms) in the lymph ducts, characterized by extreme enlargement of extremities and genital organs.

elevation (el-uh-VAY-shuhn), *n.* **1.** any rise, as a hill. **2.** an alternate term for *altitude,* used especially in describing topographical features, as mountains; see **altitude.**

ellipse (ee-LIPS), *n.* a curve similar to that of the orbits of planets or satellites. A *perfect* ellipse is the curve traced out by a point traveling around 2 other points (the *foci*) so that the sum of the distances from the foci to the traveling point remains constant.

elm family, see **Urticales.**

elodea family (el-oh-DEE-uh), see **Naiadales.**

embolism (EM-buh-lizm), *n.* sudden blocking of a vein or artery by a blood clot, or by anything else carried to the location by the blood.

embryo (EM-bree-oh), *n.* **1.** any organism in its developmental stages, before it has acquired the organs and functions necessary for independent existence. **2.** in *viviparous* animals, the earlier stages of development before birth; in humans, the stages through about the eighth week of uterine development; see also **fetus. 3.** in plants, that part of the seed that develops into the new plant. *adj.* **embryonic.**

embryology (em-bree-AHL-uh-jee), *n.* the study of the changes taking place from the fertilization of an ovum to the appearance of the adult; in viviparous animals, usually confined to the changes prior to birth.

71

Embryophyta

Embryophyta (em-bree-AHF-uh-tuh), *n.* a plant subkingdom including all those plants that have embryos, multicellular sex organs, and alternation of generations. Most *embryophytes* also have specialized conducting cells; includes all plants except thallophytes; see also **Thallophyta**.

emerald (EM-uh-ruhld), *n.* a precious gemstone of a rich green color; a variety of beryl containing some chromium; see **beryl, gem**.

emf, abbreviation for **electromotive force**.

emit (ee-MIT), *v.* **1.** to eject, as an electron from the surface of a cathode. **2.** to send out, as a radio or sound wave; to transmit. *n.* **emission**. *adj.* **emissive**.

empirical (em-PEER-i-kuhl), *adj.* related to, or found by, observation and experiment, as *empirical* data.

emu (EEM-yoo), see **Casuariformes**.

emulsion (ih-MUHL-shuhn), *n.* a colloid system in which droplets or globules of one liquid are dispersed in another liquid medium; see also **colloid**.

enamel (ih-NAM-uhl), *n.* **1.** any hard, glassy surface applied as a protective and decorative coating, usually by baking. **2.** any substance similar to this, regardless of how applied. **3.** the hard, outer covering of the teeth; see **tooth**.

encephalitis (en-sef-uh-LY-tis), *n.* inflammation of the brain; may accompany infections or may be a distinct disease caused by a virus.

endangered species, species of plant or animal that is in danger of being eliminated.

endo-, a word part meaning *within, inside*.

endocardium (en-doh-KAHR-dee-uhm), *n.* the membrane of endothelial cells lining the heart.

endocarp (EN-doh-karp), *n.* the inner layer of a fruit wall, as the hard pit around a peach seed.

endocrine gland (EN-doh-krin), any gland that secretes hormones directly into the circulatory system without ducts to carry these secretions; some glands produce hormones that are distributed without ducts and also other secretions distributed by ducts; such glands include ovaries and testes. Other endocrine glands are the pituitary, thyroid, parathyroid, adrenal, thymus, pineal, and islets of Langerhans; see **hormone**.

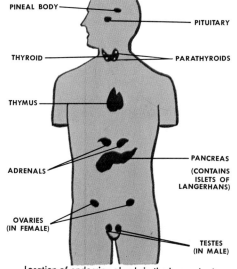

PINEAL BODY
PITUITARY
THYROID
PARATHYROIDS
THYMUS
PANCREAS (CONTAINS ISLETS OF LANGERHANS)
ADRENALS
OVARIES (IN FEMALE)
TESTES (IN MALE)

Location of endocrine glands in the human body

endocrinology (en-doh-kri-NAHL-uh-jee), *n.* the study of the endocrine glands, the hormones they produce, and the effects of the hormones on the body; a branch of internal medicine.

endoderm (EN-doh-duhrm), *n.* the innermost layer of germ cells in the embryo of many-celled animals; from it develop the gut, liver, and pancreas and many other body parts; contrast with **ectoderm, mesoderm**.

endoplasm (EN-doh-plazm), *n.* the part of the cytoplasm of a cell that surrounds the nucleus.

endoskeleton (en-doh-SKEL-uh-tuhn), *n.* a framework or skeleton on the inside of an animal; used for body support and muscle attachment; contrast with **exoskeleton**.

endosperm (EN-doh-spuhrm), *n.* the food-filled tissue around an embryo in the seed of an embryophyte plant.

endothelium (en-doh-THEE-lee-uhm), *n.* the layer of simple, flat cells, originating from mesoderm which lines the cavities in the circulatory and lymphatic system.

endothermic (en-doh-THUHR-mik), *n.* pertaining to chemical reactions that absorb heat; contrast with **exothermic**.

energy (EN-uhr-jee), *n.* the ability to do work; measured in kilowatt-hours, foot-pounds, ergs, and other units. All energy is kinetic or potential and the forms include heat, mechanical, chemical, nuclear, and radiant energies; see **kinetic energy, potential energy**.

engine (EN-juhn), *n.* a device for converting energy of any kind (especially heat energy) into mechanical work.

engineering (en-juh-NEER-ing), *n.* the applying of scientific principles and methods to useful purposes for man. Engineering as a profession has become divided into many special areas, but *engineers* come under 5 main classifications: **chemical engineering**—use of chemical processes; **civil engineering**—design and construction of large buildings, dams, railroads, etc.; **electrical engineering**—all electrical applications; **mechanical engineering**—machines and power; **mining engineering**—mining and metallurgy.

enteric (en-TAIR-ik), *adj.* pertaining to or occurring in the intestines or alimentary canal.

enterovirus (ent-uhr-oh-VY-ruhs), *n.* any of a group of viruses that lives in the human intestinal tract, of which one type causes poliomyelitis.

entomology (en-tuh-MAHL-uh-jee), *n.* the study of insects, especially of those insects helpful or harmful to man.

entropy (EN-truh-pee), *n.* **1.** in thermodynamics, a property of substances defined as the ratio of transferred heat energy to the absolute temperature of transfer. In practice, since this ratio cannot be determined, *relative entropy,* the ratio of change in amount of transferred heat energy to absolute temperature is found; the tendency is for it to keep increasing. **2.** in communication theory, the property of uncertainty of information.

environment (en-VY-ruhn-muhnt), *n.* all the factors that affect either an organism or group of organisms: air, water, soil, climate, and other organisms make up the *external* environment; conditions within the organism make up the *internal* environment. *adj.* **environmental**.

72

enzyme (EN-zym), *n.* any of numerous proteins functioning as catalysts for biological processes; most such processes involve highly specific enzymes, often identified by the word ending -*ase.*

Eocene (EE-uh-seen), *n.* a geological epoch in the early Tertiary period, that began about 60 million years ago, lasting roughly 25 million years; plants and mammals like those of the present were common; see **geologic time table.**

eosin (EE-uh-sin), *n.* **1.** a red organic dye important in microscopic staining of white corpuscles to detect disorders. The cells that take the red stain are called *eosinophils.* **2.** a characteristic red eye color in the fruit fly *Drosophila melanogaster,* much studied in genetics.

epicenter (EP-uh-sen-tuhr), *n.* the point on the surface of the earth that receives maximum shock in an earthquake, located on the surface closest to the underground origin of the quake.

epicotyl (EP-uh-kaht-uhl), *n.* the portion of a plant embryo above the cotyledon which matures into the stem and leaves; part of the *plumule.*

epicycle (EP-uh-sy-kuhl), *n.* the circle along which a heavenly body moves, according to the Ptolemaic theory; the center of the epicycle describes yet another circle around the earth.

epidemic (ep-uh-DEM-ik), *n.* an outbreak of a disease, normally uncommon in a community, that spreads rapidly to many people.

epidemiology (ep-i-dem-ee-AHL-uh-jee), *n.* the study of epidemics, including their causes and how to control them; the experts in this field are *epidemiologists.*

epidermis (ep-uh-DUHR-mis), *n.* the outermost body layer of an organism, especially one made up of cells; in vertebrates, outer skin layers.

epigenesis (ep-uh-JEN-uh-sis), *n.* the concept that fertilized ova contain only undifferentiated material that gradually changes into germ layers; formulated by Kaspar Wolff, German anatomist, in 1759; contrast with **preformation.**

epiglottis (ep-uh-GLAH-tis), *n.* a thin flap of fibro-cartilage that covers the glottis while swallowing is going on, preventing food or liquids from entering the respiratory system.

epilepsy (EP-uh-lep-see), *n.* any of several disorders characterized by variable periods of unconsciousness, in severe cases accompanied by short, mild, or violent convulsions.

epinephrine (ep-uh-NEF-ruhn), alternate name for **adrenalin.**

epiphyte (EP-uh-fyt), *n.* any nonparasitic plant, usually growing on another, but obtaining water and nutrient materials from rainfall and from the atmosphere; also called *air plant.*

epithelium (ep-uh-THEE-lee-uhm), *n.* the cellular tissue originating from ectoderm, lining the inside of most hollow organs and covering many free surfaces; *squamous, columnar, stratified,* and *cuboidal* are types of *epithelial* tissue.

epoch (EP-uhk, -ahk), *n.* a subdivision of a period in geologic time; formerly used for smaller time divisions; see **geologic time table.**

epoxy resin (eh-PAHK-see), any of a group of thermosetting plastics that are very strong and stick tightly to other materials; used in reinforced plastics and plastic cement.

equation, see **chemical equation.**

equator (ee-KWAY-tuhr), *n.* **1.** the great circle around Earth's surface, midway between the North and South poles, on a plane that passes through the center perpendicular to the axis of rotation. **2.** the *celestial* equator, the extension of the earth's equator to the celestial sphere.

equilibrium (ee-kwi-LIB-ree-uhm), *n.* a condition of stable rest or uniform motion resulting, not from absence of forces, but from the balancing of forces acting in different directions: one of the most general of all scientific concepts, extending to physical and electrical forces, chemical reactions, biological phenomena, etc. Equilibrium may be static or dynamic.

equinox (EE-kwi-nahks), *n.* a time when the sun crosses the earth's equator; occurs at the *vernal* equinox (about March 21) and the *autumnal* equinox (about September 22); day and night are each 12 hours long at the equinoxes.

Er, symbol for **erbium.**

era (EE-ruh), *n.* any of the 5 (4 in some systems) chief geologic time divisions; subdivided into *periods;* based on the quantity and kinds of living things present; see **geologic time table.**

erbium (UHR-bee-uhm), *n.* a grayish-silver, metallic chemical element in the lanthanide rare-earth series; symbol Er; *at. no.,* 68; *at. wt.,* 167.26; isolated in 1843 by Mosander.

erg (UHRG), *n.* the unit of work or energy in the cgs system: the work done (or energy used) when a force of one dyne acts through a one-centimeter distance.

ergosterol (uhr-GAHS-tuh-rohl), *n.* a steroid found in plants that change to vitamin D (calciferol) when activated by ultraviolet rays.

Ericales (er-uh-KAY-leez), *n.* an order of dicot plants, usually with flowers with stamens and petals of equal number and in whorls separate

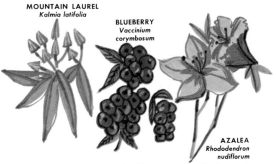

MOUNTAIN LAUREL
Kalmia latifolia

BLUEBERRY
Vaccinium corymbosum

AZALEA
Rhododendron nudiflorum

from the corolla, a double ovary, and alternate simple leaves; many have edible fruits of capsule, berry, or drupe types. Order includes 6 families; main one is the large heath family (*Ericaceae*) of rhododendron, azalea, blueberry, mountain laurel.

Types of epithelium: (1) ciliated basement cells, (2) ciliated columnar, (3) squamous, (4) goblet, (5) stratified, (6) simple cuboidal

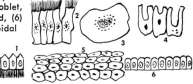

erosion (ee-ROH-zhuhn), *n.* the slow cutting down of land (soil, rock, or other forms) by the action of wind, waves, rain, or similar processes. *v.* **erode.** *adj.* **erosive.**

eruption (ee-RUHP-shuhn), *n.* **1.** the sudden release of materials under pressure inside the earth, as from geysers and volcanoes. **2.** a rash or other lesion on the skin, so called because it "breaks out." *v.* **erupt.**

erythrocyte (ih-RITH-ruh-syt), the technical term for **red corpuscle.**

Es, symbol for **einsteinium.**

escape velocity (vuh-LAHS-i-tee), the speed needed for an object to be fired from the earth or other starting place and to escape from the gravitational field.

escarpment (es-KAHRP-muhnt), *n.* in geology, a high, steep or vertical cliff, usually caused by erosion or faulting; also called *scarp.*

esker (ES-kuhr), *n.* **1.** a stratified deposit of sand, gravel, and stones, usually occurring in mounds or long winding ridges as they were laid down by flowing water. **2.** a similar ridge deposited by a stream running under a glacier.

esophagus (ee-SAHF-uh-guhs), *n.* the canal or tube that connects the animal mouth or pharynx with the stomach or crop; sometimes called *gullet;* see **digestive system.**

essential oil (uh-SEN-shuhl), an oil obtained from a plant, usually with an odor characteristic of the plant, that can be completely distilled under heat; often used in perfumery or flavoring; the name comes from *essence,* which in perfumery is the distillable scented portion of a substance.

ester (ES-tuhr), *n.* any of a group of organic compounds formed by the reaction of an acid with an alcohol, such as ethyl acetate, $C_2H_5COOCH_3$.

estivate (ES-tuh-vayt), *v.* to be in a state of drowsy inactivity and sleep during the summer or other hot, dry period; lungfishes estivate; contrast with **hibernate.** *n.* **estivation.**

estrogen (ES-truh-jen), *n.* any of a class of female sex hormones. Estrogens are steroids produced by the ovary, adrenal cortex, and testis, and are needed for developing female secondary sex characteristics, such as breast development.

estrous cycle (ES-truhs), a series of physiological changes in the sexual and other related organs of female mammals between fertile periods.

estuary (ES-choo-air-ee), *n.* a partially enclosed section of a coastal body of water where a river current meets the ocean tides, resulting in a mixture of fresh and salt water.

ethane (ETH-ayn), *n.* a colorless, odorless, flammable gaseous hydrocarbon; used as a fuel and for organic synthesis; formula, C_2H_6.

ethanol (ETH-uh-nohl), alternate name for **ethyl alcohol.**

ether (EETH-uhr), *n.* **1.** a colorless, flammable, liquid organic compound (ethyl ether), used as an anesthetic and for chemical synthesis; formula, $(C_2H_5)_2O$. **2.** one of the organic compounds (including ethyl ether) with the general formula ROR (*R* standing for some organic radical). **3.** the medium or elastic fluid that formerly was supposed to exist in all space; its existence was disproved by experiments of Michelson and Morley.

ethmoid (ETH-moyd), *n.* **1.** a sievelike bone of the human skull, located in the nasal cavity. **2.** sinus in the ethmoid bone. *adj.* **ethmoid.**

ethyl (ETH-uhl), *n.* an organic radical, C_2C_5-.

ethyl alcohol, a colorless, volatile, flammable, organic liquid with pungent odor; found in alcoholic beverages; used as a solvent and chemical intermediate; mostly synthetic, but often made from fermented grain and then called *grain* alcohol, formula, C_2H_5OH; also called *ethanol.*

ethylene (ETH-uh-leen), *n,* a colorless, flammable, gaseous hydrocarbon with a sweet odor; used for chemical synthesis; formula, C_2H_4.

ethylene series, a group of highly reactive, unsaturated hydrocarbons containing twice as many hydrogen atoms as carbons; ethylene is the first and simplest member.

ethology (e-THOL-oh-jee), *n.* study of animal behavior especially in relation to habitat.

etiology (ee-tee-AHL-uh-jee), *n.* the study of the causes of diseases.

ETO, abbreviation for **earth-to-orbit system.**

Eu, symbol for **europium.**

eugenics (yoo-JEN-iks), *n.* a branch of genetics devoted to improving man through selective mating to acquire desired hereditary characteristics.

euglena, see **Euglenophyta, Mastigophora.**

Euglenophyta (yoo-gluh-NAHF-uh-tuh), *n.* a division of plants; *englenophytes* are unicellular, usually with flagellum, so are often considered animals; chlorophyll is present; reproduce asexually; includes euglena; see **algae.**

Eumycophyta (yoo-my-KAHF-uh-tuh), *n.* a division of thallophyte plants including the true fungi, such as mushrooms; lack chlorophyll and live as parasites or saprophytes; class includes the algal, club, and sac fungi; see **Ascomycetes, Basidiomycetes, Phycomycetes.**

europium (yoo-ROH-pee-uhm), *n.* a soft, silvery, metallic element in the lanthanide series; used for nuclear control rods; symbol Eu; *at. no.,* 63; *at. wt.,* 151.96; isolated by Demarcay in 1901.

eustachian tube (yoo-STAY-kee-uhn, yoo-STAY-shuhn), a canal connecting the middle ear with the pharynx, which provides air to equalize pressure on both sides of the eardrum; see **ear.**

eutropic (yoo-TROP-ik), *adj.* related to a lake that is rich in dissolved nutrients but is probably shallow and has seasonal oxygen deficiency.

eutectic (yoo-TEK-tik), *adj.* referring to the mixture (including alloys) of any 2 or more substances with the lowest possible melting point of any mixture of these substances. *n.* **eutectic.**

ev, abbreviation for **electron volt.**

evacuate (ee-VAK-yoo-ate), *v.* to empty.

evaporate (ee-VAP-uh-rayt), *v.* **1.** to change from liquid to gas; see also **sublimation. 2.** to remove a liquid, such as water, from a substance, often by heating. *n.* **evaporation.**

evening-primrose family, see **Myrtales.**

evergreen, *adj.* not shedding its leaves each year; most gymnosperms and many angiosperms.

evolution (ev-uh-LOO-shuhn), *n.* **1.** development in general. **2.** in biology, the theory that every species of plant or animal descended with modification (mutation) from earlier species, ultimately going back to simple one-celled plants and animals; see also **natural selection.** *v.* **evolve.**

exciter (ek-SYT-uhr), *n.* anything that stimulates action in another. **1.** a nerve that stimulates activity in the body part it controls. **2.** an external generator supplying current to excite the field of an AC generator. **3.** an oscillator in a radio transmitter. **4.** the section of a radio or TV transmitting antenna that receives the signal to be radiated.

exclusion principle, *n.* in physics, the principle that no two electrons in an atom or molecule are exactly equivalent.

excrete (ek-SKREET), *v.* to discharge, eject; especially body waste. *n.* **excretion.**

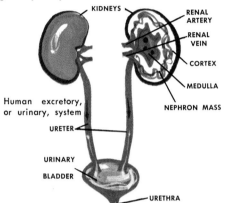

Human excretory, or urinary, system

KIDNEYS
RENAL ARTERY
RENAL VEIN
CORTEX
MEDULLA
NEPHRON MASS
URETER
URINARY BLADDER
URETHRA

excretory system (EKS-kruh-taw-ree), any cell, group of cells, organ, or organ system for elimination of nitrogenous waste products from the organism, such as kidneys in mammals.

exhale (eks-HAYL), *v.* **1.** to discharge air from the lungs by breathing. **2.** to expel into the atmosphere, as oxygen or water vapor.

exhaust (eg-ZAWST), *v.* **1.** to wear out or consume completely. **2.** to pump out air, or other gas, obtaining a vacuum; to evacuate. **3.** to draw off waste gases, as from a combustion engine. *n.* **4.** the part of an engine through which the waste gases from combustion in the cylinder are removed from the system.

exhaust velocity, the speed of the gases coming from the exhaust, as in rocket engines.

exo-, a word part meaning *outside, external.*

exocarp (EK-soh-karp), *n.* the outer layer of a fruit wall, as the skin of a peach.

exocrine gland (EKS-oh-kryn), any gland that discharges its secretions through ducts, as oil glands in skin; contrast with **endocrine gland.**

exoskeleton (ek-soh-SKEL-uh-tuhn), *n.* a protective covering, usually of hard material, on the outside of an organism, as the shell of a crayfish.

exosphere (EKS-oh-sfeer), *n.* the outermost layer of the earth's atmosphere; estimates place it anywhere from 200 to 600 miles above the earth, extending far into space.

exothermic (eks-oh-THUHR-mik), *adj.* pertaining to a chemical reaction which gives off heat; contrast with **endothermic.**

expansion (eks-PAN-shuhn), *n.* the process in which a substance increases in volume; most substances undergo expansion when they are heated. *v.* **expand.**

experiment (ek-SPEER-uh-muhnt), *n.* any test performed under controlled conditions in order to gain demonstrated knowledge on a specific subject. *adj.* **experimental.**

explode, *v.* to expand suddenly, especially by extremely rapid increase in pressure followed by sudden release of that pressure; contrast with **implode.** *n.* **explosion.**

explosive (eks-PLOH-siv), *n.* any substance that will build up pressures at very high speed and will either burst its container or force a projectile from a tube when the pressure is high enough; used for excavation, construction, mining, and for military purposes. *adj.* **explosive.**

extensor (ek-STEN-sohr), *n.* any muscle which by contraction makes the angle between 2 jointed parts larger; contrast with **flexor.**

external combustion, the combustion of a fuel in a unit separate from the power-producing device. The steam engine, in which steam under pressure is produced in a boiler and then piped to a cylinder, is a familiar example; contrast with **internal combustion.**

exteroceptor (EK-stuhr-oh-sep-tuhr), *n.* any sense organ that receives impulses from the environment external to the organism, such as those on the skin responding to heat and cold; see also **receptor.**

extraction (ek-STRAK-shuhn), *n.* **1.** the removal of a solid element from the ore in which it occurs, by heat, electrolysis, distillation, etc. **2.** the removal of a tooth from the jaw. *v.* **extract.**

extraterrestrial (eks-truh-tuh-RES-tree-uhl), *adj.* located or occurring beyond Earth and its atmosphere; beyond Earth's environment.

extremity (eks-TREM-uh-tee), *n.* a limb or appendage of the body, especially the end part of an arm or leg.

extinct (ek-STINKT), *adj.* no longer existing.

extrude (eks-TROOD), *v.* to force a substance, usually metal or plastic, through a die, thus giving it a particular shape. *n.* **extrusion.**

extrusive, *adj.* pertaining to rock formed by the crystallization of lava forced out onto the earth's surface; see also **intrusion.**

eye, *n.* the sense organ that transmits light waves to the nervous system for interpretation as sight. Invertebrate eyes are simple or compound, and some animals have both types; vertebrate eyes are like a camera with a light-tight chamber containing a lens for focusing images on the retina; see also **compound eye.**

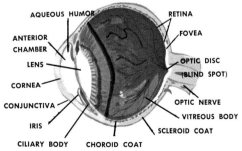

AQUEOUS HUMOR
ANTERIOR CHAMBER
LENS
CORNEA
CONJUNCTIVA
IRIS
CILIARY BODY
CHOROID COAT
RETINA
FOVEA
OPTIC DISC (BLIND SPOT)
OPTIC NERVE
VITREOUS BODY
SCLEROID COAT

eyespot, *n.* a spot on the surface of an animal; usually a light-absorbing pigment covers light-sensitive cells connected to the brain; planaria have paired eyespots in the head region.

eyetooth, see **tooth.**

F, **1.** symbol for **fluorine.** **2.** abbreviation for **Fahrenheit.**

facet (FAS-uht), *n.* **1.** a plane surface of a crystalline substance, as on a mineral; also called *face.* **2.** one of the lenses of a compound eye of an arthropod. **3.** a flat, smooth surface on a bone.

Fagales (fah-GAY-leez), *n.* an order of dicot shrubs and trees of north temperate and subtropical areas; most bear nuts with a single seeded achene or samara fruit and simple leaves. Order includes only 2 families: the birch or

PAPER BIRCH
Betula papyrifera

WHITE OAK
Querens alba

LEAVES AND SAMARA
OF WHITE BIRCH
Betula pendula

hazel-nut family (*Betulaceae*) of hazel, birch, and alder, and the beech family (*Fagaceae*) of beech, oak, and chestnut which yield valuable lumber.

Fahrenheit (FAIR-uhn-hyt), *adj.* referring to, or based on, a temperature scale with 32° as the freezing point and 212° the boiling point of water at standard pressure; the zero point is the temperature at which a strong salt solution will freeze; named for Gabriel Fahrenheit, German scientist (1686-1736). *abbr.* **F.**

faint, *v.* to become suddenly unconscious as a result of failure in the supply of oxygen and glucose to the cerebrum. *n.* **faint.**

Falconiformes (fahl-kahn-i-FAWR-meez), *n.* an order of birds that prey on other animals by day; includes eagles, hawks, vultures, and others.

Fallopian tube (fuh-LOH-pee-uhn), either of the pair of tubes connecting the ovaries with the uterus, through which the ovum reaches the uterus; the mammalian equivalent of the oviduct.

fallout, *n.* radioactive debris from an atomic (nuclear) bomb explosion, that falls gradually from the atmosphere, for periods up to months after the explosion.

fallow (FAL-oh), **1.** *n.* productive land that is deliberately left idle, usually for a season. **2.** *adj.* pertaining to unused productive land.

false berry, a simple fruit of the berry type that is also an accessory fruit. Examples are cucumber, cranberry, squash, watermelon, cantaloupe, and others; see **fruit.**

family, *n.* in biology, a group of several related genera, although may consist of one genus; groups of families comprise an order; in plants, usually has a suffix *-aceae;* in animals, *-idae.*

fan, *n.* a device for moving large amounts of a gas at atmospheric or nearly atmospheric pressure, usually by rotation of blades that exhaust (pull out) the gas or blow it (direct it inward).

fang, *n.* a sharp tooth, especially one of a venomous snake, hollowed and containing venom.

farad (FAHR-uhd), *n.* the basic unit of electrical capacitance: a capacitor has a capacitance of one farad when one coulomb of charge on the plates raises its potential difference one volt; the practical unit is the *microfarad;* named for Michael Faraday, English scientist.

faraday (FAHR-uh-day), *n.* a unit of electrical quantity (of charge): $96{,}516 \pm 2$ coulombs.

Farinales (fair-i-NAY-leez), *n.* an order of monocot plants, mainly tropical and subtropical,

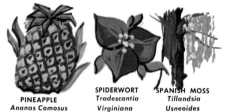

PINEAPPLE
Ananas Comosus

SPIDERWORT
Tradescantia Virginiana

SPANISH MOSS
Tillandsia Usneoides

having seeds with very mealy endosperm. Of the 5 families, the pineapple family (*Bromeliaceae*) is the largest and includes Spanish moss; order is also called *Xyridales.*

farsighted, *adj.* referring to faulty vision in which objects at a distance are clearly focused while those nearby are not because the point of focus falls behind the retina; *farsightedness* is medically named *hyperopia.*

fat, *n.* **1.** any ester of glycerol with a fatty acid, essential for energy supply in animal nutrition. **2.** in zoology, the greasy substance that is the major part of the cell cytoplasm in adipose tissue; acts as energy reserve.

fathom (FATH-uhm), *n.* a common unit for measuring depth and distance at sea: 6 feet.

fathometer (fuh-THAHM-uh-tuhr), *n.* an instrument for finding and recording depth, especially of water under a ship; see also **depth sounding.**

fatigue (fuh-TEEG), *n.* **1.** in physics, a weakening of a material such as metal or wood, caused by strain or long use. **2.** state of being tired.

fatty acid, any of the organic acids that occur in natural fats and oils, as stearic acid.

fault, *n.* in geology, a fracture in the earth's crust, with resulting displacement of both sides.

fauna (FAW-nuh), *n.* the entire animal life of a particular region or geological period of time.

Fe, symbol for **iron** (from Latin, *ferrum*).

feather, *n.* an outgrowth, originating in the epidermis, that is part of the body covering (*plumage*) of birds; or horny but light material; the 3 common types are *contour* or *vaned* feathers, *down* feathers, and *hair* or pin feathers. Parts of a

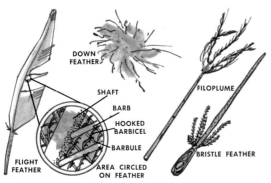

DOWN FEATHER

SHAFT

BARB

HOOKED BARBICEL

BARBULE

FLIGHT FEATHER

AREA CIRCLED ON FEATHER

FILOPLUME

BRISTLE FEATHER

feather include the *shaft* and *barbs* with addition of *barbules* and *barbicels* to the contour type.

feces (FEE-seez), *n.* waste, including undigested food and bacteria, evacuated from the intestines, normally as a solid.

feedback, *n.* **1.** energy returned from some output point in a system to an input point. **2.** in computers and automation, information returned from the output to the input to make certain that the entire system is operating properly.

feldspar (FELD-spar), *n.* any of a group of silicate minerals in igneous rocks. *Orthoclase,* $K(AlSi_3O_8)$, is light colored, white to pink. *Microcline,* with the same composition, has a green variety called *Amazon stone,* used as a gem. Sodic-calcic feldspar, called *plagioclase,* is white to dark grey or pink. All varieties are hardness 6; see **mineral** picture.

feline (FEE-lyn), *adj.* of or like a cat.

felsite (FEL-syt), *n.* a crystalline, igneous rock, composed chiefly of feldspar and quartz.

female (FEE-mayl), *n.* an organism, among those in which individuals are of different sexes, that produces the egg from which new individuals develop; also, in hermaphrodites, the portion which produces the egg. *adj.* **female.**

female flower, see **flower.**

femur (FEE-muhr), *n.* **1.** the thighbone, the bone connecting the pelvis to the knee; see **skeletal system.** **2.** a segment of an insect's leg.

fen, *n.* flat land entirely or partially under water; swamp, marsh; normally land with inadequate drainage for the water it receives.

fermentation (fuhr-muhn-TAY-shuhn), *n.* a process in which complex chemicals are decomposed into simpler ones, usually by means of bacteria or molds; lactic acid is produced; souring of milk is an example. *v.* **ferment.**

fermi (FUHR-mee), *n.* a unit of length in nuclear physics: 10^{-13} cm.

fermium (FUHR-mee-uhm), *n.* a man-made, radioactive chemical element in the actinide series; symbol Fm; *at. no.,* 100; mass number of most stable isotope, 253; isolated after a 1952 thermonuclear blast in experiments devised by Los Alamos, Argonne, and University of California laboratories.

fern (FUHRN), see **Filicineae.**

ferric (FAIR-ik), *adj.* **1.** referring to iron or its compounds. **2.** referring to compounds with iron ions of higher valence than ferrous ions.

ferrous (FAIR-uhs), *adj.* **1.** referring to iron or its compounds. **2.** referring to chemical compounds with bivalent iron ions; see also **ferric.**

fertile (FUHR-tuhl), *adj.* capable of producing, as land with soil of proper texture and chemical composition for crop raising, or ova which have been or can be fertilized by sperm.

field-ion microscope

fertilization (fuhr-ti-li-ZAY-shuhn), *n.* **1.** the union of an ovum with a sperm, activating the process of embryo formation. **2.** in botany, an alternate term for **pollination.** **3.** the treatment of soil with substances that improve its crop productivity. *v.* **fertilize.**

fertilizer, *n.* any material that makes soil more fertile or adds special chemicals.

fetus (FEE-tuhs), *n.* the prenatal state in mammals; in humans, usually the stage of development between the ninth week of pregnancy and birth; also spelled **foetus.** *adj.* **fetal.**

fever (FEE-vuhr), *n.* a condition indicated by abnormally high body temperature, usually above 98.6°F; may be a symptom of infection.

fiber (FY-buhr), *n.* **1.** in plants, a long, thick-walled cell which supports and strengthens. **2.** any threadlike cell or portion of a cell as muscle fiber or nerve fiber. *adj.* **fibrous.**

fibril (FY-bril), *n.* **1.** a threadlike filament produced by a cell and lying within it. **2.** a submicroscopic thread composed of cellulose molecules, making up cell walls.

fibrin (FY-brin), *n.* a whitish, elastic protein formed from fibrinogen in the presence of thrombin; the basic part of a blood clot.

fibrinogen (fy-BRIN-uh-juhn), *n.* the protein in blood plasma that reacts with thrombin to form fibrin, thus clotting blood; the type of fibrinogen in internal body tissues clots blood without thrombin.

fibrous root, a combination of primary, secondary, and adventitious roots in a plant; grasses have fibrous roots; contrast with **taproot.**

fibrous tissue, see **connective tissue.**

fibula (FIB-yuh-luh), *n.* one of the 2 leg or shank bones; its lower end forms the outer ankle bone; see **tibia, skeletal system.**

field, *n.* **1.** any area or space in which an activity takes place or a condition exists. **2.** in physics, a space in which action is exerted from a source at some distance; examples are magnetic fields, electrostatic fields, and gravitational fields.

field-ion microscope, a device that will enlarge the structure of an object up to 2 million times and thus show the atomic structure of crystals. A thin

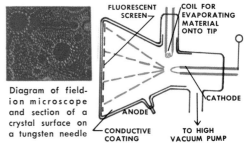

FLUORESCENT SCREEN

COIL FOR EVAPORATING MATERIAL ONTO TIP

CATHODE

ANODE

CONDUCTIVE COATING

TO HIGH VACUUM PUMP

Diagram of field-ion microscope and section of a crystal surface on a tungsten needle

needle of the substance being studied is enclosed in a glass tube containing a very small amount of helium gas; a powerful electrical field produces a positive charge on the needle, attracting neighboring helium electrons. The loss of electrons converts the helium atoms into positive ions, which are repelled by the needle tip. These ions radiate toward a fluorescent screen in the tube and create a visible image on impact; also called *field-emission microscope.*

figwort family, see **Polemoniales.**

filament (FIL-uh-muhnt), *n.* any thin, long thread or threadlike object: **1.** a wire conductor which provides resistance in electric lamps and serves as cathode in vacuum tubes. **2.** in biology, the part of a stamen that bears the anther. **3.** an alga with cells growing in long, thin strands. *adj.* **filamentous.**

filaria (fi-LAIR-ee-uh), see **elephantiasis.**

filial generation (FIL-ee-uhl), in genetics, the offspring of sexual reproduction involving the crossing of 2 genetically unlike parents; the first generation of offspring is called the F_1 generation; the second generation, with 2 F_1 parents, is the F_2 generation; see **hybrid.**

Filicineae (fi-LIS-uh-nay), *n.* a class in the subdivision *Pteropsida* containing the ferns; generally with compound leaves, underground stem, adven-

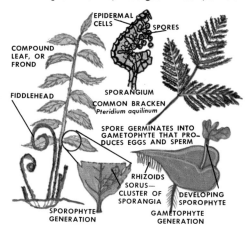

EPIDERMAL CELLS
SPORES
COMPOUND LEAF, OR FROND
FIDDLEHEAD
SPORANGIUM
COMMON BRACKEN
Pteridium aquilinum
SPORE GERMINATES INTO GAMETOPHYTE THAT PRO-DUCES EGGS AND SPERM
RHIZOIDS
SORUS—
CLUSTER OF SPORANGIA
DEVELOPING SPOROPHYTE
SPOROPHYTE GENERATION
GAMETOPHYTE GENERATION

titious roots, and no seeds; sporophyte generation is most prominent; gametophyte is not readily noticeable.

film, *n.* **1.** a thin membrane or covering, as an adsorbed layer of substance on the surface of a liquid. **2.** in photography, the thin sheet of a cellulose compound that backs the light-sensitive emulsion; a flexible and transparent sheet.

filoplume (FY-loh-ploom), *n.* a type of soft feather without barbs; serves in body insulation in birds; see **feather.**

filter (FIL-tuhr), *n.* a device or substance (paper, charcoal) used to: **1.** remove impurities or recover solids from a liquid; to remove dust and other particles from air; **2.** control flow of various electric currents; **3.** absorb or reduce sound waves; **4.** separate light waves.

filterable virus, any virus so small that it remains active after a solution containing it has passed through a fine, porcelain filter.

filtrate (FIL-trayt), *n.* a liquid solution that has been passed through a filter to remove any solid material (the *precipitate*).

fin, *n.* **1.** a winglike appendage of a fish which steers, propels, or balances the fish. **2.** a small, flat, stationary attachment of airplanes that helps stabilize aircraft. **3.** an external section of a radiator or a cylinder of an internal-combustion engine used to remove heat.

fiord (FYOHRD), *n.* a long, narrow inlet of an ocean bordered by cliffs; also spelled **fjord.**

fir, *n.* **1.** any cone-bearing, resinous, evergreen tree; usually found in cold-temperate or mountainous regions. **2.** specifically, the balsam fir, a tall conifer of the pine family.

fire, *n.* any very rapid chemical reaction accompanied by light and heat, most usually involving oxygen and another substance. The reaction is *exothermic,* and produces flame which may or may not be visible; see also **combustion.**

firedamp, methane gas formed by coal decay in mines.

fire extinguisher (ek-STING-gwish-uhr), any device for putting out fires: includes sprinkler systems, which flood the fire with water, and chemical types that usually work by smothering flame and cutting off oxygen supply.

fish, *n., pl.* **fish, fishes.** any scaled vertebrate living in water, moving by means of fins, and breathing through gills; see **Cyclostomata, Chondrichthyes, Osteichthyes.**

fission (FISH-uhn), *n.* **1.** in biology, the splitting of an organism into parts, each of which becomes a separate individual as in the ameba; a type of asexual reproduction. **2.** in physics, the breaking up of an atomic nucleus into 2 or more fragments, due to instability after capture of a nucleon, usually a neutron; results in energy release and sometimes in neutron ejection.

fissionable (FISH-uhn-uh-buhl), *adj.* able to be split due to nuclear instability, especially after neutron bombardment.

fissure (FISH-uhr), *n.* **1.** in geology, an extended crack or narrow opening in a rock surface. **2.** in anatomy, any deep fold or groove, especially one in the cortex of the brain.

fix, 1. *n.* the position of a ship or other object, usually calculated as the intersection of 2 or more lines along each of which the ship is located. **2.** *v.* in photography, to make the image formed on a film more or less permanent, usually by treatment with hypo; see also **hypo.**

fixative, *n.* a substance that makes something permanent, as a mordant that stabilizes dyes or a solution used to preserve biological specimens.

fjord, alternate spelling of **fiord.**

Flagellata (flaj-uh-LAHT-uh), see **Mastigophora.**

flagellum (fluh-JEL-uhm), *n., pl.* **-gella.** any threadlike appendage of an organism, usually from single cells, serving as an organ of locomotion.

flamingo (fluh-MIN-goh), see **Ciconiiformes.**

flammable (FLAM-uh-buhl), *adj.* easily set on fire; the term is preferred to *inflammable,* which has been misunderstood as *not* flammable.

flaps, *n.* on aircraft, adjustable sections on the trailing edges of airfoils, capable of deflection so that increased lift is available at high speeds for faster landing and takeoff.

flask, *n.* an open, bottlelike container used in laboratories; shape depends on its purpose; see also **Dewar flask.**

flatworm, see **Platyhelminthes.**

flax family, see **Geraniales.**

flea (FLEE), see **Siphonaptera.**

flesh, *n.* **1.** the soft portion of an animal's body, including fat, muscle, and skin. **2.** the pulpy portion of a fruit or vegetable.

fleshy fruit, any simple fruit whose pericarp is partly or entirely fleshy; see **fruit** picture.

flexor (FLEK-sohr, -suhr), *n.* any muscle which by contraction makes the angle between 2 jointed parts smaller; contrast with **extensor.**

flight feather, a type of contour feather found in the wings and tail of birds serving as a lift surface.

flint, *n.* a hard, crystalline form of quartz, gray to almost black in color; used by primitive man for tools and until the invention of matches for making fire or firing guns; a sharp blow on flint from a piece of steel produces sparks.

flipper, *n.* a limb modified for swimming; usually flat and broad, as on a turtle or porpoise.

floating ribs, the lowest 2 pairs of ribs in the human skeleton, not attached to the breastbone, but attached in the back to the vertebrae; see **skeletal system.**

floe (FLOH), *n.* a large mass of floating ice or ice pieces on the surface of oceans or lakes.

flood plain, the floor of the valley formed by a sediment-laden river that occasionally overflows its banks.

flora (FLOHR-uh), *n.* all of the plant life of one region at one time; see also **fauna.**

flotation (floh-TAY-shuhn), *n.* a process used to separate different solids, as minerals from waste rock. Flotation chemicals keep the unwanted solids in the mixture while the desired solids are carried to the surface and "floated" off.

flower, *n.* the reproductive portion of an angiosperm (flowering plant); a main stem bearing reproductive organs of the plant; *staminate* or male flowers have only stamens; *pistillate* or female flowers have only pistils, and *perfect* flowers have both. The flower appears as a preliminary to production of seeds and fruits.

flu, shortened term for **influenza.**

fluctuation (fluk-choo-AY-shuhn), *n.* **1.** relatively minor changes around a general measurement, position, or motion: a compass needle will *fluctuate* about the steady course of a ship. **2.** any trait variation in an organism which is not inherited.

fluid (FLOO-id), *n.* any substance that can flow or take on the shape of its container, as a gas or liquid. *adj.* **fluid.**

fluke (FLOOK), *n.* **1.** one of the broad, flat sections of a whale's tail. **2.** a parasitic flatworm; see **parasitism, Trematoda.**

fluorescent (floo-uh-RES-uhnt), *adj.* referring to substances that absorb radiation and emit visible radiation of a longer wavelength. *n.* **fluorescence.**

fluorescent lamp, a tube coated with phosphors and filled with a mixture of mercury vapor and argon. Electrical discharges through the mixture produce invisible ultraviolet radiation which is absorbed by the phosphors and emitted as visible light; see **mercury-vapor lamp.**

fluoridation (floo-ruh-DAY-shuhn), *n.* addition of a fluorine compound, as sodium fluoride, to drinking water to help strengthen tooth enamel.

fluoride (FLOO-ryd), *n.* the fluorine ion, Fl-, or a compound containing it, as sodium fluoride.

fluorine (FLOO-reen), *n.* a chemical element in the halogen family; a yellowish, poisonous gas with a sharp odor; used in chemical synthesis; symbol F; *at. no.,* 9; *at. wt.,* 18.9984; isolated by Moissan in 1886.

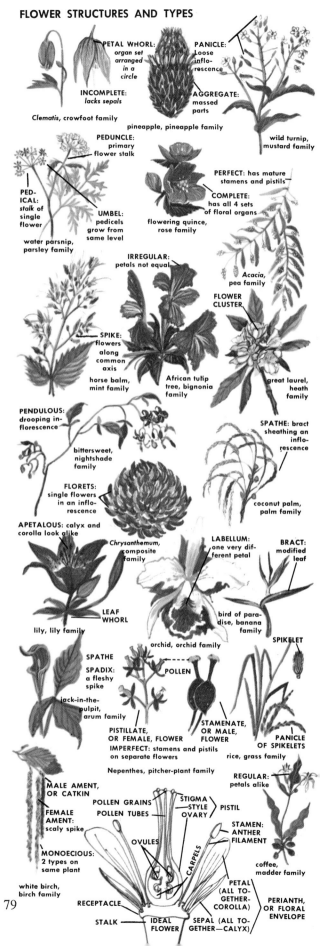

FLOWER STRUCTURES AND TYPES

79

fluorite (FLOOR-eyt), see **fluorspar.**

fluorocarbons (FLOOR-oh-KAR-buhnz), *n.* chemically inert compounds of carbon and fluorine used mainly as lubricants and to make resins and plastics.

fluoroscope (FLOOR-uh-skohp), *n.* a device for studying deep tissues and organs by use of X-rays; it consists of an X-ray tube and a fluorescent screen on which the images are projected. Since film is not used, study of the image can take place with no delay, and position can be shifted for a series of images. *adj.* **fluoroscopic.**

fluorspar (FLOOR-spahr), *n.* the naturally occurring ore of calcium fluoride, CaF_2; may be colorless or colored by various metallic oxides; used in paints, glazes, and glass; chief source of fluorine compounds; also called *fluorite.*

flux (FLUHKS), *n.* **1.** in physics, generally, flow of a quantity, or rate of flow, as: **a.** *magnetic flux,* the number of magnetic lines of force passing through a specified area. **b.** *neutron flux,* the number of neutrons incident on or passing through a specified surface in a given time. **c.** *radiant flux,* the total radiant energy incident on or passing through a specified surface per unit time. **2.** in metallurgy and chemistry, any substance added to a molten or semi-molten mass to aid in melting, to protect the liquid surface, or to free the liquid of impurities.

fly, see **Diptera.**

fly-by, *n.* the flight of a rocket past an object, close enough to make scientific observations.

flying lemur (LEE-muhr), see **Dermoptera.**

Fm, symbol for **fermium.**

FM, abbreviation for **frequency modulation.**

foal (FOHL), **1.** *v.* to bear young, said of a member of the horse family. **2.** *n.* the offspring, younger than one year, of the horse family.

foamed plastic, a man-made material that is made to foam while a liquid and then allowed to harden (set) in the foamed state; polyurethane and polystyrene are both foamed plastics.

foam rubber, a spongy rubber or elastic plastic produced by beating air or other gas into latex or urethane before vulcanizing.

focal length (FOH-kuhl), the distance between the focus of an optical system and the surface of a mirror or lens.

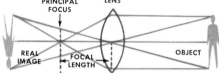

focal point, the point at which a system of rays, especially light rays, converge, or from which they diverge; *focus.*

focus (FOH-kuhs), **1.** *n.* focal point. **2.** *v.* to concentrate rays so they meet at a focal point.

foetus, an alternate spelling of **fetus.**

fog, *n.* a condensation of water vapor in the atmosphere close to the earth's surface.

fold, *n.* **1.** in geology, a region in which rock has been bent at some time after its formation. **2.** in biology, a surface formed by tissues bending back on themselves; a convolution, especially of the brain. *v.* **fold.**

foliage (FOH-lee-uhj), *n.* the entire mass of leaves of a tree or other plant.

follicle (FAHL-uh-kuhl), *n.* **1.** a dry, one-chambered fruit with one carpel, opening along one seam, as milkweed. **2.** in anatomy, a very small sac, as a *hair follicle* containing the hair root. **3.** see **Graafian follicle.**

follicle-stimulating hormone. *n.* a hormone from the anterior pituitary gland that promotes growth of the Graafian follicles in female ovaries, and stimulates the sperm-producing cells in male testes. *abbr.* **FSH.**

food chain, the interrelationship, in a given community, between the plants, the plant-eating animals (*herbivores*), the animal-eating animals (*carnivores*), and the animal- or plant-eating animals (*omnivores*).

food pyramid (PEER-uh-mid), the pyramidal arrangement according to food habits, of populations within a given area or community. Plants form the large food base for herbivorous animals which in turn form the smaller food base for carnivores. In general, the base herbivores are small and abundant while the carnivores at the apex are large and scarce.

food vacuole (VAK-yoo-uhl), a cavity in the body of a protozoan that takes in and digests food.

foot, *n.* **1.** a unit of linear measure: 12 inches. **2.** the usually enlarged end of the leg upon which vertebrates with limbs stand. **3.** any similar extremity of any animal with legs. **4.** in mollusks, the muscular ventral organ used for locomotion and attachment.

foot-and-mouth disease, alternate term for **hoof-and-mouth disease.**

footcandle, *n.* a former unit of illuminance; equivalent to lumens per square foot; see **candela.**

foot-pound, *n.* the unit of work in the fps system: the amount of work done in raising a mass of one pound a vertical distance of one foot.

foot-poundal (POWN-duhl), *n.* the unit of work in the absolute system: the work done by a force of one poundal acting through a distance of one foot.

foot-pound-second system, the basic system of measurements used in most English-speaking countries for nonscientific purposes: based on the foot as the unit of length, the pound for mass (or weight), and the second for time; contrast with **centimeter-gram-second system;** see measurement tables on page 214. *abbr.* **fps system.**

foramen (fuh-RAY-muhn), *n., pl.* **-mena.** an opening in the body, especially in bones, through which structures such as blood vessels and nerves pass.

foramen ovale (oh-VAL-ee), the oval membrane of the inner ear; also called *oval window;* see **ear.**

force, *n.* **1.** in general, any action or influence that will produce acceleration of a particle; the *push* or *pull* that causes motion; measured in pounds or grams of force. **2.** in classical physics, the product of mass and acceleration, usually measured in dynes. **3.** any push or pull.

force arm, the arm of a lever between the fulcrum and the force; see **lever.**

forceps (FOHR-seps), *n.* an instrument used to grasp or hold objects, especially during surgery; loosely miscalled *tweezers.*

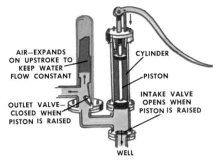

AIR—EXPANDS ON UPSTROKE TO KEEP WATER FLOW CONSTANT

CYLINDER

PISTON

INTAKE VALVE OPENS WHEN PISTON IS RAISED

OUTLET VALVE— CLOSED WHEN PISTON IS RAISED

WELL

force pump, a device for moving liquids by an arrangement of valves and a piston, arranged so that its action is not limited by air pressure in the way a lift pump is; see **lift pump.**

foreskin, see **glans.**

forestry (FAWR-uhs-tree), *n.* the management of animal and plant life and water of forests.

forge (FAWRJ), **1.** *v.* to form metal by heating it and then shaping it by hammering or by forcing it through a die. **2.** *n.* the furnace used for heating metal before shaping it.

formaldehyde (fawr-MAL-duh-hyd), *n.* a colorless gas with suffocating odor; usually used in solution for chemical synthesis and to preserve biological specimens; formula, HCHO.

formalin (FAWR-muh-lin), *n.* a colorless solution containing about 37% formaldehyde and 63% water.

formic acid (FAWR-mik), a colorless, caustic, liquid organic acid that gives off suffocating fumes; found in certain ants and in nettles; used for chemical synthesis, as a solvent, and in dyeing textiles; formula, HCOOH.

formula (FAWR-myoo-luh), *n., pl.* **-las, -lae.** an expression indicating the number of atoms of each element in a molecule of a compound, as water, H_2O, and sugar, $C_{12}H_{22}O_{11}$. These the chemist calls *molecular formulas,* to distinguish them from more complex *structural formulas,* which indicate the way the atoms are arranged in the molecule. Ethyl alcohol has a molecular formula C_2H_6O; a simplified structural formula C_2H_5OH, which shows that the oxygen and one hydrogen are combined in a hydroxyl unit; and a full structural formula CH_3CH_2OH. The structural formula distinguishes it from other compounds with the same molecular formula.

fossil (FAHS-uhl), *n.* any trace of plant or animal life of a previous geological age found in the earth's crust, such as impressions, organic parts, and wholly or partially petrified material.

fossil fuel, material from the earth used to produce heat or power by burning, e.g., coal.

Foucault pendulum (foo-KOH), a heavy metal ball hung from a long wire so as to be free to swing. Its plane of swing gives evidence of Earth's rotation; developed by J. B. L. Foucault.

four-o'clock family, see **Centrospermales.**

four-stroke cycle, a cycle in a combustion engine which is completed by 4 strokes: intake, compression, power, and exhaust.

fourth dimension, any dimension other than the classical 3 dimensions of length, width, and breadth; especially time, when used in a system of coordinates for locating an event.

fovea centralis (FOH-vee-uh sen-TRAL-is), a small pit just below the tip of the optic nerve in the retina; in higher primates, the point of most distinct vision; see **eye.**

frequency modulation

fowl, *n.* a bird, especially one of a species eaten by man, such as chicken, turkey, duck, goose, pheasant, or partridge.

fps system, abbreviation for **foot-pound-second system.**

Fr, symbol for **francium.**

fractional distillation, a distilling process for separating mutually soluble liquids that have different boiling points: usually, the vapors condense in a fractionating column with liquids having the lowest boiling points condensing on the highest plates of the column, and the higher-boiling liquids condensing on the lower plates. The liquids are separately withdrawn; see **distillation.**

fracture (FRAK-chuhr), *n.* **1.** a break in a portion of tissue, especially in a bone. **2.** the breaking of a mineral or of a metal other than along a regular plane of cleavage.

francium (FRAN-see-uhm), *n.* a radioactive chemical element, the heaviest alkaline-earth metal; symbol Fr; *at. no.,* 87; mass number of most stable isotope, 223; first identified by Perey and reported in 1939.

frankincense (FRAN-kin-sens), *n.* a pleasant-smelling, gum resin from small trees of southwest Asia and eastern Africa, important for incense.

fraternal twins (fruh-TUHR-nuhl), twins produced by development of 2 separate ova fertilized by separate sperm cells; contrast with **identical twins.**

Fraunhofer lines (FROWN-hoh-fuhr), dark lines in the spectrum of the sun's light, caused by elements in the solar atmosphere that absorb

Fraunhofer lines in part of the sun's spectrum show absorption by metallic elements

some of the radiated light; named for J. von Fraunhofer, German physicist (1787-1826).

free fall, motion in a gravitational field with no restrictions: in a satellite, after engine cutoff, everything is equally under the influence of gravitation and of no other accelerating or decelerating force; the phenomenon of weightlessness accompanies free fall. *adj.* **freely falling.**

free-living, *adj.* **1.** not attached; not sessile; able to move from place to place. **2.** not parasitic, thus not living on (*ectoparasitic*) or within (*endoparasitic*) another living organism.

freezing point, the temperature at which a liquid becomes a solid; for water, 0° C, 32° F.

frequency (FREE-kwuhn-see), *n.* **1.** in physics, a measurement of wave motion: the number of cycles per second; inversely proportional to wavelength. **2.** the number of times anything under study occurs in a group or in a time interval: the *frequency* of twins is the number of times twins are born as compared with total number of births.

frequency modulation (mahj-uh-LAY-shuhn), a system of radio broadcasting in which the car-

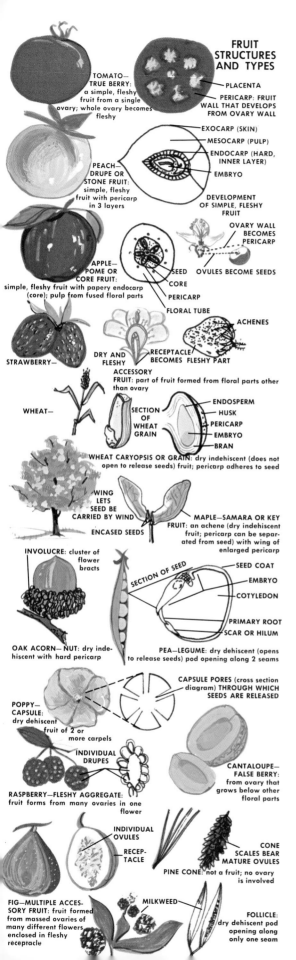

rier wave frequency (rather than its amplitude) is changed by an audio wave; sound for TV is based on this system; contrast with **amplitude modulation.** *abbr.* **FM.**

Modulation of radio wave frequency

Modulation of radio wave amplitude

friction (FRIK-shuhn), *n.* the force of resistance a body offers to motion, produced by its contact with another body; may be *rolling* friction, as with wheels or ball bearings on a surface, or *sliding* friction, as with a box being dragged over a surface.

Froehlich's disease (FROY-liks), a disease of the pituitary gland and hypothalamus, characterized by extremely overweight body and undeveloped sex organs.

frog, *n.* any of a large group of insect-eating amphibians with protruding eyes, short front and hind legs, no tail, and smooth skin; usually found near fresh water; see **Amphibia.**

frogbit family, see **Naiadales.**

frond (FRAHND), *n.* **1.** a compound leaf of many leaflets, especially a fern leaf. **2.** the leaf-like projection of some plants, such as lichens.

front, *n.* the surface between 2 different air masses; see **cold front, warm front.**

frontal (FRUHN-tuhl), *adj.* in anatomy, located in an anterior position, as the *frontal bone.*

frost, *n.* the condensation of water vapor, forming a thin covering of crystalline ice on the surface of objects colder than 32° F.

frostbite, *n.* irreversible damage to tissues of the body after prolonged exposure to freezing temperatures.

fructose (FROOK-tohs) *n.* the sweetest of the sugars; occurs naturally in fruits and honey; a yellowish-white crystalline carbohydrate used in foods and medicines; occurs as 50% of sucrose; formula, $C_6H_{12}O_6$; commonly called *fruit sugar.*

fruit, *n.* the fully matured ovary or ovaries of a plant, usually containing the seeds and varying adjacent tissues; see types of fruit: **simple, dry, fleshy, aggregate, multiple,** and **accessory.**

fruit fly, see **Drosophila.**

fry, *n., pl.* **fry.** a very small fish; especially, a newly hatched fish; offspring.

FSH, abbreviation for **follicle-stimulating hormone.**

fucus (FYOO-kuhs), see **Phaeophyta.**

fuel (FYOO-uhl), *n.* any substance which can be consumed with production of energy, especially by generation of heat, as in petroleum and coal; nuclear fuels such as uranium are included.

fuel cell, any device for production of direct-current electricity by chemical action of a *fuel* that is supplied in continuous form and of an *oxidant;* the 4 chief types under study are: *hydrox,* using hydrogen fuel and oxygen; *carbox,* using carbon compounds as fuel and oxygen; *redox,* tin salts oxidized by bromine; and *consumable electrode,* in which the fuel is the electrode, which is slowly used up.

fulcrum (FUHL-kruhm), *n.* the point around which a lever turns or tends to turn; see **lever**.

fuller's earth, a claylike substance of varying composition; a good adsorbent; used for decolorizing, and as a filler and catalyst.

fumarole (FYOO-muh-rohl), *n.* a vent in the ground from which steam or vapor escapes, especially in a volcanic or geyser area.

fumigant (FYOO-muh-guhnt), *n.* a smoke or vapor used to disinfect a building, to exterminate vermin, or to kill pests in soil. *v.* **fumigate.**

fumitory family (FYOO-muh-tohr-ree), see **Papaverales.**

function (FUHNK-shuhn), *n.* **1.** action of any portion of an organism in relation to the entire organism: the chief *function* of the kidney is the elimination of metabolic waste products. **2.** behavior of an organ or of an organism.

functional disease, any disease in which no damage to tissues is evident, detectable only by the way in which it alters bodily functions.

fundamental (fuhn-duh-MEN-tuhl), **1.** *adj.* basic; primary; referring to a main source. **2.** *n.* the basic or principal wave frequency of vibration such as the sound from a musical instrument. A c note on a piano and violin have the same fundamental, but the overtones or non-basic frequencies make the c notes sound different.

fungicide (FUHN-juh-syd), *n.* a substance that destroys or inhibits growth of fungi.

fungus (FUHN-guhs), see **Eumycophyta.**

funnel (FUHN-uhl), *n.* a device resembling an inverted cone with a long, thin tube at the apex; used in laboratories for filtering and pouring liquids.

fur, *n.* the thick hair on the skin of many mammals; usually consists of soft, fuzzy *underfur,* the layer close to the skin, and *guard hairs,* long, smooth, somewhat stiff outer hairs, often with a characteristic coloring.

fuse, *n.* **1.** a cord or similar object impregnated with explosive that carries a flame to an explosive charge in order to detonate it. **2.** any electrical wiring or other device for exploding a charge. **3.** a strip or wire of low-melting-point metal that breaks an electric circuit when overheated by excessive current. *v.* **4.** to melt (a substance). **5.** to join together: 2 gametes *fuse;* atoms may *fuse.*

fuselage (FYOO-suh-lahzh), *n.* the main, central portion of an airplane, that portion housing passengers, crew, freight, etc.

fusel oil (FYOO-zuhl), a sharp-smelling, toxic, oily liquid present in varying but tiny amounts in distilled alcoholic beverages; largely *amyl alcohol* ($C_5H_{11}OH$).

fusible (FYOO-zuh-buhl), *adj.* meltable; capable of being converted from solid to liquid by the application of heat.

fusion (FYOO-zhuhn), *n.* **1.** the turning of a solid into a liquid. **2.** the joining of substances by melting and then resolidifying. **3.** the joining of nuclei or light atoms to form nuclei of heavier atoms, as in the hydrogen fusion that creates helium in the sun and other stars; accompanied by release of large amounts of energy; not yet controllable for power production; contrast with **fission.** *v.* **fuse.**

g, 1. symbol for acceleration due to gravity; as a unit, one g is defined as this acceleration; measured by the weight of any body at sea level; a body with *0 g* is in a weightless condition. **2.** an abbreviation for **gram.**

G, symbol for the "gravitational constant," the proportionality constant in Newton's Law of Universal Gravitation; equal to 6.67×10^{-8} dyne cm^2/gm^2.

Ga, symbol for **gallium.**

gabbro (GAB-roh), *n.* a heavy, coarse-grained, greenish to dark gray, igneous rock; used as decorative stone; composed of feldspar, labradorite, pyroxene, and smaller amounts of other minerals.

gadolinite (GAD-uh-lin-eyt), *n.* a brown to greenish-black silicate ore, containing yttrium, beryllium, iron, and rare-earth metals; a species of beryl.

gadolinium (gad-uh-LIN-ee-uhm), *n.* a grayish metallic chemical element in the lanthanide series; used for control rods in nuclear reactors; symbol Gd; *at. no.,* 64; *at. wt.,* 157.25; isolated by Marignac in 1880.

gage, alternate spelling of **gauge.**

galactic (guh-LAK-tik), *adj.* **1.** aiding or increasing the flow of milk. **2.** pertaining to a galaxy (because the Milky Way was the first known galaxy).

galactose (guh-LAK-tohs), *n.* a monosaccharide (simple sugar) derived from lactose (milk sugar); a white crystalline carbohydrate used in medicines and for organic synthesis; formula, $C_6H_{12}O_6$.

galaxy (GAL-uhk-see), *n.* a vast cluster of stars, including all material such as nebulae, gases, and dust, scattered within the cluster; the whole system rotates on an axis. The Milky Way is the galaxy that contains our solar system.

gale, *n.* in meteorology, a strong wind with a velocity between about 30 and 70 miles per hour.

galena (guh-LEE-nuh), *n.* a silver-gray sulfide of lead, PbS, with hardness 2½; the chief source of lead. Often found with silver ores, it is a source of silver, as an impurity.

gall (GAWL), *n.* **1.** a substance secreted by the liver of higher animals, usually called *bile;* helps in the digestion of fats. **2.** an abnormal growth on plants resulting from plant or animal parasites or certain chemicals.

gall bladder, an organ attached to the liver and containing the bile; when infected or gallstones form, can be removed; see **digestive system.**

gallic acid

gallic acid (GAL-ik), *n.* an organic acid found in galls (growths) of trees; when pure, occurs as yellowish crystals; used in inks, for dyeing materials, and for tanning hides; formula, $C_6H_2(OH)_3COOH·H_2O$.

Galliformes (gal-i-FAWR-meez), *n.* an order of birds including domestic or wild game fowl; in wild condition often have sweeping, pointed tails, mottled brown female plumage, and brighter colored males; includes pheasants, grouse, turkeys, chickens, and others.

gallium (GAHL-ee-uhm), *n.* a bluish-gray, metallic chemical element; used as a semiconductor; symbol Ga; *at. no.,* 31; *at. wt.,* 69.72; isolated by Boisbaudran in 1875.

gallstone, *n.* one of several hard deposits formed in the gall bladder; number, size, shape, and composition vary greatly; believed to result from changes in the composition of the bile.

galvanic (GAL-vahn-ik), *adj.* having the effect of producing electricity, especially by chemical action; term derived from name of Luigi Galvani.

galvanize (GAL-vuh-nyz), *v.* to apply a thin protective coating of zinc on iron or steel objects.

galvanometer (gal-vuh-NAHM-uh-tuhr), *n.* an instrument for detecting the presence of very small electric currents; consists of a coil carrying current and a magnet system; either part may

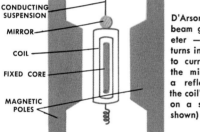

CONDUCTING SUSPENSION
MIRROR
COIL
FIXED CORE
MAGNETIC POLES

D'Arsonval light-beam galvanometer — the coil turns in response to current flow; the mirror casts a reflection of the coil's position on a scale (not shown)

move to indicate the current. The common moving-coil, or *D'Arsonval,* galvanometer has a coil suspended between poles of a magnet; a light beam may be used to reflect the position of the coil onto a scale.

gamete (guh-MEET, GAM-eet), *n.* a mature sexual reproductive cell (egg or sperm) which merges with another, becoming the zygote from which the new individual will grow; *sex cell.*

gametogenesis (guh-mee-toh-JEN-uh-sis), *n.* the development and formation of gametes in plants and animals: *spermatogenesis* is development of sperm cells; *oogenesis* is development of egg cells; see also **meiosis.**

gametophyte (guh-MEE-tuh-fyt), *n.* the gamete-producing or sexual generation of plants having an alternation of generations in their life history, as in ferns; contrast with **sporophyte.**

gamma globulin (GAM-uh GLAHB-yuh-lin), one of the proteins found in human blood serum having a large concentration of antibodies; gives passive immunity to some diseases, such as measles, mumps, and infectious hepatitis.

gamma ray, negatively charged electromagnetic radiation from the nucleus of a radioactive atom; similar to X-rays, but with a higher frequency.

ganglion (GANG-lee-uhn), *n., pl.* **-lia** (-lee-uh). **1.** a group of nerve cell bodies isolated from the central nervous system and acting as a center of nervous influence. **2.** a cyst or abnormal swelling at the wrist or hand, connected to a tendon sheath.

gangrene (GANG-reen), *n.* the dying of tissue due to interruption of the blood supply; frequently the result of disease, severe injury, frostbite, or inflammation and swelling.

gangue (GAYNG), *n.* the impurities in a mineral ore; removed in refining; also spelled **gang.**

gantry (GAN-tree), *n.* a traveling crane complete with platform and supporting towers or frames; ordinarily set on rails for missile and satellite erection and handling.

garden balsam family, see **Geraniales.**

garnet (GAHR-nuht), *n.* a group of isometric silicate minerals including pyrope and almandine, occurring in various colors, especially red, with hardness 6½-7½; used as gemstones and abrasives; see **gem.**

gas, *n.* one of the 3 phases of matter; characterized by relatively low density (in comparison with liquids and solids) and the ability to expand and contract easily. Gas molecules mix easily with molecules of other gases, and distribute themselves evenly to fill any container; many elements are found in nature as gases. *adj.* **gaseous.**

gas engine, generally, an internal-combustion engine; especially, one using a mixture of air and gas (not liquid gasoline) for fuel; see **internal combustion.**

gaseous (GAS-syuhs), *adj.* pertaining to a gas, or to the gas state of matter.

gaseous maser, a maser that uses a gas which is excited by flashing a lamp in the gas; the photon beam is reflected back and forth in the chamber and takes on a constantly increasing energy level, a process called *pumping;* see also **exciter, maser.**

gas giant, any planet of relatively large size and surrounded by a deep atmosphere of gases; especially Neptune, Jupiter, Uranus, and Saturn.

gasoline (GAS-uh-leen), *n.* a mixture of liquid hydrocarbons; used as a fuel for internal-combustion engines (automobile) as it is volatile and flammable; also used as an industrial solvent.

gastric (GAS-trik), *adj.* relating to the stomach.

gastric juice, the fluid secreted by stomach glands, containing digestive enzymes.

Gastropoda (gas-TRAH-puh-duh), *n.* a class of mollusks usually with a single valved shell often spirally coiled; a ventral, broad creeping organ

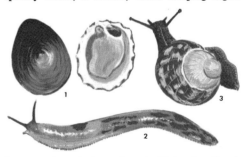

Representative univalve gastropods: (1) American limpet or sea snail (top and bottom views), *Acmaea testudinalls,* subclass Prosobranchia; (2) land slug, *Limax flavus;* (3) common brown land snail, *Helix pomatia,* both subclass Pulmonata

called a *foot;* and *radula,* a sharp, horny cutting organ in the mouth cavity; *gastropods* include snails, slugs, and limpets.

gastrovascular (gas-troh-VAS-kyuh-luhr), *adj.* serving the body functions of digestion and circulation in the more primitive groups of animals, as the *gastrovascular* cavity; see also **Coelenterata.**

gastrula (GAS-truh-luh), *n.* in animal embryos, a cavity with a wall consisting of 2 cell layers; shows the beginning of tissue differentiation into endoderm and ectoderm; the stage after *blastula.*

gas turbine (TUR-bin, -byn), an engine depending on the blast of expanding hot gases on fan blades; see also **steam turbine.**

gauge (GAYJ), *n.* **1.** any of many kinds of measuring instruments or devices, including those for measuring diameters and thicknesses; those with calibrated dials for measuring pressure; those for measuring depth of liquid, etc.; also spelled **gage.** *v.* **gauge. 2.** the thickness of metal sheets or of wires, the width of a pair of railroad tracks, etc.

gauss (GAWS), *n.* the unit of magnetic flux density in the cgs electromagnetic system of units: one maxwell per square centimeter.

electrical impulses created on collision of the particles with ionized argon gas; the impulses are counted and may be reproduced as audible clicks. They are used wherever radioactive materials are handled to detect contamination; also used by

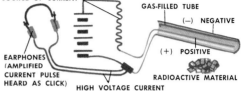

SOURCE OF CURRENT — GAS-FILLED TUBE — (−) NEGATIVE — EARPHONES (AMPLIFIED CURRENT PULSE HEARD AS CLICK) — (+) POSITIVE — RADIOACTIVE MATERIAL — HIGH VOLTAGE CURRENT

prospectors looking for radioactive metals, also called *Geiger-Müller* or *scintillation counter.*

gel (JEL), *n.* a fairly rigid colloidal dispersion of a solid in a liquid, as glue or gelatin.

gelatin (JEL-uh-tin), *n.* a yellowish, brittle, odorless protein derived from collagen; used for photographic film, adhesives, and food.

gem, *n.* any mineral substance valued for its beauty or decorative quality, as diamond, ruby, or sapphire; also called *precious stone* and called *gemstone* before polishing.

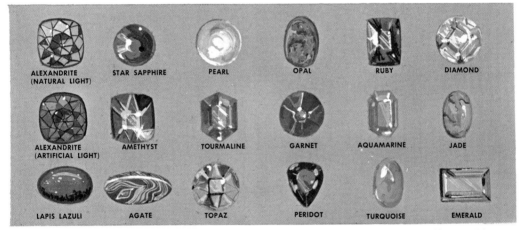

ALEXANDRITE (NATURAL LIGHT) — STAR SAPPHIRE — PEARL — OPAL — RUBY — DIAMOND
ALEXANDRITE (ARTIFICIAL LIGHT) — AMETHYST — TOURMALINE — GARNET — AQUAMARINE — JADE
LAPIS LAZULI — AGATE — TOPAZ — PERIDOT — TURQUOISE — EMERALD

Gaviiformes (gay-vee-i-FAWR-meez), *n.* an order of diving birds with webbed feet, short legs and tail, and strong, sharp beak; larger than ducks; includes loons.

Gay-Lussac's law (GAY-luh-SAK), the statement that, under standard conditions, the volumes of reacting gases and of their gas products are in the simple ratio of small whole numbers: one volume of oxygen will react with 2 volumes of hydrogen to form 2 volumes of water vapor; an important law in the study of gas behavior stated by J. Gay-Lussac, French chemist.

GCA, abbreviation for *ground-control approach,* the instrument landing system of an aircraft and the control tower guiding it.

Gd, symbol for **gadolinium.**

Ge, symbol for **germanium.**

gear, *n.* any device for changing the speed of motion or direction of motion in a machine; usually applied to toothed wheels designed for such purposes.

gecko (GEK-oh), see **lizard.**

Geiger counter (GY-guhr), a device for counting charged particles (radioactive, ordinarily) by the

GEM, abbreviation for **ground-effect machine.**

Gemini (JEM-uh-nee), *n.* **1.** the *Twins,* a zodiacal constellation best seen in winter; named for its 2 brightest stars, Castor and Pollux, 23rd and 18th brightest stars in the sky in visual magnitude. **2.** an American space project, leading to a manned lunar landing; unmanned flight tests were started in spring, 1964; so-called because the vehicle, the *Gemini* capsule, is a 2-man capsule (a modified *Mercury* capsule).

gene (JEEN), *n.* one of many small parts of a chromosome considered to be the bearers of hereditary characteristics; composed of nucleic acid molecules (DNA); see also **allele.**

genera (JEN-uh-ruh), plural of **genus.**

generalization (jen-ruhl-uh-ZAY-shuhn), *n.* in psychology, the tendency of an animal to make the same learned response to any stimulus resembling but different from the stimulus to which it has been conditioned; also called *induction;* see also **discrimination.** *v.* **generalize.**

generate (JEN-uh-rayt), *v.* **1.** to produce, to bring forth. **2.** in engineering, to convert other types of energy into electrical energy.

generation

generation (jen-uh-RAY-shuhn), *n*,   **1.** a phase in the reproductive life history of some organisms as in those exhibiting an alternation of *generations*. **2.** a single step in the natural descent of all living organisms.   **3.** the offspring of a parent or set of parents.   **4.** production or the bringing into being, as *generation* of power.

generator (JEN-uh-ray-tuhr), *n*.   a device for converting mechanical or other natural energy to electrical energy; most large-scale modern generators convert the energy of steam or falling water into electrical energy by driving a turbine connected with a set of field coils rotating about a stationary armature; see also **dynamo.**

genetic engineering (je-NE-tik en-je-NEER-ing), human maneuvering of genes. The first child (test tube baby) conceived outside the mother's body, then implanted in the mother's womb was the result of genetic engineering.

genetics (juh-NET-iks), *n*.   the branch of biology concerned with the transmission, or inheritance, of physical characteristics in organisms.

genital (JEN-i-tuhl), *adj*.   relating to reproduction or to the reproductive and associated organs.

genitourinary see **urogenital.**

genotype (JEN-uh-typ), *n*.   all of the genes present in the nucleus of a cell, both dominant and expressed, and recessive and unexpressed; contrast with **phenotype.**

gentian family (JEN-shuhn), see **Gentianales.**

Gentianales (jen-shuhn-AY-leez), *n*.   an order of dicot plants of warm areas, having petals rolled up in the bud and opposite leaves. The 6 families include the gentian family (*Gentianaceae*), the dogbane family (*Apocynaceae*)—a source of tranquilizing drugs; the olive family *(Oleaceae)*—often considered an order by itself (*Oleales*); the milkweed family (*Asclepiadaceae*); and the logania family (*Loganiaceae*) which yields the poisons curare and strychnine.

genus (JEE-nuhs), *n.*, *pl.* **genera** (JEN-uh-ruh), **1.** a subdivision in the scientific classification of plants and animals, below the family and including similar species.   **2.** the first part of the scientific name of a species in binomial nomenclature;

Representatives of order Gentianales: (1) frangipani, *Plumeria rubra;* (2) milkweed, *Asclepias syriaca;* (3) gentian, *Gentiana asclepiadea;* (4) evergreen olive, *Olea europaea;* (5) strychnine, *Strychnos nux-vomica*

Felis leo is the lion: *Felis* is the genus name for animals closely related to cats.   *adj.* **generic.**

geo-, a word part meaning *earth: geo*logy is the study of the earth.

geocentric (jee-oh-SEN-trik), *adj*.   having the earth as a center; refers especially to the Ptolemaic theory.

geochemistry, *n*.   the branch of geology that studies the chemical makeup of the earth, especially of the crust; also, the science dealing with the chemical makeup of any mineral.

geochronology (jee-oh-kruh-NAHL-uh-jee), *n*. the dating of long past events by the age of the rocks associated with them.

geodetic (jee-uh-DET-ik), *adj*.   pertaining to the size and shape of the earth and its measurement: a *geodetic survey* takes into account the shape of the earth's surface and its curvature.

geographical isolation, the separation of groups of organisms from one another by natural barriers such as deserts, mountains, and water; believed to be important in the formation of new species.

geologic time table (jee-oh-LAH-jik), a system of dating events during the history of Earth into convenient categories by time; based on the ages of rocks, especially as shown by isotope decay. Earth is probably about 4.6 billion years old, but rocks have been dated only to 3.5 billion years.

			GEOLOGIC TIME TABLE	
Era	Period	Epoch	Started	Main events for formations used in dating
CENOZOIC ("RECENT LIFE")	Quaternary ("4th period")	Recent	11,000 years ago	Withdrawal of the last glaciers; carbon-14 can be used for dating
		Pleistocene	6,000,000	4 periods of heavy glaciation; clear unconformity with Pliocene strata
	Tertiary ("3rd period"; Primary and Secondary are no longer used)	Pliocene	12,000,000	Time of solid sedimentation; main formations in Alps Mountains finished.
		Miocene	20,000,000	Sedimentation of flat strata; Himalaya and Rocky Mountains formed
		Oligocene	35,000,000	Formation of rocks not clearly Eocene or Miocene
		Eocene	55,000,000	Deposition of large oil beds
		Paleocene	65,000,000	Floods began to withdraw; plants more modern than Mesozoic
MESOZOIC ("MIDDLE LIFE")	Cretaceous ("chalk-forming")		130,000,000	Great floods, leaving marine chalk deposits
	Jurassic ("of Jura Mtns.")		185,000,000	Jura Mountains formed; abundant index fossil ammonites
	Triassic ("of 3 parts")		230,000,000	Distinct 3-part sequence of ammonite (cephalopods) fossils in the Alps
PALEOZOIC ("OLDEST LIFE")	Permian		270,000,000	Geosyncline basins in Russia (Perm is a city) and West Texas
	Pennsylvanian } (Carboniferous)		310,000,000	Great outcropping of coal in Pennsylvania
	Mississippian }		350,000,000	Limestone fossil deposits along the central Mississippi
	Devonian (from Devonshire)		400,000,000	Shale and limestone deposits with clear unconformity
	Silurian (from Silures tribe)		430,000,000	Great iron deposits; invertebrate-fossil limestone deposits in U.S.
	Ordovician (from Ordovices tribe—Wales)		490,000,000	Deposits thousands of feet thick, abundant in distinctive fossil graptolites (extinct hemichordates)
	Cambrian		700,000,000	Seas covered Earth; first fossils other than tracks and algae
PRE-CAMBRIAN	Eocambrian		700,000,000	First jellyfish and worms
	Precambrian		3,920,000,000	Much volcanic activity; mountains formed, some eroded to plains; minerals deposited; at least two glacial periods.

86

geology (jee-AHL-uh-jee), *n*, the study of the structure, composition, and history of Earth. A *geologist* may concentrate on: **physical geology** —structure and composition of the earth, including *geomorphology, mineralogy, petrology,* and *structural geology;* **historical geology**—history of the earth, including *paleontology* and *stratigraphy;* **economic geology**—study of minerals and other earth deposits for economic use, including *meteorology* and *seismology, adj.* **geological.**

geomorphology (jee-oh-mawr-FAHL-uh-jee), *n*. the study of land forms and surfaces features; see **topography** picture.

geon (JEE-ahn), *n*. a "body" in electromagnetic fields of gravitation, that behaves as if it had mass but actually consists only of radiation.

geophysics (jee-oh-FIZ-iks), *n*. the study of the physical aspects of the earth, as motion, deformations, and electric and magnetic fields.

geosyncline (jee-oh-SIN-klyn), *n*. a gradual downward warping of the earth's surface with accumulation of 1000s of layers of sediments.

geothermal power (jee-oh-THUHR-mel POU-uhr), force from internal heat of the earth.

During tnousands of years, land forms in a body of water by deposited soil eroded from high land around a geosyncline

geotropism (jee-AHT-ruh-pizm), *n*. growth movements of plants induced by their response to the earth's gravitational force.

Geraniales (juh-ray-ni-AY-leez), *n*. an order of dicot plants, mostly herbs and shrubs, with flowers in 5 parts, stamens in 2 whorls, ovules that hang down, and a variety of leaf shapes. Some of the 14 ornamental and economically valuable families are: balsam, or garden-balsam, family

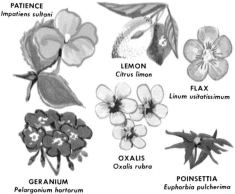

PATIENCE
Impatiens sultani

LEMON
Citrus limon

FLAX
Linum usitatissimum

OXALIS
Oxalis rubra

GERANIUM
Pelargonium hortorum

POINSETTIA
Euphorbia pulcherima

(*Balsaminaceae*)—touch-me-not and impatiens; geranium family (*Geraniaceae*); flax family (*Linaceae*); coca family (*Erythroxylaceae*)—source of cocaine; wood-sorrel, or oxalis, family (*Oxalidaceae*); spurge family (*Euphorbiaceae*)—castor oil, poinsettia, teak; citrus, or rue, family (*Rutaceae*); nasturtium family (*Tropaeolaceae*); and mahogany family (*Meliaceae*).

geranium family (juh-RAY-nee-uhm), see **Geraniales.**

geriatrics (jair-ee-AT-riks), *n*. the study of diseases common to older people, including special care and treatment because of age.

germ (JUHRM), **1.** *n*. common term used to refer to a microorganism (bacterium or virus), usually disease-producing. **2.** *adj.* capable of developing into a new organism; reproductive.

germanium (juhr-MAY-nee-uhm), *n*. a silvery-gray, brittle metallic chemical element; used as a semiconductor material for transistors and semiconductor diodes; symbol Ge; *at no.,* 32, *at. wt.,* 72.59; predicted (as *eka-silicon*) by Mendeleev in 1869 and discovered by Winkler in 1886.

German measles, a contagious disease, similar to measles, but milder; may result in birth defects when contracted by women during early pregnancy; also called *rubella.*

germ cell, a sexual reproductive cell at any stage in its development from initial cell to mature gamete (egg or sperm).

germinate (JUHR-muh-nayt), *v*. to begin to develop into a new individual from a seed, spore, bulb, or similar source; to cause such a development to begin. *n*. **germination.**

germ layer, a layer of cells formed by the first tissue differentiation in the embryonic development of multicellular animals; see **ectoderm, endoderm, mesoderm.**

gesneria family (jes-NAIR-ee-uh), see **Polemoniales.**

gestation (jes-TAY-shuhn), *n*. **1.** pregnancy. **2.** the period of pregnancy in mammals from conception to delivery (birth); about 280 days in women, 60 days in the cat.

geyser (GY-zuhr), *n*. a natural spring under pressure; intermittently discharges a fountainlike column of steam and water into the air, then builds up pressure again.

giant, *n*. any living organism much larger than the normal size for its species; especially, in man, an individual with overactive pituitary gland, more common in males than in females.

giant star, an extremely luminous star, usually considerably larger than the sun and much, much hotter; see **spectral class.**

gibberellic acid (jib-uh-REL-ik), a crystalline organic acid found in plants; a hormone that stimulates plant growth; formula, $C_{19}H_{22}O_6$.

gibbous (JIB-uhs, GIB-uhs), *adj.* convex or bulging; used of the moon when more than half but less than the entire surface is visible.

gigantism (jy-GAN-tizm), *n*. growth of an individual to abnormal size; see also **giant.**

gila monster (HEE-luh), see **lizard.**

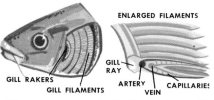

ENLARGED FILAMENTS

GILL RAY

GILL RAKERS

GILL FILAMENTS

ARTERY

VEIN

CAPILLARIES

Gill arrangement and structure in a fresh-water fish

gill, *n*. **1.** (GIL), one of the respiratory organs of some adult aquatic animals, and all chordates (at some stage of life), composed of thin, movable, vascular membranes that take in oxygen from the water or other liquid surrounding and release carbon dioxide; nonfunctional in most mammals. **2.** one of the vertical plates on the underside of mushroom caps. **3.** (JIL), a liquid measure, one-fourth pint.

gimbal (GIM-buhl), *n.* a device for mounting instruments, tools, or other objects so that they will remain in the same plane regardless of the position assumed by the vehicle in which they work; used for ship and airplane compasses.

ginger family (JIN-juhr), see **Musales.**

gingivitis (jin-juh-VY-tis), *n.* an inflammation of the *gingiva,* or gums, the tissue surrounding the teeth; caused by mouth infections, vitamin-B deficiencies, and certain drugs.

ginkgo (GINK-oh), *n.* a tree of the gymnosperm class but with fanlike leaves, yellow fruit, and sexes separate; native to China; rarely found wild, only surviving member of order Ginkgoales; also called *maidenhair tree;* also spelled **gingko.**

ginseng family (JIN-sehng), see **Umbellales.**

giraffe (ji-RAF), see **Artiodactyla.**

gizzard (GIZ-uhrd), *n.* an organ of the alimentary tract, best known in birds, similar to the stomach but having thick muscular walls and a grinding action.

glacial (GLAY-shuhl), *adj.* **1.** very cold; icelike; **2.** caused by glaciers or characteristic of the Ice Ages; Pleistocene.

Glacial, an alternate term for **Pleistocene.**

glacier (GLAY-shuhr), *n.* a massive ice sheet, wholly or partly on land, in movement or stabilized after previous periods of movement; motion is caused by gravity, with glaciers flowing slowly downhill or out from the thickest region.

gland, *n.* an organ which produces secretions or excretes waste materials, necessary to the proper functioning of the body; many variations in size, complexity, and function. *adj.* **glandular.**

glandular fever (GLAN-juh-luhr), an alternate term for **mononucleosis.**

glans (GLANZ), *n., pl.* **glandes.** the bulblike end of the penis; covered by a mucous membrane and a fold of skin called *foreskin* or *prepuce.*

glass, *n.* a brittle, transparent, amorphous substance composed of fused silica, soda ash, or similar materials; appears solid but is considered by physicists to be an undercooled liquid because its structure is not crystalline.

glaucoma (glaw-KOH-muh), *n.* an eye disease characterized by increased pressure in the eyeball often causing blindness; exact cause unknown; occurring in middle age or later.

glide, **1.** *v.* in aircraft, to come down slowly in a shallow angle without enough power for level flight. **2.** *n.* the path of an aircraft descending in this way, usually for landing.

glider, *n.* an aerodyne similar to an airplane, but with no power plant; also called *soarplane.*

global (GLOH-buhl), *adj.* **1.** spherical. **2.** pertaining to the entire Earth.

globular (GLAHB-yuh-luhr), *adj.* **1.** pertaining to a globe; global. **2.** pertaining to a small spherical object or *globule.*

globulin (GLAHB-yuh-lin), *n.* one of the proteins that do not dissolve in pure water but do in weak salt solutions, such as actin and gamma globulin.

glomerulus (glah-MAIR-yuh-luhs), *n.* *pl.* **-uli,** a cluster of blood capillaries in the kidney surrounded by a Bowman's capsule; brings blood with its wastes to renal tubule; see **nephron.**

glottis (GLAH-tis), *n.* a slitlike opening into the mouth from the upper part of the larynx and trachea in higher vertebrates.

glucose (GLOO-kohs), *n.* **1.** a thick, syrupy, yellowish liquid composed of dextrose, maltose, dextrins (various viscous polysaccharides), and water; used in foods and medicines. **2.** D(+)-glucose, biochemical name for dextrose; present in sucrose (common sugar).

glutamic acid (gloo-TAM-ik), *n.* a nonessential amino acid found in all complete proteins; used in medicine and flavoring; occurs in several isomers as colorless crystals; formula, $C_5H_9O_4N$.

glycerol (GLIS-uh-rohl), *n.* a colorless to yellowish, odorless, syrupy alcohol; occurs in nature as its esters, called *glycerides* (fats and vegetable oils); used for many organic products; formula, $C_3H_5(OH)_3$.

glycogen (GLY-kuh-jen), *n.* a white, amorphous polysaccharide stored in the animal liver and converted into glucose for use in the body; formula, $(C_6H_{10}O_5)_n$; also called *animal starch.*

glycol (GLY-kawl), *n.* **1.** *ethylene glycol,* a clear, colorless, syrupy alcohol; used as an automobile antifreeze, solvent, and organic intermediate; formula, $C_2H_4(OH)_2$. **2.** any of a group of alcohols containing 2 hydroxyl groups, including ethylene glycol.

glycolysis (gly-KAHL-uh-sis), *n.* the series of enzyme reactions in metabolism that breaks down glycogen and glucose, releasing energy, without using oxygen; results in formation of lactic acid in some bacteria and all animal muscle. When the animal rests, the liver reconverts the acid into glycogen; also called *anaerobic respiration;* see also **fermentation.**

glyptodon (GLIP-tuh-dahn), *n.* any of several giant, prehistoric, armadillo-like animals with a

Glyptodon, a fossil edentate, about 8 or 9 feet long; lived during the Pleistocene

shell of fused thick bony plates; ranged in southern United States; also spelled **glyptodont.**

gm, abbreviation for **gram.**

gneiss (NYS), *n.* a metamorphic rock, made up chiefly from granite in irregular bands of different composition and colors; see **rock.**

gnomon (NOH-mahn), *n.* **1.** the pointer or similar vertical part on a sundial, whose shadow indicates the time. **2.** the sundial itself.

goiter (GOY-tuhr), *n.* a tumor or enlargement of the thyroid gland; one type is due to insufficient iodine in food and water for normal functioning of the gland.

gold, *n.* a deep-yellow, soft, metallic chemical element; used in alloys for coins, jewelry, and decoration; symbol Au; *at. no.,* 79; *at. wt.,* 196.967; known to early man.

gonad (GOH-nad), *n.* an organ of multicellular animals in which cells for sexual reproduction are formed; *ovary, testis,* or combination.

gonorrhea (gahn-uh-REE-uh), *n.* a contagious disease of genital organs and urethra often involving other reproductive organs; caused by a coccus bacterium.

goosefoot family, see **Centrospermales.**

gourd family, see **Campanulales.**

gout (GOWT), *n.* a disease characterized by acute inflammation of joints, particularly in the big toe, and an excess of uric acid in the blood; attacks are usually recurring.

governor (GUHV-uhr-nuhr, GUHV-nuhr), *n.* a regulator; especially, a device attached to a rotating shaft that regulates the velocity of rotation of the shaft; an increase in velocity of the shaft increases the angular velocity of the governor, causing, in turn, a resultant decrease in the angular velocity of the shaft, and vice versa.

Graafian follicle (GRAHF-ee-uhn FAHL-uh-kuhl), one of the many tiny, bladderlike cavities within the ovary; the ovum develops in it and is discharged from it at the time of ovulation.

gradient (GRAY-dee-uhnt), *n.* the amount of change per unit length. For example, *temperature gradient* is the ratio of the temperature difference at 2 points to the length between the points; *potential gradient* is the ratio of the difference in charge at 2 points to the length. A *steep-gradient* aircraft is one capable of climbing rapidly, such as a VTOL.

grain alcohol, a common term for **ethyl alcohol.**

grain boundary, in a crystalline metal, the surface where 2 different grains meet. The grains are the result of crystal deformation in the metal, often propagated for greater metallic strength.

gram, *n.* **1.** in the metric system, a unit of weight equal to 1/1000 kilogram; equal to 0.0326 ounce avoirdupois. *abbr.* **g., gm. 2.** a unit of force: weight of a gram mass at the earth's surface. *abbr.* **gf., gm. 3.** a stain used in classifying bacteria; see **bacterium.**

gram atom, the weight of an atom of any element expressed in grams; makes chemical calculations much easier. Since copper has an atomic weight of 63.54, we can weigh out 63.54 grams of copper to react with a gram atom of sulfur; see also **atomic weight.**

gramicidin (gram-uh-SY-duhn), *n.* an antibiotic isolated from soil bacteria; useful in local infections but harmful if enters blood stream.

Graminales (gram-i-NAY-leez), *n.* an order of monocot plants with spike-like leaves and small, simple flowers which have small or missing petals and sepals and an achene or caryopsis-type of fruit. The order includes the large and economically important grass family (*Gramineae*) of wheat, corn, bamboo, rice, sugar cane, etc., and the sedge family (*Cyperaceae*) of papyrus, bulrush, and sweet flag.

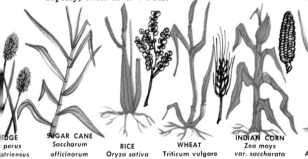

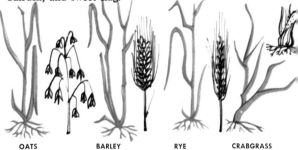

SEDGE *Cyperus striensus*   SUGAR CANE *Saccharum officinarum*   RICE *Oryza sativa*   WHEAT *Triticum vulgare*   INDIAN CORN *Zea mays var. saccharata*   OATS *Avena sativa*   BARLEY *Hordeum vulgare*   RYE *Secale cereale*   CRABGRASS *Digitaria sanguinalis*

graduate (GRAJ-oo-wuht), *n.* a tall, narrow glass cylinder accurately marked in units and used in laboratories for measuring liquids.

graft, *n.* **1.** a part of a plant (*cion*) joined to a second plant (*stock*) to produce new plants; 4

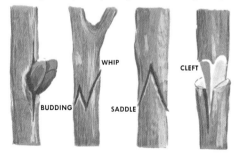

WHIP   CLEFT   BUDDING   SADDLE

basic methods of *grafting* are used. **2.** in surgery, a piece of living tissue transplanted to another part of the body or to another animal.

grain, *n.* **1.** the fruit of a cereal plant, as wheat or rice; see **caryopsis, Graminales. 2.** a unit of weight; see **troy system. 3.** an individual crystal making up a metal, usually with its true shape disturbed by bordering crystals.

gram molecule, the weight of one molecule of an element or compound expressed in grams; the sum of the atomic weights in grams.

granite (GRAN-uht), *n.* a granular, crystalline, igneous rock composed chiefly of feldspar and quartz; used for decorative and building stone; see **rock.**

granulation (gran-yoo-LAY-shuhn), *n.* **1.** the process of forming granules or grains. **2.** in medicine, the formation of granules in the healing process.

granule (GRAN-yuhl), *n.* any small grain or particle; granules of carbon are found in the telephone receiver; especially: **1.** in medicine, any of the small red grains of tissue formed by capillaries in healing wounds. **2.** in astronomy, any of the short-lived bright spots or waves on the sun's photosphere; hotter and brighter than surrounding material. *adj.* **granular.**

granulite (GRAN-yoo-lyt), *n.* a grayish, fine-grained metamorphic rock, often banded; composed of quartz, feldspar, and small, brownish garnets.

graphite (GRAF-eyt), *n.* a steel-gray to black, soft (hardness 1-2), lustrous, crystalline form of carbon; used in "lead" pencils, for electrodes, and as a neutron moderator for nuclear reactors; see **mineral** picture.

graphite-moderated reactor, a thermal-neutron reactor in which graphite is used as the moderator to slow down the neutrons and increase the efficiency of neutron capture.

grass family, see **Graminales.**

grasshopper, see **Orthoptera.**

grating (GRAY-ting), *n.* any structure of close parallel bars and crossbars, often of fine wire; especially, a device used to separate the components of white light or to analyze light obtained from heating an unknown substance so its com-

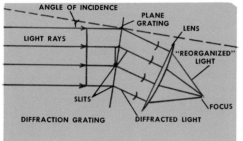

ANGLE OF INCIDENCE — PLANE GRATING — LENS — LIGHT RAYS — "REORGANIZED" LIGHT — SLITS — FOCUS — DIFFRACTION GRATING — DIFFRACTED LIGHT

position can be determined; consists of a large number of very fine equidistant grooves ruled on a plane glass or metal surface.

gravid (GRAV-id), *adj.* pertaining to the condition of pregnancy; pregnant.

gravimeter (gruh-VIM-uh-tuhr), *n.* **1.** a device for measuring specific gravity, similar to a hydrometer. **2.** a device for measuring the force of the gravitational field: as weights are added to a delicate spring, the extension produced by the added weight is measured.

gravitation (grav-uh-TAY-shuhn), *n.* a force of attraction between 2 bodies, proportional to the product of the masses of the bodies and inversely proportional to the square of the distance between them. *adj.* **gravitational.**

gravity (GRAV-uh-tee), *n.* the gravitational force between the earth and a body near it; see **g.**

gray matter, a dark, reddish-gray nervous tissue in the spinal cord and brain consisting chiefly of nerve cell bodies and fibers without myelin.

great circle, a circle on the surface of a sphere formed by the points on the surface that intersect a plane passing through the sphere's center; a great circle on the earth is the shortest distance between any 2 points; see **azimuth** picture.

Great Red Spot, a large, oval patch on the planet Jupiter; its cause is unknown.

grebe (GREEB), see **Podicipediformes.**

green algae see **Chlorophyta.**

greenhouse effect, 1. heating of an enclosed space by the sun's rays shining on or through its surface to raise the temperature within to be higher than that outside. **2.** heating of the earth by the penetration of the atmosphere by absorption of short wavelengths of solar radiation.

greenockite (GREE-nuh-kyt), *n.* a yellowish-orange, crystalline mineral composed of cadmium sulfide, with hardness 3-3½; usually found with sphalerite.

greenstick fracture, fracture of a bone not completely breaking through its width; usually cracked on one side, but only bent on the other.

Greenwich mean time (GRIN-ij, GREN-ich), the mean solar time at Greenwich, England, at the prime meridian, 0°; see **standard time.**

Gregorian telescope (gruh-GAWR-ee-uhn), a reflecting telescope with a concave parabolic mirror with an opening through it, and a smaller ellipsoidal mirror set beyond the focus; light is reflected from the smaller mirror through the opening to an eyepiece; one of the first reflecting telescopes; also called *Cassegrainian.*

grid, *n.* **1.** in an electron tube, that electrode that controls the electron stream passing from cathode to anode; made of a spiral or fine wire mesh; often called *control grid.* **2.** any network of evenly spaced horizontal and vertical lines used as a coordinate system.

groin (GROYN), *n.* the section of the lower abdomen adjoining the thighs, or that general area.

ground-effect machine, a vehicle operated by air blast against ground or water surface; so-called because it uses the surface of the ground to provide much of its needed aerodynamic lift; a continual supply of air replaces air lost at the sides; also called *air-cushion vehicle, abbr.* **GEM.**

ground station, 1. the transmitting and receiving equipment on the ground used for communication by satellite or receiving information from and tracking satellites and missiles. **2.** similar equipment on the ground used in airplane navigation.

ground water, water underneath the surface of the earth; specifically, water that forms the water table; see **water table.**

ground wire, a connection between an electrical circuit and a very large conductor, usually the earth itself; used to keep voltages in electrical circuits at safe levels, regardless of faults that may develop in the circuit.

growing pains, dull, unlocalized pain in the limbs, occurring frequently in children; possibly due to a mild tetany or calcium deficiency.

grub, *n.* the soft, white, bulky larva of certain insects, especially of some beetles.

Gruiformes (groo-uh-FAWR-meez), *n.* an order of birds found along waterways, with long legs, short wings, and long slender beaks; includes rails, coots, and cranes.

guanine (GWAH-neen), *n.* a purine-type base, one of the 4 fundamental units in both DNA and RNA; always pairs with cytosine.

guard cell, one of 2 epidermal cells that surround a stoma, a tiny opening in plant epidermis; they control size of the opening, permitting exchange of gases and transpiration; see **stoma.**

guidance system, a system for directing missiles toward distant objects: consists of *sensor equipment* for observation of location, speed, direction, etc.; *computer* to convert this information into instructions for changes in speed, direction, or other controllable variable; and *control system*—whatever automatic piloting equipment is installed to regulate these factors; may be on ground or on board the missile.

guided missile, any missile with automatic systems installed for controlling its flight path; may be either unmanned, as are most destructive missiles, or manned.

guide fossil, alternate term for **index fossil.**

gulf, *n.* a large indentation in the coastline of an ocean or sea, partially surrounded by land.

gull, see **Charadriiformes.**

gullet, an alternate term for **esophagus.**

gum, *n.* **1.** the fleshy inside covering of the jaws of animals, covering the necks of the teeth; also called *gingiva.* **2.** any of various dried excretions of plants, as resins and rubber. **3.** specifically, any plant excretion with colloidal properties; water-soluble or swell with water, as agar and dammar; composed chiefly of carbohydrates.

guncotton, *n.* a material composed primarily of nitrocellulose; looks like ordinary cotton; used in the manufacture of dynamite and other explosives; formula, $C_6H_7O_2(ONO_2)_3$.

gunpowder, *n.* a mixture of varying composition, containing potassium nitrate (saltpeter), sulfur, and charcoal; used for explosives.

gut, *n.* **1.** generally, a section of the alimentary canal from the intestine to the anus in higher animals. **2.** the intestines of an animal when commercially treated for use as violin strings, in tennis rackets, fishing lines, and the like. **3.** the alimentary canal.

gutta-percha (GUHT-uh-PUHR-chuh), *n.* a rubberlike material derived from latex of *Palaquium* and *Payena* trees; used for waterproofing and insulating electric wires; formula, $(C_{10}H_{16})x$.

gymnosperm (JIM-noh-spuhrm), *n.* any plant of class *Gymnospermae* in subdivision *Pteropsida,* containing the most primitive seed plants; they lack flowers and fruits; seeds are exposed and usually borne on scales of cones; leaves are usually evergreen needles; examples include cycads, conifers, and ginkgo.

gynecology (gy-nuh-KAHL-uh-jee), *n.* the study of the functions, diseases, and disorders of the female reproductive and related organs.

gypsum (JIP-suhm), *n.* a soft (hardness 2) crystalline mineral, usually white; composed of hydrated calcium sulfate, $CaSO_4 \cdot 2H_2O$; used in cements, plasters, and tile; see **mineral.**

gyration (jy-RAY-shuhn), *n.* the revolution of an object about any point or axis.

gyrocompass (JY-roh-kuhm-puhs), *n.* a gyroscope that incorporates a pendulum or other heavy object free to swing, installed on ships to insure accurate pointing to true north; the installation is mounted on gimbals to permit correct alignment.

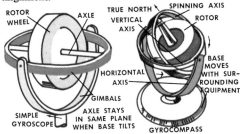

gyroscope (JY-ruh-skohp), *n.* a rotating wheel mounted so that its axis is free to turn; it can maintain a fixed absolute position regardless of changes in position of its mountings; used in gyrocompasses to indicate true north, and in *gyrostabilizers* which help eliminate a ship's roll.

gyrus (JY-ruhs), see **convolution.**

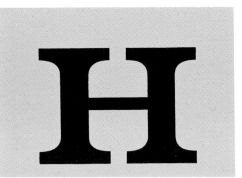

H, symbol for **hydrogen.**

habitat (HAB-uh-tat), *n.* the natural environment of a particular animal or plant; marshy land is the *habitat* of ducks.

hafnium (HAF-nee-uhm), *n.* a silvery, dense metallic element; resembles zirconium in crystalline structure and chemical properties; symbol Hf; *at. no.,* 72; *at. wt.,* 178.49; isolated by Coster and Hevesy in 1923.

hahnium *n.* chemical element. *at no.,* 105; *at. wt.,* 260; discovered by Soviet scientists in 1967.

hail, *n.* small, layered pellets of ice, formed by freezing raindrops; occurs most often during thunderstorms.

hair, *n.* **1.** one of the many fine, threadlike structures of varying lengths growing from the skin of most mammals; see **skin. 2.** an outgrowth from the bodies of insects. **3.** in plants, an outgrowth of the epidermal layer.

half-life, the amount of time it takes for a radioactive substance to decay to half its original amount; used as a measure of radioactivity: the *half-life* of thorium-233 is 23.5 minutes; see element table on page 214.

halite (HAL-eyt), *n.* NaCl, a mineral produced naturally by the evaporation of sea water, isometric, white or colored by impurities, hardness 2½. It is mined as a source of sodium chloride; also called *rock salt;* see also **mineral** picture.

halitosis (hal-uh-TOH-sis), *n.* any unpleasant smell borne on the breath, arising from decomposing food or secretions of the mouth, pharynx, or stomach; may be a symptom of a disorder.

Halley's comet (HAL-ee), a comet famed for the ease with which it can be seen by the naked eye, orbiting the sun with a period of roughly 76 years; named for the English astronomer Edmund Halley (1656-1742), who accurately predicted its orbit. It will next appear in 1986.

halo (HAY-loh), *n.* a ring or series of rings of light surrounding the sun or moon, caused when light rays are refracted or reflected by the tiny ice crystals in the atmosphere.

halogen (HAL-uh-juhn), *n.* any of the 5 highly reactive elements in group VII-A of the periodic table: fluorine, chlorine, bromine, iodine, and astatine; see **periodic table.**

haltere (HAHL-teer), *n.* one of a pair of club-shaped, threadlike balancing organs that represent the hind wings of insects in order Diptera.

ham, a common name for an amateur radio operator.

Hansen's disease, alternate term for **leprosy.**

haploid

haploid (HAP-loyd), *adj.* having half the number (n) of chromosomes for a given species; found in gametophyte plant body cells and in all germ cells following meiosis.

hardening of the arteries, see **arteriosclerosis.**

hardness, see **Mohs hardness scale.**

hard palate (PAL-uht), the roof of the mouth in front of the palate bone; also called *bony palate;* see **palate.**

hard water, any otherwise useful water that has the disadvantage of containing certain dissolved minerals that precipitate soap and leave soiling deposits on objects.

hardwood, *n.* **1.** wood that has an abundance of wood fiber cells for support, producing a dense wood and xylem cells for conduction; wood from the angiosperm trees rather than from the conifers. **2.** any tree yielding such wood, as the oak, hickory, maple, and cherry.

hare, see **Lagomorpha.**

harelip, *n.* a lip, usually the upper, that did not form correctly, resulting in a vertical cleavage between lip and nostril; corrected by surgery.

harmonic (hahr-MAHN-ik), *n.* a whole-number multiple (overtone) of a fundamental frequency. The fundamental is the *first harmonic;* twice the fundamental is the *second harmonic,* etc. In musi-

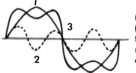

(1) Fundamental wave, (2) third harmonic of that wave, (3) third harmonic added to the fundamental

cal instruments, overtones, harmonics, as well as the fundamental frequencies, are different, resulting in a distinguishable sound for each instrument.

hatch, *v.* **1.** to emerge from an egg. **2.** to incubate, or to produce young by incubating, an egg.

Haversian canal (huh-VUHR-shuhn), any of the numerous channels through bone tissue that carry blood vessels.

hawk, see **Falconiformes.**

hay fever, allergic sensitivity to pollens of certain plants, notably ragweed; results in irritation of the eyes and the membranes of the upper respiratory tract.

hazel-nut family, see **Fagales.**

H-bomb, shortened term for **hydrogen bomb.**

He, symbol for **helium.**

health (HELTH), *n.* the state when all parts of an organism function normally; being free from sickness. *adj.* **healthy.**

hearing, *n.* the sensory response to sound waves, in humans limited to waves ranging from about 16 cycles per second to about 20,000; the intensity limits are much more variable than the frequency limits, with partial or total deafness in a person depending on both factors; see **ear.**

heart, *n.* the main organ of muscular tissue that keeps the blood circulating through the body by contractions and dilations; may have one, 2, 3, or 4 chambers for the passage of blood; man has 4; see **circulatory system.**

heartbeat, *n.* the throbbing of the heart; one beat includes a full cycle of *systole* (contraction) and *diastole* (expansion).

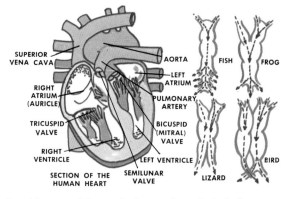

SECTION OF THE HUMAN HEART

heart-lung machine, a device, used particularly in open-heart surgery, in which a pump is substituted for heart action and an oxygenator for the lungs; impure blood from the body is shunted through the oxygenator and purified (and sometimes cooled); then the artificial heart pumps the blood back into the body, by-passing the heart which can then be stopped during the surgery.

heart murmur, a low sound (as heard through the stethoscope) produced in the heart, due to imperfect valve closure or other defect; not necessarily indication of a serious defect.

heartwood, *n.* the dense wood formed in the center of a tree trunk when the xylem cells become filled with resins, gums, and tannins and no longer conduct sap; also called *duramen.*

heat, *n.* **1.** the total *kinetic* energy of the molecules of a material. Heat is absent only if the molecules of a material cease moving (at absolute zero). **2.** generally, the state of being hot. *v.* **3.** to cause the temperature of something to be raised.

heat capacity, a quantity of heat: that quantity of heat required to raise the temperature of any given mass one degree centigrade; stated in calories per degree centigrade. The heat capacity of a material is found by multiplying its specific heat by its weight in grams.

heat exchange, the transfer of heat from one material to another; especially, heat transfer from a gas or liquid to another gas or liquid when the 2 are separated by a heat-conducting barrier; important in boilers, refrigerators, distillation equipment, and other applications.

heath family (HEETH), see **Ericales.**

heat of fusion, the amount of heat needed to convert a solid to a liquid at its melting point, measured in calories per gram or Btu per pound. The heat of fusion of melting ice is 79.6 calories per gram.

heat of reaction, the quantity of heat emitted or absorbed in a chemical reaction; if the reaction produces heat, it is *exothermic;* if it absorbs heat, it is *endothermic.*

heavier-than-air aircraft, see **aerodyne.**

heavy hydrogen, an alternate term for **deuterium.**

heavy water, water composed of deuterium atoms and ordinary oxygen atoms; formula, D_2O; occurs in nature in about 1 part per 5,000 of ordinary water; used in nuclear reactors as a moderator and coolant; also called *deuterium oxide.*

hectare (HEK-tair), *n.* a unit of area in the metric system: 100 meters by 100 meters or 10,000 sq. meters; see also **are.**

hedgehog, see **Insectivora.**

Heidelberg man (HY-duhl-buhrg), the earliest form of modern man; anatomy was reconstructed from a lower jaw found near Heidelberg, Germany; dates from about 750,000 years ago; his scientific name is *Homo heidelbergensis.*

helicopter (HEL-uh-kahp-tuhr, HEE-luh-), *n.* an aerodyne making use of large rotor blades

Modern helicopter for rapid travel or freight service

instead of wings to provide aerodynamic lift; capable of vertical ascent and descent, hovering, or flying in any direction.

helio-, a word part meaning *sun.*

heliocentric (hee-lee-oh-SEN-trik), *adj.* having the sun as the center of a system, as the Copernican theory.

heliotropism (hee-lee-AHT-ruh-pizm), *n.* a growth movement of plants resulting in their turning toward or away from the sun as a response to sunlight.

helium (HEE-lee-uhm), *n.* a chemical element in the rare gas family; a colorless and odorless light gas; used to fill balloons and luminous sign tubes, and to dilute anesthetic gases in medicine; symbol He; *at. no.,* 2; *at. wt.,* 4.0026; identified by Ramsay in 1895. *Liquid* helium, with lowest known freezing point (1.1°K at high pressure) at which it is superfluid, is used extensively in cryogenic research.

helix (HEE-liks), *n., pl.* **-lices** (-luh-seez). **1.** a spiral or an object having a spiral shape: the DNA molecule is believed to be a double helix. **2.** the spirally curved fold of the outer ear.

Helobiales (hee-loh-bee-AY-leez), an alternate term for **Naiadales.**

hematite (HEE-muh-tyt), *n.* a black, reddish-black, or brick-red mineral with hardness 5½-6½; luster is metallic to dull; composed of iron oxide (Fe_2O_3) and impurities; used as a source of iron and as pigment.

hematoma (hee-muh-TOH-muh), *n.* accumulation of blood in body tissues forming a local swelling; caused by an injury that ruptures the vessels.

hemi-, a word part meaning *half.*

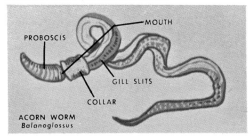

MOUTH
PROBOSCIS
GILL SLITS
COLLAR
ACORN WORM
Balanoglossus

Hemichordata (hem-ee-kohr-DAH-tuh), *n.* a subphylum in phylum Chordata of animals with wormlike body made up of a proboscis, collar,

and trunk; notochord continues to proboscis, nerve cord, and gill slits in the collar. Examples are acorn and tongue worms.

Hemiptera (hem-IP-tuh-ruh), *n.* an order of insects made up of the true bugs; front wings are partly leatherlike and partly membranous; hind wings are entirely membranous; bugs have gradual metamorphosis and mouth parts that can pierce and suck; includes the stink bugs, chinchbugs, bedbugs, water bugs, squash bugs, and many others; see **Insecta.**

hemisphere (HEM-uh-sfeer), *n.* **1.** half of a sphere. **2.** half of Earth, as the Northern or Southern, Eastern or Western, hemispheres. **3.** in astronomy, a projection of a terrestrial (Earth) hemisphere into space; half of the celestial sphere. **4.** in anatomy, half of the cerebrum; the 2 halves are joined by a mass of nervous tissue called the *corpus callosum.*

hemo-, a word part meaning *blood.*

hemoglobin (HEE-muh-gloh-buhn), *n.* a compound of the protein *globin* with the nonprotein organic molecule *heme,* containing one atom of iron; carries oxygen and is responsible for the red color of vertebrate blood.

hemolysis (hee-MAHL-uh-sis), *n.* the rupturing of red blood cells when placed in a salt solution of lower salt concentration than blood plasma; releases hemoglobin. *v.* **hemolyze.**

hemophilia (hee-muh-FIL-ee-uh), *n.* a hereditary disease characterized by a tendency to bleed excessively from minor injuries, with improper coagulation of the blood; cause unknown; a sex-linked recessive character found almost exclusively in males, but transmitted by females.

hemorrhage (HEM-uh-rij), *n.* loss of blood from blood vessels due to physiological causes, physical injury, or numerous pathological causes; may be internal and therefore not obvious or external.

hemostat (HEE-muh-stat, HEM-uh-), *n.* a device for pinching off a blood vessel to stop blood flow or hemorrhage.

hemp family, see **Urticales.**

hen, *n.* the female of any chickenlike bird, domesticated or wild.

henry, *n., pl.* **rys.** the basic unit of electrical inductance; when current in a conductor changing at the rate of one ampere a second induces an electromotive force of one volt in the conductor (or in another conductor), the self-inductance (or the mutual inductance between the conductors) is one henry; named for Joseph Henry, American physicist.

hepatic (hi-PAT-ik), *adj.* **1.** referring to the liver. **2.** belonging or pertaining to the bryophyte group of plants called *liverworts.*

Hepaticae (heh-PAT-i-see), *n.* a class of bryophytes containing the liverworts; plant body is small, flat, and branching; flat or leafy types with unicellular rhizoids; found in moist, shady locations on soil, rocks, and trees; see also **Bryophyta.**

hepatitis (hep-uh-TY-tis), *n.* a liver disease caused by a virus or by chemical poisoning, characterized by fever, weakness, jaundice, and inflamed liver; virus form is highly infectious; *serum* hepatitis is transmitted through blood transfusions; formerly called *jaundice.*

herb

herb (UHRB), *n.* **1.** any seed-bearing plant without a woody stem. *adj.* **herbaceous. 2.** a plant or part of a plant used especially for flavoring.

herbivore (UHR-bi-vohr), *n.* a plant-eating animal. *adj.* **herbivorous.**

herbicide (UHR-bi-seyd), *n.* substance or preparation for killing plants, especially weeds.

heredity (huh-RED-uh-tee), *n.* the genetic characteristics inherited from parents through the transmission of genes. *adj.* **hereditary.**

hermaphrodite (huhr-MAF-ruh-dyt), *n.* an animal or plant having male and female reproductive organs in one individual. *adj.* **hermaphroditic.**

hermetic (huhr-MET-ik), *adj.* airtight; sealed so that no gases can enter or escape.

hernia (HUHR-nee-uh), *n.* the projection or rupture of an organ or portion of tissue through an abnormal opening or weak place in the surrounding walls; this condition usually treated surgically.

heroin (HAIR-oh-in), *n.* a white, odorless, crystalline chemical, derived from morphine; habit-forming, no longer used medicinally in U.S.; formula, $C_{21}H_{23}NO_5$.

herpetology (huhr-puh-TAHL-uh-jee), *n.* the study of reptiles and amphibians, a branch of zoology.

hertz (huhrtz), *n.* unit of frequency which is one cycle per second.

hetero-, a word part meaning *different.*

heterodyne (HET-uh-ruh-dyn), *adj.* describing any electric circuit that makes accented waves (beats) by combining 2 different wavelengths; the beat waves thus obtained have been changed from wave rates too fast to hear (*radio frequency*) down to lower audible rates (*audio frequency*); see also **superheterodyne.**

heterogeneous (het-uhr-uh-JEE-nee-uhs), *adj.* different in kind: air is a *heterogeneous* mixture of gases; contrast with **homogeneous.**

heterosexual (het-uh-roh-SEK-shoo-uhl), *adj.* **1.** relating to the other sex. **2.** pertaining to male and female sex organs located in separate individuals of the same species.

heterosis (het-uhr-OH-sis), see **hybrid vigor.**

heterozygote (het-uh-roh-ZY-goht), *n.* an organism to which parents have contributed unlike genes for one or more inherited characters, although the organism may resemble one parent because of gene dominance; contrast with **homozygote.** *adj.* **heterozygous.**

hexagonal (heks-AG-uh-nuhl), *adj.* **1.** 6-sided. **2.** referring to any crystal with 3 equal, one-plane axes crossing at 120° and a fourth axis perpendicular to the others; see **crystal system.**

Hf, symbol for **hafnium.**

Hg, symbol for **mercury.**

hibernate (HY-buhr-nayt), *v.* to spend a period of time in an inactive state with a much lowered metabolic rate and temperature; usually occurs in winter among certain non-migratory mammals. *n.* **hibernation.**

hiccough (HIK-up), *n.* a sudden, involuntary contraction of the glottis and diaphragm from variety of causes; severe attacks may require medical treatment; also spelled **hiccup.**

high, *n.* in meteorology, an area of high atmospheric pressure; an *anticyclone.*

high blood pressure, 1. an increase of blood pressure against the inner walls of vessels, especially in the heart ventricles; also called *hypertension.* **2.** a symptom of arterial disease common in old age; also a symptom of various other disorders such as kidney disease.

high fidelity (fi-DEL-uh-tee), sound reproduction that faithfully duplicates the original sound; ordinary sound reproduction loses some of the highest and lower tones and distorts others; used particularly of phonographs and FM receivers.

high-octane, *adj.* referring to gasoline that has a high octane number, thus reducing knocking in gasoline engines; see **octane number.**

high-pressure center, the center of an anticyclone, normally accompanied by clear, dry weather. Such centers normally move eastward across North America; the air rotates clockwise about the center in the Northern Hemisphere, counterclockwise in the Southern.

high-tension wire, wire carrying electrical current at high voltages, in the range from 11,000 to 330,000 volts; at high voltages, much less power is lost by leakage.

hilum (HY-luhm), *n., pl.* **hila** (HY-luh). **1.** the mark on a seed caused by its separation from its stalk. **2.** the central cavity of a starch grain.

hinge joint, a type of joint permitting back-and-forth motion of members in one plane: the knee and elbow are examples of hinge joints in the skeletal system.

hippopotamus (hip-uh-PAHT-uh-muhs), see **Artiodactyla.**

histamine (HIS-tuh-meen, -myn), *n.* a chemical found in many animals, and made synthetically. It causes dilation of blood vessels; its action is related to allergic symptoms (asthma, hay fever); formula, $C_5H_9N_3$; see **antihistamine.**

histology (his-TAHL-uh-jee), *n.* the study of the microscopic structure of living organisms, especially the specialization and organization of cells into tissues and organs.

histone (HIS-tohn), *n.* a protein that is strongly basic and is soluble in dilute acid; inhibits the release of RNA by the chromosomes, thus controlling embryonic cell differentiation.

hit theory, a theory in nuclear physics accounting for radiation damage to cells and the probability of such damage; states that when certain vital regions in the cell (called *sensitive sites*) are "hit" by ionizing radiation, the region will be "killed" and permanent damage done to the cell chromosomes. If the vital region is not hit, no permanent damage results.

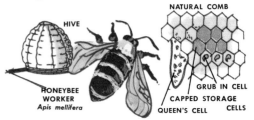

hive, *n.* the structure built by honeybees and various other social insects, in which they live, store food, and raise young.

hives, *n.* an allergic reaction with skin eruptions and itching; has several causes, including sensitivity to certain proteins and drugs; known medically as *urticaria.*

Hn, symbol for **hahnium.**

Ho, symbol for **holmium.**

hoarfrost, an alternate term for **frost.**

hole, *n.* an electron energy level from which the electron is missing; important in semiconductors, in which the hole may move in space when electrical fields are applied.

holly family, see **Sapindales.**

holmium (HOHL-mee-uhm), *n.* a metallic chemical element in the lanthanide series; symbol Ho; *at. no.,* 67; *at. wt.,* 164.930; discovered by Cleve in 1879 but pure element has not yet been isolated.

homeostasis (hoh-mee-oh-STAY-sis), *n.* a steady internal state possessed in some degree by all living organisms and produced by regulating mechanisms which, if successful, allow an organism to become more or less independent of environmental changes; physiological equilibrium of the organism as a whole.

homeotherm (HOH-mee-uh-thuhrm), *n.* an animal that is warm-blooded; also spelled **homoiotherm.** *adj.* **homeothermal, -thermic.**

homing, *adj.* **1.** referring to devices or systems that guide a missile toward a target or guide aircraft toward targets, airfields, or other objects. Missile homing devices may depend on light-sensitivity, heat-sensitivity, or other factors. **2.** descriptive of a pigeon which can find its way home from long distances: the *homing pigeon.*

homo-, a word part meaning *identical* or *similar.*

homogeneous (hoh-muh-JEE-nee-uhs), *adj.* the same kind: a *homogeneous* bed of coal is uniform throughout; contrast with **heterogeneous.**

homogenize (hoh-MAH-juh-nyz), *v.* to make consistent in composition, or homogeneous, usually by mixing and emulsifying, as *homogenized* milk.

homologous (hoh-MAH-luh-guhs), *adj.* **1.** in chemistry, pertaining to the same chemical type, as fatty acids are *homologous* organic compounds. **2.** in biology, pertaining to the same structure and ancestral origin, but not always the same function; as the wings of birds are *homologous* to the arms of man; contrast with **analogous. 3.** in immunology, pertaining to the relationship between bacteria and serum obtained from them.

Homoptera (hoh-MAHP-tuh-ruh), *n.* an order of insects with 2 pairs of wings of uniform thickness, piercing and sucking mouth parts, and gradual metamorphosis. Examples are cicadas, aphids, and scale insects.

Homo sapiens (HOH-moh SAP-ee-uhnz), scientific name (genus and species) of modern man in the primate family of animals; Latin for *wise man.*

homozygote (hoh-moh-ZY-goht), *n.* an organism whose parents contribute similar genes for some inherited character; contrast with **heterozygote.** *adj.* **homozygous.**

honeysuckle family, see **Rubiales.**

hoof, *n.* the hard, hornlike (*keratinized*) covering of part of the foot in certain animals such as the horse.

hoof-and-mouth disease, a highly contagious, acute disease, especially in cattle, caused by a virus that produces severe eruptions in the mouth and feet, and fever; humans may contract the disease; also called *foot-and-mouth disease.*

hookworm, see **Nematoda.**

hook, *n.* a spit or cape in a body of water, which curves back toward the mainland; usually develops by wave action.

horizon (huh-RY-zuhn), *n.* the line or arc where the earth and sky apparently meet, created by the curvature of Earth.

hormone (HAWR-mohn), *n.* any chemical substance produced by the endocrine glands which stimulates the activity of other glands or organs within the body; also, products in plants that function in a similar way, such as *auxins;* see **endocrine gland.**

	GLAND: HORMONE	MAIN ACTIVITY
BODY MAINTENANCE	Adrenal cortex:	carbohydrate, protein, and
	Corticosteroids	salt metabolism
	Adrenal medulla: Adrenalin	blood pressure in stress
	Noradrenalin	normal blood pressure
	Pancreas islets: Insulin	glucose usage
	Glucagon	glycogen breakdown
	Parathyroid: Parathormone	P & Ca concentration
	Posterior pituitary: Pituitrin	smooth muscle contraction
	(oxytocin & vasopressin)	(bladder, uterus, etc.)
	Thyroid: Thyroxine	basal metabolism
ORGAN STIMULATION	Anterior pituitary:	
	3 gonad stimulators	sex hormone secretion;
	(FSH, ICSH, LH)	ovum maturation
	3 metabolic stimulators	thyroid & adrenal cortex
	(thyrotrophin, ACTH,	secretion; general body
	growth hormone)	growth & development
	Gonads, especially	female secondary sex char-
	ovary: Estrogens	acters; ovulation cycle
	Progesterone	preparation for & maintenance of pregnancy
	Gonads, especially	male secondary sex charac-
	testis: Androgens	ters; muscle development

horn, *n.* **1.** a hard, translucent substance containing keratin produced by epidermal cells of certain animals; nails, hoofs, and claws are horn. **2.** a hard projecting outgrowth of varying shape and size appearing on the head of certain mammals; not made of bone; usually in pairs; the ox has horns; contrast with **antler.**

hornblende, *n.* one of the blackish mineral varieties of amphibole containing aluminum, with hardness 5-6; see **mineral** picture.

horse, see **Perissodactyla.**

horse-chestnut family, see **Sapindales.**

AMERICAN BISON
Bison bison
(PERMANENT HORNS)

MALE WHITE-TAILED DEER
Odocoileus virginianus
(ANTLERS ALL BONE, NO TRUE HORN)

BIGHORN SHEEP
Ovis canadensis
(HORNS OF BONE COVERED WITH HORN)

RHINOCEROS
Rhinoceros unicornus

(HORN OF MASSED

horse latitudes, the high-pressure belts lying north and south of the doldrums, around 30° latitude; they give rise to the trade winds.

horsepower, *n.* a unit of power defined as 746 watts, or 550 foot-pounds per second.

horseshoe crab, any member of a primitive group of arthropods (order *Xiphosurida*) with horseshoe-shaped carapace, unsegmented abdo-

Atlantic horseshoe crab, *Limulus* (or *Xiphosurus*) *polyphemus,* about 18 inches long

men ending in a long spine, and 6 jointed walking legs; also called *king crab;* see also **Crustacea.**

horsetail, see **Sphenopsida.**

host, *n.* a plant or animal that provides food, shelter, or other living condition for a parasite.

hot cell, a heavily shielded room or enclosure specially equipped for the handling, processing, etc., of highly radioactive materials by remote means and for the temporary storage of such "hot" materials.

humid (HYOO-muhd), *adj.* referring to humidity; moist, damp.

humidify (hyoo-MID-uh-fy), *v.* to make moist or humid, as by adding water vapor to air.

humidity (hyoo-MID-uh-tee), *n.* the water vapor content of the air. *Absolute humidity* is the actual amount of water vapor present, in grams per cubic meter or other measure; *relative humidity* is the ratio of water vapor present in the air to the amount that would saturate the air at the same temperature.

hummingbird, see **Apodiformes.**

humerus (HYOO-muhr-uhs), *n.* the bone of the upper arm; see **skeletal system.**

humor (HYOO-muhr), *n.* any fluid within the body; see **aqueous humor, neurohumor, vitreous humor.**

humus (HYOO-muhs), *n.* the dark-brown organic substance found in soil formed by the decay of organic matter; a natural fertilizer.

hurricane (HUHR-i-kayn), *n.* **1.** a storm over a wide area, generally starting over water in the tropics; contrast with **tornado. 2.** wind of over 75 miles per hour.

hyaline (HY-uh-luhn), *adj.* glasslike, transparent, or translucent: *hyaline cartilage* is a translucent, bluish cartilage occurring especially in joints and respiratory passages.

hybrid (HY-brid), *n.* an animal or plant produced by parents of differing strains of the

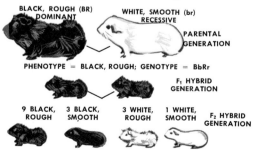

BLACK, ROUGH (BR)
DOMINANT
WHITE, SMOOTH (br)
RECESSIVE
PARENTAL GENERATION

PHENOTYPE = BLACK, ROUGH; GENOTYPE = BbRr
F₁ HYBRID GENERATION

9 BLACK, ROUGH
3 BLACK, SMOOTH
3 WHITE, ROUGH
1 WHITE, SMOOTH
F₂ HYBRID GENERATION

same species or of different species; shows characteristics of both the parents, according to Mendelian inheritance. *v.* **hybridize.** *n.* **hybridization.**

hybrid vigor, the increased strength and healthy growth shown by hybrids, usually resulting from a cross between 2 not closely related pure varieties. Corn raised from hybrid seed produces a larger eared and more evenly kerneled type of corn than either of the parent types; also called *heterosis.*

hydra (HY-druh), see **Hydrozoa.**

hydrate (HY-drayt), **1.** *n.* any chemical compound containing one or more water molecules, usually loosely bonded, as copper sulfate, $CuSO_4 \cdot 5H_2O$. **2.** *v.* to combine with water or its elements.

hydraulic (hy-DRAW-lik), *adj.* **1.** worked by water or other liquid. **2.** referring to pressure of a liquid forced through a small pipe.

hydrazine (HY-druh-zeen), *n.* a colorless, corrosive, liquid nitrogenous base that gives off poisonous fumes; used in jet and rocket fuels and as a chemical intermediate; formula, H_2NNH_2.

hydride (HY-dryd), *n.* a compound containing hydrogen ions, H^+, as sodium hydride, NaH.

hydro-, a word part meaning *water* or *hydrogen.*

hydrocarbon (HY-droh-kahr-buhn), *n.* one of a series of organic compounds formed from only hydrogen and carbon, such as ethane, C_2H_6.

hydrochloric acid (hy-droh-KLOH-rik), a strong inorganic acid; a colorless to yellowish, fuming, poisonous water solution of hydrogen chloride; used to activate oil wells, reduce ores, and as a chemical intermediate; the dilute acid is found in the mammalian stomach; formula, HCl; also called *muriatic acid.*

hydrocyanic acid (hy-droh-sy-AN-ik), a colorless, low-boiling acid with an odor like bitter almonds; gives off poisonous fumes; used as a chemical intermediate and fumigant; formula, HCN; also called *prussic acid* and *hydrogen cyanide.*

hydrodynamics (hy-droh-dy-NAM-iks), *n.* the study and application of the behavior of moving liquids; includes behavior at boundaries with stationary solids (such as pipe walls) and with solids immersed in liquids (ship travel).

hydroelectric, *adj.* pertaining to electrical power generated by the fall of water.

hydrofoil (HY-druh-foil), *n.* a body functioning in water as an airfoil functions in the atmosphere; used for rapid surface vessels; it provides *hydrodynamic lift* just as an airfoil provides aerodynamic lift; this lessens the water drag on the vessel; also called *hydroplane.*

hydrogen (HY-druh-juhn), *n.* the lightest and simplest chemical element, consisting of one proton and one electron; a colorless, odorless, highly flammable gas; used in making chemical compounds and as a reducing agent; symbol H; at. no., 1; at. wt., 1.00797; properties first studied by Cavendish about 1766.

hydrogenated (HY-droh-juh-nay-tuhd), *adj.* pertaining to substances that have been treated with hydrogen, as *hydrogenated vegetable oils.*

hydrogen bomb, an explosive with power derived from release of tremendous amounts of energy when hydrogen nuclei undergo fusion at extremely high temperatures to form helium nuclei; also called *H-bomb.*

hydrogen cyanide (SY-uh-nyd), an alternate term for **hydrocyanic acid.**

hydrogen peroxide, a colorless, unstable chemical compound; used in bleaching, dyeing, and as a rocket fuel oxidizer; formula, H_2O_2.

hydrolysis (hy-DRAH-luh-sis), *n.* a chemical reaction in which a substance is converted into one or more different substances by the action of water, as the ionization of salts in water. Many enzymes function in the hydrolysis of food materials being digested. *v.* **hydrolyze.** *adj.* **hydrolytic.**

hydrometer (hy-DRAHM-uh-tuhr), *n.* a device for determining specific gravities of liquids,

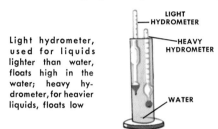

Light hydrometer, used for liquids lighter than water, floats high in the water; heavy hydrometer, for heavier liquids, floats low

consisting of a float attached to a calibrated scale; the point on the scale at the surface of the liquid indicates specific gravity.

hydrophobia, an alternate term for **rabies.**

hydrophone, an underwater receiver that is sensitive to sound waves and converts sound waves into electric signals much as a microphone does; used in underwater equipment such as sonar.

hydroplane (HY-droh-playn), *n.* **1.** alternate term for **hydrofoil. 2.** a type of speedboat with hydrofoils, or one with a hull shaped in steps, so that most or all of the hull is lifted out of the water in travel. **3.** any seaplane. **4.** a horizontal submarine rudder for changing the vessel's depth.

hydroponics (hy-druh-PAHN-iks), *n.* the cultivation of plants by use of liquid nutrient solutions of controlled composition as a growing medium instead of soil.

hydrosphere, *n.* the part of the earth covered by water.

hydrotropism (hy-DRAHT-ruh-pizm), *n.* growth movements of plants in response to water.

hydroxide (hy-DRAHKS-eyd), *n.* a compound containing the hydroxyl radical; see also **base.**

hydroxyl (hy-DRAHKS-uhl), *n.* an oxygen-hydrogen chemical radical, —OH, as in sodium hydroxide, NaOH.

Hydrozoa (hy-druh-ZOH-uh), *n.* a class of coelenterates including both single and colonial forms; often with asexual polyps and sexual medusae stages, although one of these may be reduced or absent; examples are hydra and Portuguese man-of-war; see **Coelenterata.**

hyena (hy-EE-nuh), see **Carnivora.**

hygiene (HY-jeen), *n.* the branch of knowledge dealing with protection of health in all its aspects, including physical, mental, and emotional. *adj.* **hygienic.**

hygrodeik (HY-gruh-dyk), *n.* a direct-reading hygrometer, usually a psychrometer mounted above a relative-humidity scale and connected to the pointer; see **psychrometer.**

hygrograph (HY-gruh-graf), *n.* a recording hygrometer; a pen is attached to hairs or other organic threads that contract or expand with moisture changes; the pen moves over a mechanically operated revolving drum, tracing out a continuous record of humidity changes.

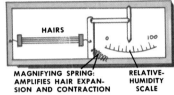

HAIRS

MAGNIFYING SPRING: AMPLIFIES HAIR EXPANSION AND CONTRACTION

RELATIVE-HUMIDITY SCALE

The *hair hygrometer,* a direct-reading type, indicates relative humidity in response to changes in length of hairs or other organic fibers

hygrometer (hy-GRAHM-uh-tuhr), *n.* an instrument for calculating humidity, the amount of water in the air or in other substances; one type depends on expansion and contraction of organic materials, such as hair, with change in moisture content; see also **hygrodeik, psychrometer.**

Hymenoptera (hy-muh-NAHP-tuh-ruh), *n.* an order of insects with 2 pairs of membranous wings hooked together (absent in some), chewing or sucking mouth parts, and complete metamorphosis; both social and solitary species; examples include ants, bees, and wasps.

hyper-, a word part meaning *more than usual* or *excessive.*

hyperacidity (hy-puhr-uh-SID-uh-tee), *n.* a condition in which the stomach glands secrete excessive amounts of hydrochloric acid.

hyperon (HY-puhr-ahn), *n.* an elementary particle of unstable nature, with mass between that of a neutron and a deuterium nucleus.

hyperopia (hy-puhr-OHP-ee-uh), the medical term for *farsightedness;* see **farsighted.**

hyperplasia (hy-puhr-PLAY-zhuh), *n.* **1.** an unnatural increase in the number of normal cells in otherwise normal tissue; contrast with **hypertrophy. 2.** the enlarged part of an organism resulting from such an increase.

hypersonic (hy-puhr-SAHN-ik), *adj.* referring to speeds at least 5 times the speed of sound; thus, referring to speeds greater than Mach 5 (3,800 miles per hour).

hypertension (hy-puhr-TEN-shuhn), medical term for **high blood pressure.**

hyperthyroidism (hy-puhr-THY-roy-dizm), *n.* overactivity of the thyroid gland often causing fatigue, weight loss, nervousness, irritability, increased appetite and basal metabolism, and goiter.

hypertonic (hy-puhr-TAHN-ik), *adj.* of solutions, having a higher concentration of solute than a comparable solution, thus a higher osmotic pressure; often used in comparing solutions with those existing in the body; see also **isotonic.**

hypertrophy (hy-PUHR-truh-fee), *n.* an enlargement of tissue not produced by cell division, as occurs in animal thyroids and plant galls;

hypha

usually caused by growth disorders or by parasites; contrast with **hyperplasia.**

hypha (HY-fuh), *n., pl.* **hyphae** (HY-fee). a threadlike filament characteristic of fungi, from which the plant body is formed; see also **mycelium.**

hypo (HY-poh), *n.* **1.** sodium thiosulfate, a common photographic fixing agent; short for *hyposulfite,* the old name. **2.** shortened term for **hypodermic.**

hypo-, a word part meaning *below, less than normal.*

hypoacidity (hy-poh-uh-SID-uh-tee), *n.* a condition in which insufficient hydrochloric acid is secreted by the stomach glands.

hypocotyl (HY-puh-kaht-uhl), *n.* the portion of a plant embryo between the radicle and cotyledons which may develop into part of the stem; see **seed.**

hypodermic (hy-poh-DUHR-mik), **1.** *adj.* pertaining to the region (*hypodermis*) just underneath the outer skin; intended for injection in this subcutaneous region of the skin. **2.** *n.* a syringe or needle for such injection, or a drug to be so administered.

hypoplasia (hy-poh-PLAY-zhuh), *n.* a condition of underdeveloped structural parts due to an abnormal deficiency of cells.

hypotension (hy-poh-TEN-shuhn), medical term for **low blood pressure.**

hypothalamus (hy-poh-THAL-uh-muhs), *n.* that part of the brain with centers for regulating temperature, water balance, sleep, and other body functions; see **brain.**

hypothesis (hy-PAHTH-uh-sis), *n.* an unproved statement made for the purpose of experimentation or testing; such experiments or tests may have the special purpose of testing the truth, or validity, of the hypothesis. *adj.* **hypothetical.**

hypothyroidism (hy-poh-THY-roy-dizm), *n.* **1.** abnormally low activity of the thyroid gland often causing a disease of adults, called *myxedema,* characterized by weight gain, slowing of bodily functions, anemia, and low metabolism; when present at birth, called *cretinism.*

hypotonic (hy-poh-TAHN-ik), *adj.* having a lower solute concentration, thus a lower osmotic pressure; see also **hypertonic, isotonic.**

Hyracoidea (hy-rah-KOY-dee-uh), *n.* an order of mammals resembling short-eared rabbits

Rock hyrax, *Procavia capensis,* of Asia; about 10 inches long

with rhinocerous-like teeth, 4 hoofed toes on the front limbs and 3 on the hind, and with pads on the feet; includes only the *hyrax,* also called *coney,* but this term tends to confuse hyrax with pika, a true lagomorph sometimes called coney.

hysteresis (his-tuh-REE-sis), *n., pl.* **-ses.** a time lag in the effect of any motion or action; especially, a lag in the magnetizing of a substance in response to a change in magnetizing force. *adj.* **hysteretic.**

I, symbol for **iodine.**

ibis (EY-buhs), see **Ciconiiformes.**

ICBM, abbreviation for **intercontinental ballistic missile.**

ice, *n.* the solid state of water, obtained by cooling below 0°C (32°F); such as hail or snow.

ice age, 1. any period when glaciers covered much of the surface of Earth. **2.** the Pleistocene or most recent epoch of glaciation; see **Pleistocene.**

iceberg, *n.* a huge body of ice floating freely in the ocean with most of its mass under the surface of the water; a chunk of glacial ice.

Iceland spar, a form of calcite that is transparent and can polarize light; utilized in polarizing microscopes and optical stress analysis of materials.

ichthyology (ik-thee-AHL-uh-jee), *n.* the scientific study of fishes.

iconoscope (ey-KAHN-uh-skohp), see **image iconoscope.**

identical twins (ey-DEN-tuh-kuhl), 2 individuals of the same sex and appearance who have developed from a single fertilized ovum which separated at early cleavage stages; contrast with **fraternal twins.**

igneous (IG-nee-uhs), *adj.* pertaining to, or formed by, heat or fire; especially, pertaining to any rock formed by the melting action of heat followed by slow or rapid cooling of a magma, with or without crystallization; see **rock.**

ignite (ig-NYT), *v.* to heat or burn intensely.

ignition point, alternate term for **kindling temperature.**

ileum (IL-ee-uhm), *n.* the last section of the small intestine leading to the large intestine; about 14 feet long in man; see **digestive system.**

iliac (IL-ee-ak), *adj.* pertaining to the bones forming the pelvic girdle in vertebrates.

ilium (IL-ee-uhm), *n.* one of 2 hipbones in the pelvic girdle; see **skeletal system.**

illuminate (ih-LOO-mi-nayt), *v.* to supply light. *n.* **illumination.**

ILS, abbreviation for **instrument landing system.**

image (IM-uhj), *n.* **1.** the optical equivalent of a real object, produced by light in an optical system such as a lens or mirror; the system may be natural or man-made; see also **real image, virtual image. 2.** any similar equivalent of a real object produced by non-optical (electronic or other) methods.

image iconoscope, a TV camera tube with the electron image produced by a photoemissive surface focused on one side of a separate target, which is then scanned on the *same* side by a beam of high-velocity electrons that are attracted to the charged particles left; one of the earliest camera tubes; contrast with **image orthicon.**

image orthicon (ORTH-uh-kahn), a TV camera tube with the electron image produced by a photoemissive surface is focused on one side of a separate target, which is then scanned on the *opposite* side by a beam of low-velocity electrons; many times more sensitive than the image iconoscope.

Image orthicon tube compared to image iconoscope

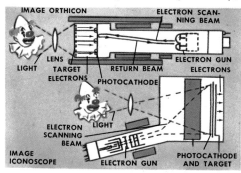

immunity (im-YOO-nuh-tee), *n.* ability to resist certain infectious diseases; may be natural or acquired through inoculation or actual infection. *adj.* **immune.**

immunization (im-yoo-ni-ZAY-shuhn), *n.* the acquiring of immunity. *v.* **immunize.**

immunology (im-yoo-NAHL-jee), *n.* the branch of medicine that deals with immunity from a particular disease and the production of immunity, as by use of vaccines.

impact (IM-pakt), *n.* a collision between 2 bodies, or the force of such a collision.

impacted (im-PAK-tuhd), *adj.* pertaining to a tooth incapable of erupting from the jaw.

impedance (im-PEE-duhnts), *n.* resistance to the flow of alternating current in a circuit; consists of *inductive reactance,* due to change in magnetic field; *capacitative reactance,* due to a capacitor resistance; and *circuit resistance.*

impeller (im-PEL-uhr), *n.* **1.** a rotor or rotor blade; see **rotor.** **2.** specifically the rapidly rotating wheel which forces air into a centrifugal compressor. *v.* **impel.**

imperfect flower, a flower having either male parts (stamens) or female parts (pistils), regardless of the number of other floral parts absent or present; see **flower.**

impetigo (im-puh-TY-goh), *n.* a contagious skin disease characterized by pustules which break, form yellow crusts, and heal without scarring; caused by streptococci bacteria.

impetus (IM-puh-tuhs), *n.* the force exerted by a moving body in overcoming resistance and in maintaining its motion.

implode (im-PLOHD), *v.* to shatter, often with great violence, with all force directed inward by atmospheric pressure; contrast with **explode.** *n.* **implosion.**

imprinting (im-printing-ing), *n.* **1.** producing a mark on something by pressure. **2.** fixing firmly in the consciousness.

impulse (IM-puhls), *n.* **1.** an abrupt increase in force or energy, especially electrical energy. **2.**

change in momentum of an object. **3.** in biology, the electrochemical passage of a stimulus over nerve fibers, producing a reaction to the stimulus.

impurity (im-PYOO-ruh-tee), *n.* a small quantity of a material found in an otherwise homogeneous material; especially, a small quantity of another element (usually arsenic or boron) introduced into pure crystalline germanium (or silicon) to make it a semiconductor; often called *donor impurity* or *acceptor impurity.* *adj.* **impure.**

In, symbol for **indium.**

inanimate (in-AN-uh-muht), *adj.* not living.

incandescence (in-kuhn-DES-uhnts), *n.* the state in which a substance glows with white heat, often so that it can be used for artificial lighting, as in the *incandescent lamp.* *v.* **incandesce.** *adj.* **incandescent.**

incidence (IN-suh-duhnts), *n.* contact with a surface, as in a light ray reaching a liquid or solid surface; see also **angle of incidence.**

incision (in-SIZH-uhn), *n.* a cut into body tissues, especially one made deliberately during surgery to reach internal organs.

incisor (in-SY-zuhr), see **tooth.**

inclination (in-kluh-NAY-shuhn), *n.* the angle by which anything differs from the perfectly horizontal or vertical, as in the tilt of the earth's axis from the vertical, or the tilting that may occur at the *inclination joint* on a microscope. *v.* **incline.**

inclined plane, a simple machine for easy moving of loads; a plane surface placed at an angle

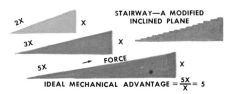

of less than 90° so that it forms a slope; the load moves a longer distance, but with less effort per unit of distance.

inclinometer (in-kluh-NAHM-uh-tuhr), *n.* an instrument for measuring angle of slope, usually from the horizontal; used on ships and planes to show relation to the horizon; also called *clinometer.*

incombustible (in-kuhm-BUHS-ti-buhl), *adj.* cannot be ignited.

incomplete dominance, a genetic cross in which heterozygous individuals are like neither of the parents because neither of the pair of genes (*alleles*) responsible for the trait is completely dominant: a red flowered four-o'clock, when crossed with a white, yields pink four-o'clocks.

incomplete flower, a flower in which one or more of the normal floral parts (stamens, pistils, petals, and sepals) is missing.

incubator (IN-kyuh-bay-tuhr), *n.* a device for maintaining proper temperature so eggs can develop and hatch. **2.** an apparatus for controlling temperature, oxygen, etc., permitting development of living organisms, particularly those used for bacterial or mold cultures, or for controlling the environment of prematurely born human infants.

incus (IN-kuhs), *n.* the small, anvil-shaped bone in the ears of all mammals; see **ear.**

indehiscent (in-duh-HIS-uhnt), *adj.* of fruit, not opening at maturity; see **fruit** picture.

index fossil, fossil remains with a fairly sharply defined time span, whose occurrence in a rock can be used for dating purposes, or for establishing a sequence of events; also called *guide fossil;* see **geologic time table.**

index of refraction, the ratio of speed of any electromagnetic radiation in one medium to its speed in a second medium; especially, for light, the ratio of its speed in a vacuum to its speed in another medium; a constant for light of a particular color and a particular medium; also expressed as the ratio between the sines of the angle of incidence and the angle of refraction.

Indian summer, a short period of moderate, calm weather in late fall, often with some haze; usually occurs after the first freezing spell; caused by a polar air mass developing into a relatively stationary high-pressure area.

indicator (IN-di-kay-tuhr), *n.* **1.** in chemistry, a substance used to show the state of a reaction, especially one such as litmus, used to indicate the endpoint of neutralization reactions by color change; others show endpoints of oxidation-reduction reactions; see also **litmus. 2.** an instrument pointer.

indigenous (in-DIHJ-uh-nuhs), *adj.* pertaining to or originating from a particular region, as kangaroos are *indigenous* to Australia.

indigestion (in-duh-JES-chuhn), *n.* difficulty in the digestion of food usually accompanied by fullness, belching, and heartburn; may occur as a symptom of a number of diseases.

indigo (IN-duh-goh), *n.* a dark-blue, crystalline, organic dye from plants in genus *Indigofera* of the pea family; used to dye textiles; formula, $C_{16}H_{10}N_2O_2$; now almost entirely replaced by the synthetic chemical.

indium (IN-dee-uhm), *n.* a shiny, silvery-white, soft, metallic chemical element; used in alloys for dental work and in low-melting-point alloys; symbol In; *at. no.,* 49; *at. wt.,* 114.82; isolated by Reich and Richter in 1863.

inductance (in-DUHK-tuhnts), *n.* the circuit property that responds to a changing current by development of an electromotive force in the circuit (or in a nearby circuit) that opposes the change in current; expressed in henrys.

induction, *n.* the process by which an object having electrical or magnetic properties creates a similar property in a nearby object. *v.* **induce.**

induction coil, a device for converting direct current to alternating current or for boosting the voltage of DC; current is induced in a secondary coil by a pulsating or interrupted DC current in the primary coil; used in the telephone.

inductive reasoning, reasoning that proceeds from the specific to the more general; usually it begins with observations and generalizes by interpreting the observations consistently; the statement of a scientific law is induction after a series of observations; contrast with **deductive reasoning.**

inductor (in-DUK-tuhr), *n.* a conductor or group of conductors in electrical equipment in which voltage is induced by the cutting of lines of magnetic flux.

inelastic, *adj.* not able to resume original size and shape after an applied force has been removed; contrast with **elastic.**

inert (in-UHRT), *adj.* lacking or deficient in power, action, or motion, as the *inert gases* (neon, argon, etc.) which do not react chemically under ordinary conditions.

inertia (in-UHR-shuh), *n.* resistance to motion when at rest, or to change of motion or direction when moving; one of the fundamental properties of matter.

inertial guidance, a guidance system for missiles and other vehicles in which all sensing and control devices are contained within the vehicle, preventing interference from outside systems possible with remote control.

infantile paralysis, former term for **poliomyelitis.**

infection (in-FEK-shuhn), *n.* **1.** the process by which disease-producing agents invade organisms. **2.** the disease resulting from this invasion, as an *infected* wound. *v.* **infect.**

infectious (in-FEK-shuhs), *adj.* communicable; transferable from one organism to another by means of various agents such as bacteria, insects, air, and water.

inferior (in-FEER-ee-uhr), *adj.* lower or underneath, in relation to other parts of an anatomical structure; contrast with **superior.**

infest, *v.* to overrun, such as may be done by annoying insect pests. **2.** to enter or live on as a parasite. *n.* **infestation.**

infinity (in-FIN-uh-tee), *n.* any quantity or dimension that has no limiting value; a concept for expressing the increase of any value beyond any assignable limit. *adj.* **infinite.**

inflammable (in-FLAM-uh-buhl), *adj.* a common but misleading term for **flammable.**

inflammation (in-fluh-MAY-shuhn), *n.* a reaction of the body to infection or some irritation, shown by redness, heat, swelling, and pain. *adj.* **inflamed.**

inflorescence (in-floh-RES-uhnts), *n.* a cluster of flowers on one stalk, as in geranium; may look like a single flower.

influenza (in-floo-EN-zuh), *n.* a highly contagious disease of the respiratory tract characterized by fever, physical exhaustion, inflammation of the mucous membranes, and pains in back and limbs; caused by several viruses; may be mistaken for the milder common cold; often called *flu.*

infrared (in-fruh-RED), *n.* the portion of the electromagnetic spectrum between the shortest radio waves and red light, with a wavelength longer than that of red light (about 0.8 to 300 microns); emitted by all objects at temperatures above absolute zero; used to detect structural flaws and hidden objects.

Infusoria (in-fyoo-ZOHR-ee-uh), an alternate term for **Ciliata.**

ingestion (in-JES-chuhn), *n.* the taking of food into a vacuole, cavity, or digestive system for the purpose of digestion. *v.* **ingest.**

ingot (ING-guht), *n.* a bar of some metal, usually iron or steel, made by pouring the molten metal into a mold, made for convenience of handling.

inhale (in-HAY-uhl), *v.* to breathe or take in air; contrast with **exhale.** *n.* **inhalation.**

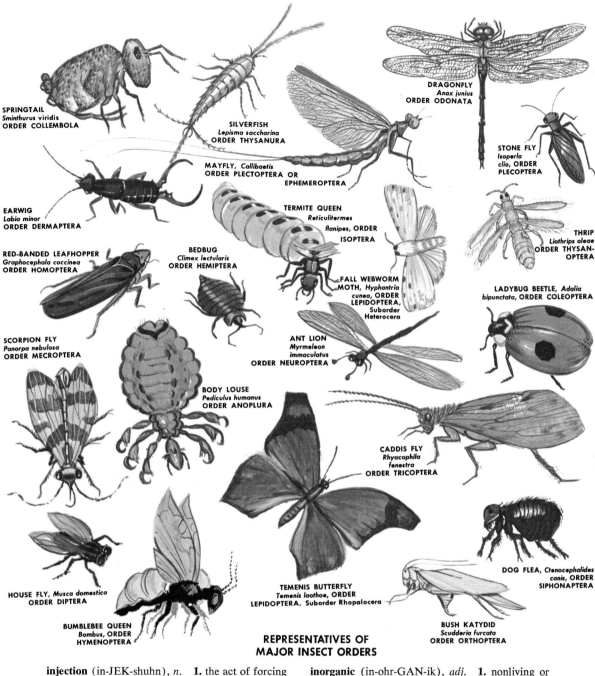

SPRINGTAIL
Smithurus viridis
ORDER COLLEMBOLA

SILVERFISH
Lepisma saccharina
ORDER THYSANURA

MAYFLY, *Callibaetis*
ORDER PLECTOPTERA OR
EPHEMEROPTERA

DRAGONFLY
Anax junius
ORDER ODONATA

STONE FLY
Isoperla
clio, ORDER
PLECOPTERA

EARWIG
Labia minor
ORDER DERMAPTERA

TERMITE QUEEN
Reticulitermes
flanipes, ORDER
ISOPTERA

THRIP
Liothrips oleae
ORDER THYSAN-
OPTERA

RED-BANDED LEAFHOPPER
Graphocephala coccinea
ORDER HOMOPTERA

BEDBUG
Climex lectularis
ORDER HEMIPTERA

FALL WEBWORM
MOTH, *Hyphantria*
cunea, ORDER
LEPIDOPTERA,
Suborder
Heterocera

LADYBUG BEETLE, *Adalia*
bipunctata, ORDER COLEOPTERA

SCORPION FLY
Panorpa nebulosa
ORDER MECROPTERA

ANT LION
Myrmeleon
immaculatus
ORDER NEUROPTERA

BODY LOUSE
Pediculus humanus
ORDER ANOPLURA

CADDIS FLY
Rhyacophila
fenestra
ORDER TRICOPTERA

HOUSE FLY, *Musca domestica*
ORDER DIPTERA

BUMBLEBEE QUEEN
Bombus, ORDER
HYMENOPTERA

TEMENIS BUTTERFLY
Temenis laothoe, ORDER
LEPIDOPTERA. Suborder Rhopalocera

BUSH KATYDID
Scudderia furcata
ORDER ORTHOPTERA

DOG FLEA, *Ctenocephalides*
canis, ORDER
SIPHONAPTERA

**REPRESENTATIVES OF
MAJOR INSECT ORDERS**

injection (in-JEK-shuhn), *n.* **1.** the act of forcing a fluid, drug, serum, or vaccine into a tissue, vein, or organ; usually made with a syringe and needle called *hypodermic.* *v.* **inject.** **2.** the fluid that is injected.

ink sac, a saclike organ present in most cephalopods containing a black, inky fluid which, when expelled, throws a black protective screen around the animal, enabling it to escape; see also **Cephalopoda.**

innate (in-NAYT), *adj.* pertaining to something existing from birth and not acquired; inborn.

inoculate (in-AHK-yuh-layt), *v.* to inject dead or weakened disease-producing microorganisms into the body so as to produce a mild form of the disease and thus establish future immunity. *n.* **inoculation.**

inorganic (in-ohr-GAN-ik), *adj.* **1.** nonliving or not derived from living organisms, as many minerals. **2.** in chemistry, pertaining to substances that do not contain carbon; contrast with **organic.**

input, *n.* **1.** the energy put into a device, usually electrical but can be mechanical. **2.** the point at which energy is fed into a device.

Insecta (in-SEK-tuh), *n.* a class of air-breathing arthropods with 2 antennae, 6 legs, a body divided into head, thorax, and abdomen, and usually 2 pairs of wings; the *insects* include flies, beetles, wasps, ants, bees, grasshoppers, butterflies, moths, and many others.

insecticide (in-SEK-ti-syd), *n.* a substance or chemical preparation used to kill insects; usually applied by spraying, dusting, fumigating, or the use of aerosols.

Insectivora (in-sek-TIV-uh-ruh), *n.* an order of primarily insect-eating mammals with flat feet, 5 toes, and undifferentiated teeth; front limbs are

SHORT-TAILED
SHREW, *Blarina brevicanda*

COMMON MOLE
Scalopus aquaticus

often modified for digging. *Insectivores* include moles, shrews, and hedgehogs.

insectivore (in-SEK-tuh-vawr), *n.* **1.** the common name for a mammal in order Insectivora. **2.** any plant or animal adapted for eating insects, as the pitcher plant. *adj.* **insectivorous.**

insertion (in-SUHR-shuhn), *n.* the more movable end of a muscle; contrast with **origin.**

insoluble (in-SAHL-yoo-buhl), *adj.* incapable of being dissolved in water or other specified liquids, as *insoluble* salts.

instinct (IN-stinkt), *n.* an inborn response or reaction to a stimulus, found in some animals; also a natural pattern or inclination determined by heredity, which does not have to be learned. *adj.* **instinctive.**

instrumentation (in-struh-men-TAY-shuhn), *n.* the design, manufacture, installation, and operation of a group of instruments regarded as a unit for a major operation; *spacecraft instrumentation* involves all the instruments installed on the craft as well as remote-control devices.

instrument flying, the operation of aircraft without visual aids; the pilot controls all details of operation solely by consulting his instruments; used for night flying and in bad weather.

instrument landing system, a radio navigation system for guiding aircraft to landing when visibility is poor or nonexistent; involves beams showing the pilot both vertical and horizontal location at every moment. *abbr.* **ILS.**

insulator (IN-suh-lay-tuhr), *n.* a nonconducting material surrounding a substance used to prevent the loss or gain of heat, sound, or electricity. *v.* **insulate.**

insulin (IN-suh-luhn), *n.* a complex protein substance secreted by the islets of Langerhans in the pancreas of animals; essential to sugar metabolism and used in treatment of diabetes.

intake, *n.* **1.** the point at which substances are taken into an organism or a device; an opening to admit substances into a system, as through an *intake* valve. **2.** anything taken into a system.

integument (in-TEG-yuh-muhnt), *n.* **1.** the outer layer (or 2 layers) of cells surrounding the ovule in an undeveloped plant seed and developing into the seed coat after fertilization. **2.** in animals, the skin and its outgrowths, such as hair, glands, scales, and feathers.

inter-, a word part meaning *within, among;* often used for *among* in distinction to **intra-,** when reserved for *within.*

intercellular, *adj.* occurring between or among cells, as *intercellular* matter.

interceptor (in-tuhr-SEP-tuhr), *n.* a swift fighter aircraft, able to climb rapidly to head off invading bombing planes: the *Convair F-106A* is an advanced all-weather *interceptor.*

intercontinental ballistic missile, a missile with a range of at least 5,000 miles, such as the *Atlas;* see also **ballistic missile.** *abbr.* **ICBM.**

interference (in-tuhr-FEER-uhnts), *n.* **1.** in electronics, anything that prevents reception of an undistorted signal. **2.** in optics, the effect at a point where 2 light waves from the same source cross and either reinforce (*constructive interference*) or cancel (*destructive*) each other. Brilliant colors that appear in thin films such as soap bubbles are due to interference. **3.** in sound, the effect at a point where 2 waves of identical frequency and amplitude meet and either reinforce or cancel each other. *v.* **interfere.**

interferometer (in-tuhr-fuhr-AHM-uh-tuhr), *n.* an optical instrument, consisting mainly of 2 reflecting surfaces, used for measuring small differences between 2 optical path lengths (distance along the path times index of refraction of material in the path).

interferon (in-thur-FEER-ahn), *n.* a chemical recently isolated by a British physician from body cells being attacked by a virus; appears to be a successful viricide (virus killer).

interglacial (in-tuhr-GLAY-shuhl), *adj.* happening or taking shape during an interval between glacial periods.

intermediate (in-tuhr-MEE-dee-uht), **1.** *adj.* located or occurring between 2 objects, extremes, times, etc. **2.** *n.* a compound produced as a necessary step between raw materials and desired compound.

intermediate range ballistic missile, a missile with a range of between 1,000 and about 3,000 miles, such as the *Polaris;* see also **ballistic missile.** *abbr.* **IRBM.**

internal (in-TUHR-nuhl), *adj.* existing within a substance, body, or system.

internal combustion, an explosion or burning that takes place within an engine (such as an automobile engine) that generates power, instead of in a separate furnace.

internal medicine, an area of medicine concerned with the diagnosis and treatment of disorders and diseases occurring on the inside of the body. A physician in internal medicine is an *internist.*

international date line, an imaginary line located in the Pacific Ocean, generally following the 180th meridian from the North Pole to the South Pole; the calendar is adjusted by one day at this line, a day being dropped when traveling from east to west or gained when traveling from west to east.

internode, *n.* the section or region between 2 nodes, as on a tree branch; see **bud.**

interplanetary (in-tuhr-PLAN-uh-tair-ee), *adj.* existing or occurring in the region of the solar system; often used in referring to space travel from one planet to another.

interstellar (in-tuhr-STEL-uhr), *adj.* relating to the region in space that separates the stars; also used of space travel to the stars.

interstitial (in-tuhr-STISH-uhl), *adj.* located in, or pertaining to, the area between things; especially, *interstitial tissue,* such as connective tissue between organs.

intestine (in-TES-tuhn), *n.* the lower portion of the digestive system in higher animals, from the posterior end of the stomach or gizzard to the anus or rectal opening; secretes digestive enzymes which act upon sugars and proteins; see **digestive system.** *adj.* **intestinal.**

intoxicant (in-TAHK-si-kuhnt), *n.* **1.** any substance that partially or entirely stupefies (dulls) the organism by chemically suppressing cell activity (especially nerve cells). **2.** any alcoholic beverage.

intra-, a word part meaning *within, among;* often used for *within* in distinction to **inter,** often reserved for *among.*

intragalactic space (in-truh-guh-LAK-tik), the region of space within a galaxy.

intramuscular (in-truh-MUHS-kyuh-luhr), *adj.* found or taking place within a muscle.

intravenous (in-truh-VEE-nuhs), *adj.* within or into a vein, as an *intravenous* injection.

intrusion (in-TROO-zhuhn), *n.* **1.** a mass of igneous rock forced into other rocks or between other rocks; *magma* (the solidified product) is an

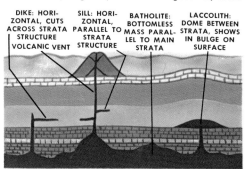

DIKE: HORI-ZONTAL, CUTS ACROSS STRATA STRUCTURE VOLCANIC VENT   SILL: HORI-ZONTAL, PARALLEL TO STRATA STRUCTURE   BATHOLITE: BOTTOMLESS MASS PARALLEL TO MAIN STRATA   LACCOLITH: DOME BETWEEN STRATA, SHOWS IN BULGE ON SURFACE

intrusion. Four basic types are *batholiths, laccoliths, dikes,* and *sills,* based on the intrusion's position in relation to surrounding strata. **2.** the action that produces an intrusion. *adj.* **intrusive.**

inverse proportion, the dependence of one quantity upon the reciprocal (1 divided by a quantity) of another; as one quantity grows larger, the other grows smaller.

inverse-square law, a law stating a relation inversely proportional to the square of the distance between objects; thus the Universal Law of Gravitation states that gravitational force between 2 objects follows the inverse-square law: if the distance between them is doubled, the force is only one-fourth as great.

inversion (in-VUHR-zhuhn), *n.* **1.** the state of being inside out or upside down; see also **temperature inversion.** *v.* **invert. 2.** in genetics, a rearrangement of the genes within the chromosome.

invertase (in-VUHR-tays), *n.* an enzyme that allows the diassacharide sucrose to be converted to dextrose and fructose; found in the gastric juices of animals and in yeasts; also called *sucrase.*

invertebrate (in-VUHR-tuh-bruht), *n.* any animal without a backbone or endoskeletal axis; all animals except those in chordate subphylum *Vertebrata* (including the fishes, amphibians, reptiles,

birds, and mammals); see also **Chordata, Vertebrate.**

in vitro (VEE-troh), under artificial conditions rather than natural ones; a bacterial culture in agar is one *in vitro*: Latin, *in glass.*

involuntary muscle (in-VAHL-uhn-tair-ee), a muscle that reacts without *conscious* control, independent of the will, controlled by the autonomic nervous system. Examples include muscles regulating the size of the eye pupil and those of the intestinal wall; also called *non-striated* or *smooth muscle;* see also **voluntary muscle** picture.

iodide (EY-uh-dyd), *n.* the iodide ion, I–, or any compound containing it, as sodium iodide, NaI.

iodine (EY-uh-dyn), *n.* a heavy, grayish solid chemical element in the halogen family; readily gives off a purplish vapor; poisonous and corrosive; used in medicines, dyes, and for making organic compounds; iodine-131 is used in diagnosis; symbol I; *at. no.,* 53; *at. wt.,* 126.9044; obtained in 1811 by Courtois.

iodoform (ey-OH-duh-fawrm), *n.* a yellowish, crystalline organic compound with a penetrating odor; used as a bactericide or disinfectant; formula, CHI_3.

ion (EY-uhn), *n.* an electrically charged atom or group of atoms resulting from the gain or loss of electrons; see also **anion, cation.**

ion engine, an engine converting energy from nuclear reactions or solar radiation into mechanical energy, as for space-vehicle propulsion; based on extremely high-speed discharge of ions, as in plasma engines.

ion exchange, the purification of liquids or the separation of dissolved materials by contact with solids containing ions of similar positive or negative charge to ions in the liquid; see also **zeolite.**

ionic bond (ey-AHN-ik), an alternate term for **electrovalent bond.**

ionization (ey-uh-nuh-ZAY-shuhn), *n.* a chemical process in which molecules of a substance, usually in solution, dissociate (separate) into positive and negative ions, as NaCl, a salt, dissociates into Na^+ and Cl^-. Ionization of gases usually occurs by means of electrical discharge, resulting in positively and negatively charged atoms or groups of atoms. *v.* **ionize.**

ionosphere (ey-AHN-uh-sfeer), *n.* the outer layer of the atmosphere between the stratosphere and the exosphere, containing ionized particles; also called the *Kennelly-Heaviside* layer.

Ir, symbol for **iridium.**

IRBM, abbreviation for **intermediate range ballistic missile.**

iridescent (eer-uh-DES-uhnt), *adj.* having or displaying different colors of the rainbow, as the plumage of pigeons and certain other birds. *n.* **iridescence.**

iridium (ih-RID-ee-uhm), *n.* a shiny, silvery-white metallic chemical element; used with platinum in alloys for jewelry and electronic equipment; symbol Ir; *at. no.,* 77; *at. wt.,* 192.2; isolated by Tennant in 1804.

iris (EY-ris), *n.* the opaque diaphragm in front of the lens of the eye, which controls the amount of light passing through the pupil; see **eye.**

iris family

iris family, see **Liliales.**

iron (EY-uhrn), *n.* a grayish, metallic chemical element; highly malleable and ductile; essential for all plants and animals; used chiefly for making steel; symbol Fe; *at. no.,* 26; *at. wt.,* 55.847; known since early times.

iron pyrite, see **pyrite.**

irradiate (ih-RAY-dee-ayt), *v.* to expose to radiation; especially, to expose to radioactivity or to ultraviolet radiation; foods may be *irradiated* to produce or increase vitamin-D content. *n.* **irradiation.**

irrigation (eer-uh-GAY-shuhn), *n.* **1.** a process in which water is artificially supplied to land areas by means of canals, ditches, etc. **2.** in medicine, a process in which a cavity or canal of the body is flushed with water or other fluid. *v.* **irrigate.**

irritability (eer-uh-tuh-BIL-uh-tee), *n.* the ability to respond to stimuli, one of the general characteristics of all protoplasm, and a function which is increasingly specialized as animal nervous systems evolve.

ischium (IS-kee-uhm), *n.* one of the 3 fused bones of the pelvic girdle; see **skeletal system.**

isinglass (EY-suhn-glas), *n.* **1.** a white, odorless, tasteless gelatin derived from swim bladders of certain fishes, especially sturgeons; used as an adhesive. **2.** an alternate term for **mica,** especially when it occurs in thin sheets.

islet of Langerhans (EY-luht, LAHN-guhr-hahns), any of the cells in the pancreas that function as endocrine glands; they secrete *insulin* which controls glucose and fat metabolism; also called *island;* see **endocrine gland.**

iso-, a word part meaning: **1.** *equal, uniform, similar.* **2.** *isomeric,* as a prefix to the name of a chemical.

isobar (EY-suh-bahr), *n.* **1.** an imaginary line on the earth's surface connecting points of equal

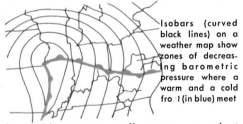

Isobars (curved black lines) on a weather map show zones of decreasing barometric pressure where a warm and a cold front (in blue) meet

barometric pressure; or a line on a map or chart showing such points. **2.** an atom of the same weight but of different atomic number from another; carbon-14 and nitrogen-14 are isobars.

isogonal (ey-SAHG-uh-nuhl), *n.* a line on a magnetic map showing all the places of equal magnetic declination; also called *isoclinic line.*

isolate (EY-soh-layt), *v.* **1.** in chemistry, to separate an element or compound in pure form from the substances in which it is mixed or chemically combined. **2.** in bacteriology, to grow a pure culture of bacteria. **3.** in medicine, to separate a patient with a contagious disease from other persons. *n.* **isolation.**

isomer (EY-soh-muhr), *n.* any of 2 or more chemical compounds that have the same molecular formula but different molecular structures, and, usually, different physical properties: butyl alcohol, C_4H_9OH, and ethyl ether,

$(C_2H_5)_2O$, have the same molecular formula, $C_4H_{10}O$. *adj.* **isomeric.**

isometric (ey-soh-MET-rik), *n.* **1.** in thermodynamics, a line that indicates the changes in temperature and pressure at constant volume. **2.** *adj.* in crystallography, an alternate term for **cubic.**

isomorphic (ey-suh-MAWR-fik), *adj.* having the same shape as something else, as crystals with the same shape, and frequently the same size, as the crystals of another substance, but differing in color; formulas are usually similar. *n.* **isomorph.**

isoprene (EY-suh-preen), *n.* a colorless, liquid, double-bond hydrocarbon which is a basic constituent of all natural rubber; the basic "building block" of many volatile plant oils; formula, $CH_2:CHC(CH_3):CH_2.$

isopropyl (ey-soh-PROH-puhl), *n.* an organic isomer of the propyl radical, $(CH_3)_2CH$-, as in *isopropyl alcohol* of industrial and skin-rub use, $(CH_3)_2CHOH.$

Isoptera (ey-SAHP-tuh-ruh), *n.* an order of social insects without wings except on sexual forms; have chewing mouth parts and gradual metamorphosis. Examples are termites, often wrongly called *white ants.*

isostasy (ey-SAH-stuh-see), *n.* balance in the level of large sections of the earth's crust due to their floating on the denser material underneath; less dense material of the crust is thus raised above more dense material.

isotherm (EY-soh-thuhrm), *n.* the line on a weather map joining points having the same temperature.

isothermal, *adj.* **1.** referring to the same amount of heat in 2 or more objects. **2.** referring to a change in volume or pressure when heat is added or removed from a body whose temperature is kept constant. **3.** referring to an isotherm.

isotonic (ey-soh-TAHN-ik), *adj.* having the same osmotic pressure, especially applied to a fluid that is to be injected into the bloodstream. Such a fluid must also have the same solute concentration as the blood.

isotope (EY-suh-tohp), *n.* a form of an element that has the same atomic number as another form, but a different atomic weight or mass number, due to a different number of neutrons in the nucleus: chlorine is a naturally occurring mixture of 2 *isotopes:* Cl^{35} and Cl^{37}. Artificial isotopes of elements are produced by bombarding the nuclei of atoms; see also **isobar, radioactive isotope.**

isotopic generator (ey-suh-TAHP-ik), a thermoelectric generator using heat from radioactive decay to generate electricity; used in satellites, unmanned weather stations, etc.; also called *atomic battery.*

isthmus (IS-muhs), *n.* **1.** a narrow strip of land that connects 2 larger bodies of land, with water on both sides. **2.** in anatomy, a narrow strip of tissue between 2 organs, or a narrow passage between 2 cavities in the body.

-itis, a word part meaning *inflammation of:* meningitis is *inflammation of* the meninges.

ivory (EYV-uh-ree), *n.* a hard, whitish type of dentine, harder than bone, found in the tusks of some mammals, especially the elephant.

J

jade, *n.* an extremely hard gem variety of jadeite (true jade) or nephrite.

jadeite (JAY-dyt), *n.* a tough, translucent mineral member of the pyroxene group, $NaAlSi_2O_6$, with hardness 6½-7; white to deep green in color; used as a gemstone, known as *jade.*

jasper (JAS-puhr), *n.* an opaque form of quartz with extremely fine crystal structure, occurring in various colors, usually reddish to brown.

jaundice (JAWN-duhs), *n.* a disorder caused by bile in the blood giving a yellowish color to skin, tissues, body fluids, and eyes; often accompanies other disease symptoms.

Java man (JAHV-uh), a prehistoric race of man whose fragments of remains were found on the island of Java; reconstructions indicate an ape-like appearance and the ability to walk upright; scientific name is *Pithecanthropus.*

jejunum (juh-JOO-nuhm) *n.* part of the small intestine following the duodenum; 8 feet long in man; see **digestive system.**

jellyfish, see **Scyphozoa.**

jet, *n.* **1.** a black mineral (compressed lignite) formerly popular as a gem because of the high glossy polish it takes. **2.** a high-velocity stream of fluid (gas or liquid) through a nozzle or other small opening. *adj.* **jet.**

jet engine, see **reaction engine, turbojet.**

jet propulsion (proh-PUL-shuhn), the movement of a body (vehicle, missile, etc.) by reaction; the force moving the body is the reaction to the force of a fluid jet expelled from the body; see **reaction engine.** *adj.* **jet-propelled.**

jet stream, an area of high-speed, westerly winds circling Earth; about 30,000 feet high, 300 miles wide, and 4 miles thick; they hinder or speed air travel.

jettison (JET-uh-suhn), *v.* to drop materials from a ship, aircraft, or other vessel in motion in order to reduce load, as in an emergency.

joint, *n.* **1.** in anatomy, the junction of 2 bones, particularly such a junction permitting motion;

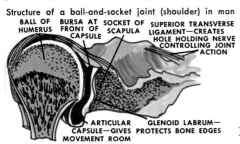

Structure of a ball-and-socket joint (shoulder) in man

BALL OF HUMERUS — BURSA AT FRONT OF CAPSULE — SOCKET OF SCAPULA — SUPERIOR TRANSVERSE LIGAMENT—CREATES HOLE HOLDING NERVE CONTROLLING JOINT ACTION

ARTICULAR CAPSULE—GIVES MOVEMENT ROOM — GLENOID LABRUM— PROTECTS BONE EDGES

see **ball-and-socket joint, hinge joint, skeletal system. 2.** in geology, a crack in rocks at the earth's surface due to expansion and contraction beneath the surface.

joule (JOOL, JOWL), *n.* the unit of work in the mks system: 0.7376 foot-pounds or 10 million ergs; work done by a one-neutron force in moving a body one meter in the direction in which the force is applied.

Joule-Thomson effect, the change in temperature which occurs when a gas is forced through a small opening when the pressure of the gas is different on each side; used to liquefy gases, particularly in the manufacture of liquid air and the production of liquid oxygen and nitrogen from liquid air.

Juglandales (juh-gluhn-DAY-leez), *n.* an order of dicot deciduous trees and shrubs with compound, pinnate leaves and bearing nut fruit in a leathery husk formed from fused bracts. The

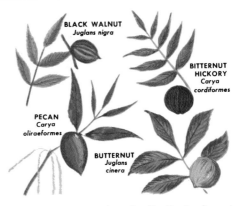

BLACK WALNUT
Juglans nigra

BITTERNUT HICKORY
Carya cordiformes

PECAN
Carya oliraeformes

BUTTERNUT
Juglans cinera

only family is the walnut family (*Juglandaceae*) of walnut, hickory, pecan, and butternut which yield valuable timber and edible nuts.

jugular (JUHG-yuh-luhr), *adj.* relating to the neck or throat, as the *jugular* vein.

junction JUHNK-shuhn), *n.* a point at which 2 or more objects meet; especially applied to diodes or transistors which use the barrier between 2 regions of opposite conductivity to produce the effect of a rectifier.

jungle (JUHN-guhl), *n.* a thick region of vegetation in tropical areas characterized by dense undergrowth.

Juno (JOO-noh), *n.* **1.** one of the largest asteroids, having a diameter of about 120 miles; its orbit is between that of Mars and Jupiter. **2.** any of a series of relatively small American booster rockets used until 1960 to launch satellites.

Jupiter (JOO-pi-tuhr), *n.* **1.** the largest of the sun's planets, with a diameter of about 85,000 miles, about 11 times that of Earth, and an average distance of 485 million miles from the sun; the fifth planet from the sun, only one-fourth as dense as Earth. **2.** an intermediate range ballistic missile, with range of over 1,500 miles; replaced by *Polaris.*

Jurassic (juh-RAS-ik), *n.* a geologic period of the Mesozoic era that began about 185 million years ago and lasted about 45 million years; reptiles were the major animal life; see **geologic time table.**

k, an abbreviation for **kilogram.**

K, 1. symbol for **potassium** (from Latin, *kalium*). **2.** abbreviation for **Kelvin.**

kaleidoscope (kuh-LY-duh-skohp), *n.* a tube with loose colored particles between 2 glass sheets at one end, and with 2 mirrors running the length of the tube, usually at an angle of 30° to each

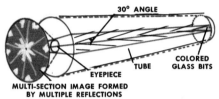

30° ANGLE

COLORED
GLASS BITS
TUBE
EYEPIECE
MULTI-SECTION IMAGE FORMED
BY MULTIPLE REFLECTIONS

other; when an observer looks through an eyepiece and turns the tube, symmetrical colored patterns are seen.

kangaroo (kan-guh-ROO), see **Marsupialia.**

kaolin (KAY-uh-luhn), *n.* a fine, white to gray clay composed of hydrous aluminum silicates; used as a filler, and for rubber, ceramics, and cement; also called *China clay.*

karat (KAIR-uht), *n.* a unit for measuring the purity (fineness) of gold, equal to 1/24 of the total, so that 24-*karat* gold is pure; contrast with **carat.**

keel, *n.* **1.** the median ventral projection of the sternum (breastbone) in flying birds and a few flightless birds to which wing muscles are attached. **2.** a similar projection on the hull of a boat that serves in balance. **3.** the common name for constellation Carina.

keloid (KEE-loyd), *n.* **1.** a type of fibrous tumor which forms hard, irregular, clawlike outgrowths on the skin. **2.** a typical scar formed after flesh burns, with thick, fibrous tissue.

kelp, see **Phaeophyta.**

Kelvin (KEL-vuhn), *adj.* referring to or based on a temperature scale in which absolute zero (−273.16°C) is 0° and the freezing point of water is 273.16°. Temperatures given in degrees Kelvin can be converted into degrees centigrade by subtracting 273.16. The scale is especially important in thermodynamics and cryogenics; named for Lord Kelvin; also called *absolute scale. abbr.* **K.**

Kennelly-Heaviside layer, an alternate term for **ionosphere.**

Keplerian trajectory (kep-LUHR-ee-uhn), the path of a body whose motion obeys Kepler's 3 laws of planetary motion; a regular ballistic path.

Kepler's laws (KEP-luhrz), laws of motion of the planets in the solar system, stated by Johannes Kepler, German astronomer: **1.** the planets revolve about the sun in elliptical orbit, with the sun as one focus. **2.** a planet's motion is fastest when it is nearest the sun, slowest when farthest away. **3.** the square of a planet's period of revolution about the sun is proportional to the cube of its average distance from the sun.

keratin (KAIR-uh-tin), *n.* an almost insoluble protein material present in the external layers of the skin of reptiles, birds, and mammals, from which nails, horns, claws, hoofs, and scales are formed. *adj.* **keratinous.**

kernel (KUHR-nuhl), *n.* **1.** a single seed, usually of a cereal grain. **2.** the soft, innermost portion of a nut or drupe.

kerosene (KAIR-uh-seen), *n.* a mixture of hydrocarbons distilled from petroleum; boiling range, 150-300° C; used as fuel for heating and jet engines, and as solvent; also spelled **kerosine.**

ketone (KEE-tohn), *n.* any of a group of organic compounds containing the carbonyl radical and with the general formula RCOR (where R stands for hydrocarbon radicals), as acetone, CH_3COCH_3. Naturally occurring ketones in plants and a few animals are important in flavoring and perfumery.

kg, an abbreviation for **kilogram.**

kidney (KID-nee), *n.* either of 2 solid, bean-shaped, glandular organs; consists of masses of tubes and nephrons; main function is the excretion of nitrogenous wastes in urine; see **excretory system, nephron.**

kilo, short for **kilogram.**

kilo-, a word part meaning *thousand.*

kilocycle (KIL-oh-sy-kuhl), *n.* a unit of wave frequency used in standard-band radio: 1,000 cycles per second.

kilogram (KIL-uh-gram), *n.* the basic unit of weight in the meter-kilogram-second system of units: the mass of the international kilogram, a platinum-iridium cylinder held at Paris, France; thus, 1 gram would be 1/1000 of the international kilogram. *abbr.* **kg** or **k.**

kilowatt-hour (KIL-uh-waht), a unit of electrical energy: the amount expended by 1,000 watts of power for one hour.

kindling temperature, the lowest temperature at which a combustible substance will catch fire and continue to burn; differs with various substances; also called *ignition point.*

SAMPLE KINDLING TEMPERATURES OF COMMON MATERIALS
(specific temperature depends on volatile impurities)

Acetylene, 580°F (304.4°C)	Hardwood, 400°F−550°F (204°C−288°C)
Benzene, 1000°F (537.8°C)	Hydrogen, 1070°F (576.7°C)
Coal, Anthracite, 900°F (482.2°C)	Kerosene, 500°F (260°C)
Coal, Bituminous, 700°F (371.1°C)	Paper, 220°−290°F (104°−143°C)
Coal gas, 1200°F (648.9°C)	Red phosphorus 495°F (257.2°C)
Gasoline, 600°F (315.5°C)	Softwood, 280°−300°F (138°−149°C)

kinematics (kin-uh-MAT-iks), *n.* the mathematical description of any object's motion as related to time; a branch of physics.

kinescope (KIN-uh-skohp), *n.* **1.** the picture tube of a television receiver, consisting basically of an electron gun which beams electrons to a fluorescent screen, scanning the screen at the same rate as the transmission equipment; produces a light image in a process that is the reverse of the production of an electron image during transmission; see also **image orthicon. 2.** a motion picture made from the images on the picture tube, seldom used now because of magnetic tape pictures.

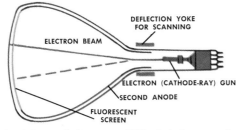

DEFLECTION YOKE FOR SCANNING
ELECTRON BEAM
ELECTRON (CATHODE-RAY) GUN
SECOND ANODE
FLUORESCENT SCREEN

kinesiology (kuh-nees-ee-AHL-oh-jee), *n.* the study of the muscles of the human body and their relationships to movement and exercise.

kinesthetic sense (kin-uhs-THET-ik), a sense especially noted inside tendons, joints, and muscle tissue, that indicates position and detects motion in relation to surroundings; the sense communicates by nerves from the organs involved; also called *muscle sense.*

kinetic (kuh-NET-ik), *adj.* relating to the motion of substances.

kinetic energy, the energy a system has due to its motion; the energy in water flowing over a dam is *kinetic;* contrast with **potential energy.**

kinetic theory, an explanation of the behavior of substances in terms of temperature and pressure; based on all matter consisting of molecules in motion, with the motion becoming more rapid as the temperature increases; also called *kinetic molecular theory.*

king crab, an alternate name for **horseshoe crab.**

kingdom, *n.* the largest taxonomic division of living organisms, dividing them into 2 large groups: the plants (kingdom *Plantae*) and the animals (kingdom *Animalia*).

kingfisher, see **Coraciiformes.**

kiwi (KEE-wee), see **Apterygiformes.**

klieg light (KLEEG), a carbon-arc lamp used for its intense light.

klystron tube (KLY-strahn), a vacuum tube in which electrical fields cause bunching of electrons; used in ultra-high frequency transmission.

knot (NAHT), *n.* **1.** in navigation, a unit of speed equal to one nautical mile (6,076 ft.) per hour. **2.** a cross section of a branch showing on a surface of wood cut from the main stem. **3.** an abnormal growth on trees caused by a fungus.

Kr, symbol for **krypton.**

krypton (KRIP-tahn), *n.* a rare chemical element in the noble-gas family; colorless and odorless; used to fill luminous sign tubes; symbol Kr; *at. no.,* 36; *at. wt.,* 83.80; first identified by Ramsay and Travers in 1898.

kurchatovium, *n.* chemical element. *at no.,* 104; *at. wt.,* 260; discovered by Soviet scientists in 1964.

kymograph (KY-muh-graf), *n.* a device for tracing a record of motion or pressure on paper; useful especially in physiology for recording chest, heart, or even arterial, movement.

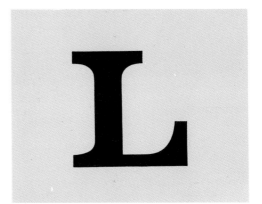

La, symbol for **lanthanum.**

labradorite (LAB-ruh-doh-ryt), *n.* a variety of plagioclase feldspar; gray with iridescent luster; see **feldspar.**

labyrinth (LAB-uh-rinth), *n.* the intricate passages of the inner ear, divided into the *osseous* (bony) labyrinth and the *membranous* labyrinth, inside the osseous; a fluid called *perilymph* separates the 2, and one called *endolymph* is

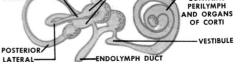

SEMICIRCULAR CANALS—PLANES AT RIGHT ANGLES TO EACH OTHER
SUPERIOR
AMPULLAE
COCHLEA—CONTAINS PERILYMPH AND ORGANS OF CORTI
VESTIBULE
POSTERIOR
LATERAL
ENDOLYMPH DUCT

contained in the membranous labyrinth; it controls the equilibrium of the body and adjusts to motion.

lac, *n.* a resinous material deposited by a scale insect on various trees in southern Asia; used in manufacturing shellac, varnishes, sealing wax, and a red coloring material.

laccolith (LAK-uh-lith), *n.* a thick, dome-shaped intrusion of igneous rock; has a flattened bottom; see **intrusion.**

lacerate (LAS-uh-rayt), *v.* to mutilate by tearing; to scrape unevenly, as to *lacerate* the skin.

lacrimal gland (LAK-ruh-muhl), a tear-secreting gland located at the inside edge of the eye; tears keep the eye lubricated and wash out dust.

lactase (LAK-tays), *n.* an enzyme found in both animals and yeasts that breaks down lactose into glucose and galactose.

lactation (lak-TAY-shuhn), *n.* **1.** the production of milk by a female mammal. **2.** the period during which milk is produced. *v.* **lactate.**

lacteal (LAK-tee-uhl), **1.** *n.* one of the very small vessels located in the villi of the small intestine; carries digested fats, especially *chyle* (a whitish, fatty lymph), into the lymphatic system and then into the veins. **2.** *adj.* pertaining to or like milk.

lactic acid (LAK-tik), *n.* an odorless, yellowish, syrupy, organic acid produced in the body by glycolysis; formula, $C_2H_4(OH)COOH$.

lactogen (LAK-toh-jen), *n.* any substance which tends to produce milk formation in the mammary glands, as *prolactin,* secreted by the anterior pituitary.

lactose (LAK-tohs), *n.* the sugar present in milk; in pure form, a sweet, white crystalline or powdered disaccharide obtained from whey; used in foods and pharmaceuticals; formula, $C_{12}H_{22}O_{11} \cdot H_2O$; also called *milk sugar.*

lacuna (luh-KYOO-nuh), *n., pl.* **-nae.** in anatomy, any small gap, depression, or other pit in a structure; especially, a space occupied by separate bone cells in true bony tissue.

lag, *n.* **1.** the time between one event or phenomenon and another occurring after, as the time between one wave and another following wave; see also **hysteresis. 2.** a charge that persists in a TV camera after the image is scanned.

Lagomorpha (LAG-oh-mor-fuh), *n.* an order of mammals with 2 pairs of incisor teeth in the

(Left) White-tailed jack rabbit (a hare), *Lepus townsendi;* (center) cottontail rabbit, *Sylvilagus floridanus;* (right) American pika, *Ochotona princeps*

upper jaw, long ears, and long hind legs for jumping; *lagomorphs* include rabbits, hares, and pikas; see also **Hyracoidea.**

Lamarckianism (luh-MAHR-kee-uhn-izm), *n.* a theory of organic evolution stating that traits (physical or behavioral) of an organism are acquired because it needs them, and are inheritable. Continued inheritance depends on use of the trait; disuse leads to gradual disappearance; originated by J. Lamarck; see also **Darwinism.**

lamella (luh-MEL-uh) *n., pl.* **-mellae.** any thin plate or scale, especially those that make up the gills of mollusks and fishes, or that contain the mineral and organic matter in bony tissue.

laminar flow, 1. flow in a fluid in which the streamlines are separate along their whole length. **2.** flow without turbulence, parallel to any solid boundaries in the fluid; important in hydrodynamics and aerodynamics.

lamination (lam-uh-NAY-shuhn), *n.* **1.** a process in which thin layers of the same or different materials are united with adhesives, usually under pressure, as in making plywood. **2.** a crack in a plane parallel to the surface of sheet metal.

lamp, *n.* any device for producing artificial light; often called *bulb.*

lamprey (LAM-pree), see **Cyclostomata.**

lancelet (LAN-suh-luht), see **Cephalochordata.**

lancet (LAN-sit), *n.* a slender, pointed, 2-edged knife used in surgical operations.

land bridge, an area of land connecting great land masses which, during the course of geologic change, has disappeared, leaving the larger land masses disconnected; the Bering Strait between Asia and North America is an example.

landing gear, the wheels, or other devices (skis, pontoons, etc.) and shock absorbers that carry the weight of an aircraft during landing or takeoff.

lanolin (LAN-uh-luhn), *n.* a yellowish-white, greasy substance, mainly esters of cholesterol, obtained from sheep wool; used for ointments, cosmetics, and soap.

lanthanide series (LAN-thuh-nyd), the chemical elements with atomic numbers 58 through 71 in the periodic table; also called the *rare-earth* elements; see **periodic table.**

lanthanum (LAN-thuh-nuhm), *n.* a white, malleable, metallic chemical element in the lanthanide series; used in alloys and in salts for camera lenses; symbol La; *at. no.,* 57; *at. wt.,* 138.91; isolated by Mosander in 1839.

lapis lazuli (LAP-uhs LAZ-you-lee), see lazurite.

Laplace theory (luh-PLAHS), an alternate term for **nebular hypothesis.**

large calorie, an alternate term for **Calorie.**

larva (LAHR-vuh), *n., pl.* **larvae.** an intermediate form of many invertebrate animals that undergo metamorphosis in their development; in 4-

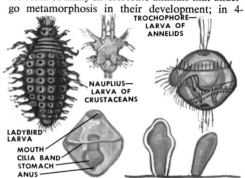

TROCHOPHORE—LARVA OF ANNELIDS
NAUPLIUS—LARVA OF CRUSTACEANS
LADYBIRD LARVA
MOUTH
CILIA BAND
STOMACH
ANUS
DIPLEURULA—HYPOTHETICAL ANCESTRAL LARVA OF ECHINODERMS
PLANULA—LARVA OF COELENTERATES

stage metamorphosis, the larva is the form hatched from the egg, which later becomes a pupa; see also **metamorphosis.** *adj.* **larval.**

laryngitis (lair-uhn-JY-tis), *n.* inflammation of the larynx, often accompanying upper respiratory infections or colds; hoarseness.

larynx (LAIR-inks), *n.* **1.** in man, the chamber or box at the upper end of the trachea containing the vocal cords; see **vocal cord. 2.** a corresponding structure in other vertebrates.

laser (LAY-zuhr), *n.* a device that filters and amplifies a visible light beam by the stimulation of

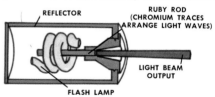

REFLECTOR
RUBY ROD (CHROMIUM TRACES ARRANGE LIGHT WAVES)
LIGHT BEAM OUTPUT
FLASH LAMP

high-energy atoms; named for *L*ight *A*mplification by *St*imulated *E*mission of *R*adiation; sometimes called an *optical maser.*

latent (LAY-tuhnt), *adj.* **1.** in biology, an alternate term for **dormant. 2.** in physics, an alternate term for **potential.**

lateral (LAT-uh-ruhl), *adj.* at or on a side: human arms are normally *lateral* to the body.

latex (LAY-teks), *n.* a milky liquid that oozes from a cut in certain plants such as dandelions, poppies, and the rubber tree; commercial source of rubber and chicle.

latitude (LAT-uh-tyood), *n.* **1.** in geography, the angular distance of any point north or south of the equator; measured in degrees from the

LEAF STRUCTURES AND TYPES

equator, at 0°. Latitudes can be shown as parallel lines around the earth. **2.** in astronomy, the angular distance of a star or planet measured from the plane of the earth's movement around the sun.

lattice (LAT-uhs), *n.* the way in which atoms are arranged to form a crystal; a 3-dimensional arrangement of points specific for each crystalline substance; important in semiconductor devices where one atom in the crystal lattice is replaced by an impurity atom.

launch (LAWNCH), **1.** *n.* the very first motion of a satellite or rocket from rest. **2.** *v.* to initiate takeoff of a rocket or missile.

launch vehicle (VEE-uh-kuhl), the carrier which thrusts a space vehicle or satellite from Earth to its orbit position, often consisting of several stages which drop off.

laurel family (LAWR-uhl) see **Ranales.**

lava (LAH-vuh), *n.* **1.** fluid, hot rock flowing from a volcano during eruption or from a crack in the earth in a volcanic region. **2.** such igneous rock after cooling and solidifying.

law, *n.* in science, any statement of the relationship between observable things or events, usually regarded as an unchanging description of relationships.

lawrencium law-REN-see-uhm), *n.* a radioactive element, last in the actinide series; the most recent of the man-made elements; symbol Lw; *at. no.,* 103; mass number of most stable isotope, 257; produced in 1961 by Ghiorso, Sikkeland, Larsh, and Latimer.

laxative (LAKS-uh-tiv), *n.* a substance or drug that causes the bowels to be evacuated.

lazurite (LAZ-yuh-ryt), *n.* a deep-blue, lustrous mineral silicate of aluminum and sodium with sulfur; has hardness 5-5½; makes up the main part of lapis lazuli, a semiprecious stone.

lb., abbreviation for **pound.**

leaching (LEE-ching), *n.* the process of removing either good or harmful products from soil by the slow draining, solvent-action of a liquid.

lead (LED), *n.* a soft, gray, metallic chemical element; heavy, malleable, and ductile; used for metal products such as pipes, chemicals (as tetraethyl lead), and pigments (as red lead); symbol Pb; *at. no.,* 82; *at. wt.,* 207.19; known since early Roman days.

lead acetate, a poisonous white, crystalline compound; used in medicines and as a mordant in dyeing textiles; formula, Pb $(C_2H_3O_2)_2 \cdot 3H_2O$.

leading edge (LEED-ing), the part of an airfoil that first contacts the air; see **airfoil.**

lead poisoning, illness caused by eating of or extensive skin exposure to lead, its compounds, or lead-containing mixtures such as certain paints. Symptoms are varied, involving digestive and blood disorders; also called *plumbism.*

leaf, *n., pl.* **leaves.** one of the usually green, expanded stem outgrowths on a plant, consisting of a variously shaped *blade* usually borne on a slender stalk or *petiole;* carries the chlorophyll that makes it a "factory" for photosynthesis; regulates exchange of gases in the plant; carries on transpiration.

leaf margin, the outer edge of a leaf which may be lobed, serrated, smooth, undulated, parted, or combinations; useful in identification.

leap year, a year of 366 days which occurs every 4th year except century years that are not divisible by 400; necessary to keep the calendar in phase with the seasons since one revolution of Earth is nearer 365¼ days than 365.

leech, see **Annelida.**

legume (LEG-yoom), *n.* **1.** any plant of the pea family, particularly those used for food or soil improvement. **2.** the dry, pod-shaped fruit of plants of the pea family which splits open along 2 sides when ripe. *adj.* **leguminous.**

lemur (LEE-muhr), see **Primates.**

lens, *n., pl.* **lenses.** any object through which light can pass, especially: **1.** a transparent, nearly spherical body in the eye that focuses light rays; see **eye. 2.** an artificial body (of glass or

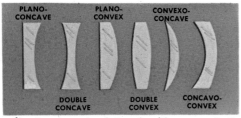

other transparent substance) with one or both sides curved, through which light rays are passed to control their point of focus; see **concave, convex.**

lenticel (LEN-tuh-sel), *n.* any of the small pores through the cork layer of woody plants; serves as pore for gaseous exchange.

Leo (LEE-oh), *n.* the *Lion,* a constellation of the zodiac best seen in late spring and early summer. The bright star Regulus is the lion's front paw; see also **Regulus.**

Leonids (LEE-uh-nids), *n.* meteoric showers that appear near constellation Leo; visible in November with special brightness every 33 years.

lepidolite (leh-PID-uh-lyt), *n.* a mica-type mineral, commonly lilac or rose; see **mica.**

Lepidoptera (lep-uh-DAHP-tuh-ruh), *n.* an order of insects with 2 pairs of wings partially covered with small scales, and sucking mouths in the adult stage and chewing mouth parts in the larva; complete metamorphosis; includes butterflies, moths, and skippers; over 100,000 known species. *adj.* **lepidopterous.**

leprosy (LEP-ruh-see), *n.* a chronic, infectious disease caused by a bacillus; characterized by lack of pain, red-brown ulcers, patches of thickened skin, and gradual death of infected tissues. Unless treated, the patient may suffer from loss of fingers and toes; also called *Hansen's disease.*

lesion (LEE-zhuhn), *n.* any injury or wound; a diseased area, or area of tissue breakdown.

lethal (LEE-thuhl), *adj.* **1.** deadly; fatal. **2.** pertaining to, or capable of causing, death: a *lethal* gene may, if its character is expressed, cause the organism's death.

leucine (LOO-seen), *n.* an essential amino acid produced by hydrolysis of proteins during pancreatic digestion; occurs as white crystals; used in biological research; formula, $C_6H_{13}NO_2$.

leucite (LOO-syt), *n.* a white to gray, lustrous mineral found in cavities of basalt, $K(AlSi_2O_6)$, with hardness 5½-6.

leucocyte (LOO-coh-cyt), medical name for **white corpuscle.**

leucoplast (LOO-koh-plast), *n.* one of the colorless bodies within plant cells acting as centers of starch formation; found in storage cells of roots and underground stems of plants.

leukemia (loo-KEE-mee-uh), *n.* a generally fatal disease that attacks bone marrow; symptoms include unusually large numbers of white cells, anemia, general weakness, fever, and enlargement of the spleen and lymphatic glands.

lever (LEV-uhr, LEE-vuhr), **1.** *n.* a simple machine used to multiply force in moving or holding a weight; consists of a bar along which force is exerted at one point, the weight is at a second point, and the bar pivots or rotates at a third point called the *fulcrum.* Levers are grouped into 3 classes according to the positions of these 3

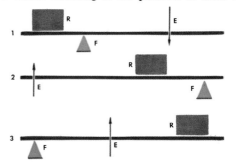

First class lever (1): fulcrum (F) between weight, or resistance (R), and effort (E), or force; 2nd class (2): R between E and F; 3rd class (3): E between F and R

points. Baseball bat, crowbar, and nutcracker are examples of levers. **2.** *v.* to move something with a lever.

Leyden jar (LY-duhn), a glass jar covered with a thin metal foil inside and out, used chiefly to demonstrate the action of a capacitor.

Li, symbol for **lithium.**

Libra (LY-bruh, LEE-), *n.* the *Balance,* a constellation of the zodiac, best seen in the spring; has no conspicuous features or bright stars.

libration (ly-BRAY-shuhn), *n.* the irregular movement of a planet or satellite in its orbit.

lichen (LY-kuhn), *n.* a symbiotic partnership of 2 kinds of plants, an alga and a fungus; the greater part of the lichen is composed of hyphae

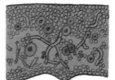

Microscopic cross section of a lichen; chlorophyll-bearing algae are scattered through mycelia filaments of the fungus

from the fungus; the plant is a tiny perennial growing in crustlike patches or bushlike forms on rocks, trees, or ground; see also **symbiosis.**

life cycle, the course of development of an organism from the fertilization of the egg to the formation of a new generation of new germ cells; life history: birth, growth, reproduction, and death.

life science, the study of life; see **biology.**

life support system, the complete installation needed to maintain human life outside the earth's atmosphere; the typical system for the moon might include control, ecological, laboratory, and maintenance sections.

lift, *n.* the force perpendicular to the relative wind which keeps an airfoil airborne even though it is heavier than air: lift occurs because air passes over the curved upper surface of an airfoil faster than it passes under the flat lower surface; pressure above the airfoil is lower than that below, and the airfoil is pushed upward; see also **airfoil.**

liftoff, *n.* takeoff, especially the initial motion taken by a missile or space vehicle on launch.

lift pump, a pump used for forcing liquids to higher levels, depending on partial vacuum created in an airtight cylinder; the liquid is forced upward through valves by differences in air pressure; maximum lift possible is about 32 feet, equivalent to atmospheric pressure; see also **force pump.**

ligament (LIG-uh-muhnt), *n.* a band of very tough tissue which connects bones or supports internal organs; may be fibrous or a fold in membranes attaching organs.

light, *n.* any electromagnetic radiation in the range between the wavelengths of infrared and ultraviolet; light is required for the eye to see; see **electromagnetic spectrum.**

lighter-than-air aircraft, see **aerostat.**

lightning, *n.* the sudden discharge of electric current through the air, visible as a bright flash of light; caused by accumulation of opposite electrostatic charges between clouds and earth or between one cloud and another.

light-year, *n.* a measure of distance used by astronomers: the distance light will travel during a year; since the speed of light is about 186,000 miles per second, a light-year is about 5,730,000,000,000 miles.

lignite (LIG-nyt), *n.* a brownish-black form of coal between the stages of peat and sub-bituminous coal; also called *brown coal.*

(1) Wild onion, *Allium cernuum;* (2) Turk's-cap lily, *Lilium superbum;* (3) dogtooth violet, *Erythronium;* (4) wild oats, *Uvularia sessilifolia;* (5) painted trillium, *T. undulatum;* (6) wild hyacinth, *Camassia scilloides*

Liliales (lil-ee-AY-leez), *n.* a large order of monocot plants with flower parts that occur in 3s or groups of 3, and a seed with fleshy or horny endosperm. Though there are 7 families, one-half of the species belong to the lily family

(*Liliaceae*), which provides food (asparagus, onion, garlic), fiber, drugs, and ornamentals (tulips, lily-of-the-valley, crocus). Some other families are the iris family (*Iridaceae*), the yam family (*Dioscoreaceae*), and the amaryllis family (*Amaryllidaceae*), which is often considered to include the agave family (*Agavaceae*).

lily family, see **Liliales.**

lime, n. **1.** in chemistry, calcium oxide, a white, powdery alkali obtained by roasting limestone; has many industrial uses in iron and steelmaking, glass and ceramics manufacture, in mortar, and as a base in neutralizing acids; formula, CaO; see **quicklime, slaked lime. 2.** loosely, any of various calcium compounds, as calcium hydroxide (*slaked lime*), calcium carbonate, etc. **3.** a small citrus tree of the rue family, and its round, green fruit.

limestone, *n.* a hard sedimentary rock composed mostly of calcite; occurs in various colors and in modified forms, as dolomite, marble; used for building stone and as a flux.

limewater, *n.* a colorless, water solution of calcium hydroxide, $Ca(OH)_2$, used in medicines, and to react with carbon dioxide, forming an insoluble calcium carbonate precipitate.

limnology (lim-NAHL-uh-jee), *n.* the study of fresh-water lakes and ponds including physical and geographical features and classification, and flora and fauna.

linden family, see **Malvales.**

lineal (LIN-ee-uhl), *adj.* **1.** referring to a line. **2.** descending in a direct line from an ancestor: Julian S. Huxley is a *lineal* descendant of Thomas H. Huxley.

linear (LIN-ee-uhr), *adj.* having the characteristics of a straight line.

linear accelerator, a particle accelerator in which a particle's speed and energy are increased by impulses from a straight-line series of alternating electric fields; may lead to a synchrotron.

linear venation, an alternate term for **parallel venation.**

lines of force, imaginary lines representing the direction of force of a magnetic field surrounding a magnet; see **magnet.**

linkage (LINK-uhj), *n.* **1.** the way in which units of any kind are joined together into a larger whole, as in the way carbon atoms are *linked* to form complex organic compounds. **2.** the tendency of 2 or more genes to stay in association in heredity, attributed to their occupying fixed and relatively neighboring positions on the same chromosome; crossing-over measures the degree of linkage; see also **sex-linkage.**

Linnaean (luh-NEE-uhn), *adj.* pertaining to the binomial (2-name) system of scientific classification of organisms devised by Carolus Linnaeus.

lipase (LY-pays), *n.* one of the enzymes produced by the pancreas, liver, and other digestive organs; converts fats and oils into glycerol and fatty acids.

lipid (LIP-uhd), *n.* any of a group of organic compounds (aliphatic hydrocarbons) including fats, oils, waxes, and steroids that are energy sources in all living tissue; also spelled **lipide.**

liquefy (LIK-wuh-fy), *v.* to change into a liquid, usually applied to condensation of gases by

liquid

reduction of temperature or increase of pressure. *n.* **liquefaction.**

liquid (LIK-wuhd), *n.* one of the 3 states of matter; the state between gas and solid; free-flowing as a gas, but denser; has definite volume as does a solid, but no definite shape. *adj.* **liquid.**

liquid hydrogen, a colorless liquid; hydrogen gas liquefied under very high pressure and below −240° C; used as a propellant for nuclear engines and in low-temperature research.

liquid measure, a system for the measurement of liquids by volume, used in the British Commonwealth and the United States. While both use the same names and quantity relationships (in general), the British imperial gallon contains 277.42 cubic inches; the U.S. gallon contains 231.00; see measurement tables on page 214.

liquid oxygen, a bluish liquid; oxygen gas under high pressure and below −118° C; used for explosives and rocket oxidants. *abbr.* **LOX.**

Listerism (LIS-tuhr-izm), *n.* a method of producing antisepsis by spraying the parts of the body undergoing surgery with carbolic acid (phenol) solution; named for the British surgeon, Sir Joseph Lister; see also **asepsis.**

liter (LEE-tuhr), *n.* the basic unit of volume (capacity) in the metric system: the space occupied by one kilogram of water at 4° C; about 1.06 U.S. quarts.

lith-, a word part meaning *stone.*

lithification (lith-uh-fi-KAY-shuhn), *n.* **1.** the formation of small, stony masses in organs such as the gall bladder, kidney, and others. **2.** the hardening of sediments into sedimentary rock.

lithium (LITH-ee-uhm), *n.* a soft, silvery, metallic chemical element; the lightest alkali metal; used as a reducing agent, to harden alloys, and in thermonuclear reactions, such as for power; symbol Li; *at. no.,* 3; *at. wt.,* 6.939; identified by Arfvedson in 1817.

lithology (lith-AHL-uh-jee), *n.* the study of mineral characteristics of rocks, usually restricted to descriptive, nonmicroscopic study; see also **petrology.**

lithosphere (LITH-uh-sfeer), *n.* the rocky outer portion of the earth, averaging about 60 miles in depth; often called the *crust* of the earth.

litmus (LIT-muhs), *n.* a product obtained from certain lichens, used as an acid-base indicator in analytical chemistry: it turns red in acid solution and blue in alkaline solution.

litter (LIT-uhr), *n.* **1.** all of the young, usually mammals, born at one time to an animal. **2.** the accumulation of dried leaves, twigs, decaying branches, seeds, and fruits (particularly dry fruits, as nuts or acorns) found on the forest floor; also called *leaf mold.*

Little Dipper, a group of stars in Ursa Minor that has the shape of a water dipper; *Polaris,* the North Star, is the end of the handle.

live-bearer, *n.* any of various fishes with females producing living young; guppies are an example; see also **ovoviviparous.**

liver, *n.* a lobed, reddish-brown, glandular organ of the digestive system of vertebrates; secretes bile, destroys worn-out red blood cells, forms nitrogenous wastes from excess protein, and ab-

sorbs products of carbohydrate digestion from the blood and stores them as glycogen; see **digestive system.**

liver fluke (LIV-uhr flook), see **alternation of hosts, Platyhelminthes.**

liverwort (LIV-uhr-wuhrt), see **Bryophyta, Hepaticae.**

lizard (LIZ-uhrd), *n.* any animal in the order *Squamata* of reptiles with short legs, long tail, eyelids, and skin covered with small scales; of varying lengths; found in many environments; includes chameleon, gecko, gila monster; see also **Reptilia.**

lizard-hipped dinosaur, see **Saurischia.**

LNG, abbreviation for *liquefied natural gas;* natural gas that has been liquefied by cooling to and maintaining at a temperature of 100° K; occupies 1/600 of the space of the same mass of gas.

load, *n.* **1.** the weight borne by any structure, or the force resulting from that weight. **2.** the power delivered by electrical equipment at any time. **3.** the power required to overcome external resistance; both power and resistance may be mechanical or electrical.

loam (LOHM), *n.* a fertile, dark soil composed of varying amounts of clay, sand, and humus.

lobar (LOH-buhr), *adj.* of a lobe, especially a lobe of the lung.

lobe (LOHB), *n.* any division of a bodily organ, or visibly separate part, as the *lobe* of the ear (the fleshy lowest part), or *lobes* of the liver, lungs, and cerebrum.

lobelia family (loh-BEEL-yuh), see **Campanulales.**

lobotomy (loh-BAHT-uh-mee), *n.* a surgical procedure involving cutting into the frontal lobes of the brain and severing nerve fibers; used in treating certain physical and mental disorders.

lobster (LAHB-stuhr), see **Crustacea.**

lockjaw, a common term for **tetanus.**

locomotion (loh-kuh-MOH-shuhn), *n.* **1.** the ability (characteristic of most animals) to change location, regardless of means used. **2.** any movement.

locus (LOH-kuhs), *n., pl.* **loci. 1.** in mathematics, the set of points lying in a surface whose positions satisfy a specified set of equations or conditions: a circle is the set of all points in a plane equidistant from a fixed point. **2.** in genetics, the specific location of a gene on a chromosome, as defined by its relation to other genes on the chromosome.

lode (LOHD), *n.* a well-defined, veinlike deposit of metal ore, usually within rock.

lodestone, see **magnetite.**

loess (LOH-uhs), *n.* an extremely fertile, fine, yellowish soil usually deposited by wind; generally rich in calcium carbonate from shells.

logania family (loh-GAN-yuh), see **Gentianales.**

longitude (LAHN-juh-tood), *n.* the angular distance of any point in degrees east or west of a prime meridian running north and south on the earth's surface; the most used prime meridian, selected as 0°, is the Greenwich meridian, and any point on the earth's surface is described in degrees east or west of the prime meridian, up to a maximum of 180°.

loon, see **Gaviiformes.**

loran (LOH-ran), *n.* a navigation system depending on the time interval between radio signals from 2 different stations at known locations; named from *Long-Range Navigation.*

lordosis (lohr-DOH-sis), *n.* a condition in which the spinal ˙column has a forward, convex curve.

lotus family, see **Ranales.**

louse (LOWS), see **Anoplura.**

low, *n.* in meteorology, an area of low atmospheric pressure.

low blood pressure, a reduction in systolic and diastolic blood pressure; may be due to numerous conditions, including inadequate blood volume; also called *hypotension.*

low-pressure center, the center of a region of low atmospheric pressure, around which air spins in a counterclockwise direction in the Northern Hemisphere; in the Southern Hemisphere, the spin is clockwise; also called *cyclone.*

LOX, abbreviation for **liquid oxygen.**

Lu, symbol for **lutetium.**

lubricate (LOO-bri-kayt), *v.* to reduce friction between 2 objects, especially using a slippery substance (*lubricant*), as oil. *n.* **lubrication.**

lumbago (luhm-BAY-goh), *n.* a condition of acute pain in the lumbar region of the back due to infection or sprain of muscles; also results from a slipped disc between vertebrae.

lumbar (LUM-bahr), see **vertebra.**

lumen (LOO-muhn), *n.* **1.** the unit of luminous flux, equal to the luminous flux through a steradian (unit solid angle) from a source of one candle. **2.** a passageway in a gland.

luminescent (loo-muh-NES-uhnt), *adj.* capable of giving off visible or invisible "cold light" (not incandescent), as light from fireflies and phosphor crystals; see also **fluorescent, phosphorescent.**

luminosity (loo-muh-NAHS-uh-tee), *n.* **1.** light; the state of being luminous. **2.** brightness, or quantity of radiant energy, especially: **a.** the energy given off by a star, a function of surface temperature and mass; expressed in ergs per second or in units based on comparison with the sun (*solar luminosity*). **b. absolute magnitude.**

luminous (LOO-muh-nuhs), *adj.* **1.** giving off, or capable of giving off, light. **2.** brightly lighted.

luminous flux, radiant flux in the visible part of the electromagnetic spectrum; see **flux.**

lunar (LOO-nuhr), *adj.* of or near the moon.

lung, *n.* either of 2 internal, saclike organs of the respiratory system, composed of many tiny chambers (*alveoli*) in a spongy mass of tissue containing muscle and elastic fibers, where oxygen and carbon dioxide are exchanged; see **respiratory system.**

lungfish, *n.* any of various fishes with an air bladder serving as a lung, in addition to gills; see **Osteichthyes.**

luni-, a word part meaning *moon.*

lunisolar (loo-nuh-SOH-luhr), *adj.* of or caused by both the sun and the moon, as *lunisolar precession,* that part of the precession of the equinoxes due to the combined action of sun and moon.

luster (LUHS-tuhr), *n.* a glow occurring by reflecting light, as minerals with a *metallic luster;* a gleaming appearance. *adj.* **lustrous.**

luteinizing hormone (LOOT-ee-uhn-eyz-ing), one of the secretions from the anterior pituitary lobe that stimulates the development of a hormone-secreting ovarian structure, the *corpus luteum,* forming in empty follicles after ovulation; see also **graafian follicle.**

lutetium (loo-TEE-shee-uhm), *n.* a silvery, metallic chemical element, the heaviest member of the lanthanide series; symbol Lu; *at. no.,* 71; *at. wt.,* 174.97; first isolated by Urbain in 1906; also spelled **lutecium.**

lux (LUHKS), *n.* a unit for measuring illumination; the amount of illumination received on a surface one meter from a unit light source; equal to 0.0929 foot-candle.

Lw, symbol for **lawrencium.**

Lycopsida (ly-KAHP-suh-duh), *n.* a subdivision of tracheophyte plants containing the club mosses; a *lycopsid* has clublike clusters of sporo-

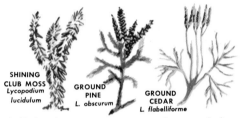

SHINING CLUB MOSS *Lycopodium lucidulum*   GROUND PINE *L. obscurum*   GROUND CEDAR *L. flabelliforme*

phylls bearing spore cases; no real economic importance but advanced structures over psilopsids show evolutionary trends; see also **Psilopsida.**

lymph (LIMF), *n.* a clear, yellowish fluid derived from blood plasma that has filtered through the blood capillaries into the tissues; minus red corpuscles and any of the proteins with molecules too large to diffuse through capillary walls; supplies nourishment to tissues.

lymphatic system (lim-FAT-ik), a system of vessels that supplements the blood system in vertebrates; collects and carries lymph from the tissues and returns it to veins for circulation.

lymph gland, any of the glandlike bodies, or nodes, occurring in the lymphatic vessels, which remove toxic and infectious bacteria from lymph and produce lymphocytes; also called *lymph node* or *lymphatic gland.*

lymphocyte (LIM-fuh-syt), *n.* a type of white blood cell or leucocyte produced by lymph glands and other lymphoid tissue such as the spleen and tonsils; numbers in the blood increase greatly in certain diseases.

Lyra (LY-ruh), *n.* the *Lyre,* a northern constellation, best seen in the summer; contains Vega, fifth brightest star in the sky in visual magnitude, as one of its features.

lyrebird, see **Passeriformes.**

lyse (LYS, LYZ), *v.* to undergo disintegration, or to cause to undergo disintegration, used especially of cells. *n.* **lysis.**

lysin (LY-suhn), *n.* any substance that causes lysis of cells.

lysine (LY-seen), *n.* an amino acid essential for animal nutrition; formula, $C_6H_{14}N_2O_2$.

lysosome (LY-soh-sohm), *n.* a type of microscopic, variously shaped body or organelle in animal cells; contains digestive enzymes and functions in cellular digestion.

m, abbreviation for **meter.**

MA, abbreviation for **mechanical advantage.**

machine (muh-SHEEN), *n.* any device used to do work by increasing force or changing its direction or increasing speed; all machines are based on 6 simple kinds: lever, wheel and axle, pulley, inclined plane, screw, and wedge.

machine-tool computer, a computer used to control machine tools; controls an entire machining process from feeding in raw materials to packaging finished parts, and also signals when more raw materials are required or repair is needed; may be self-repairing for certain faults.

Mach number (MAHK), the ratio of an object's speed to the speed of sound: *Mach 1* applies to objects at the speed of sound; *Mach 2,* to objects moving at twice the speed of sound, etc.

mackerel sky (MAK-uh-ruhl), a sky overcast with altocumulus or cirrocumulus clouds in a rippled pattern like the dorsal scales of the mackerel.

macro-, a word part meaning *large.*

macronucleus (mak-roh-NOO-klee-uhs), *n.* a large nucleus occurring in many one-celled organisms, usually accompanied by one or more small nuclei.

madder family, see **Rubiales.**

Magdalenian (mag-duh-LEE-nee-uhn), *adj.* belonging to an Upper Paleolithic culture, 10,000 to 20,000 B.C., when man used refined flint tools, and showed advanced painting techniques.

Magellanic cloud (maj-uh-LAN-ik), either of the 2 nebulous galaxies nearest to the Milky Way, easily seen by eye from the Southern Hemisphere.

maggot (MAG-uht), *n.* the legless, soft-bodied larva of certain 2-winged flies in order *Diptera;* feeds on decaying organic matter.

magma (MAG-muh), *n.* **1.** rock inside the earth, able to move; comprises both solid and liquid material; solidification of magma forms igneous rock. **2.** any thin, pasty mass.

magnesia (mag-NEE-shuh, -zhuh), *n.* a pure form of magnesium oxide, MgO, a tasteless, white powder, insoluble in water; used in high-temperature ceramic materials, electrical insulation, and medicines.

magnesium (mag-NEE-zee-uhm), *n.* a grayish-white, metallic chemical element; very reactive and light; easily machined; used in lightweight alloys for airplane construction, and as a reducing agent; symbol Mg; *at. no.,* 12; *at wt.,* 24.312; first identified by Black in 1775 and isolated by Davy in 1808.

magnet, *n.* **1.** any body that will attract iron, nickel, or cobalt, and produce a magnetic field outside itself; the property (*magnetism*) is believed to be caused by electron rotation that is not compensated. **2.** any piece of iron, steel, etc., in which magnetism has been induced; see also **electromagnet.**

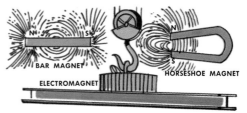

magnetic compass (mag-NET-ik), a needle or bar of iron or steel which has been magnetized; if freely suspended, one end will point north and the other south; used for navigation; see also **gyrocompass.**

magnetic dip, the angle that a freely suspended magnet makes with the horizontal at a particular place; especially, the angle such a magnet makes when its magnetic axis is lined up with Earth's magnetic field; dip will be 90° at a magnetic pole; also called *magnetic inclination.*

magnetic field, the space near any magnet, which has lines of magnetic force through it; electric currents also generate magnetic fields.

magnetic flux, the number of magnetic lines of force passing through a specific area.

magnetic north, the direction in which a magnetic compass points, toward the magnetic North Pole, at some distance from the geographic North Pole and moving a little each year.

magnetic storm, an abrupt and appreciable disturbance of a magnetic field in space; thought to be responsible for sunspots and other disturbances on the sun; may affect radio reception.

magnetite (MAG-nuh-tyt), *n.* a black mineral composed of iron oxide, Fe_3O_4, and impurities, with hardness 6; dull to metallic luster; often magnetic; an ore of iron; also called *lodestone,* when it has magnetic polarity.

magneto (mag-NEE-toh), *n.* an alternating-current generator with a permanent magnet in the rotor; used on aircraft, formerly in automobile engines, to supply high voltages to spark plugs that ignite fuel.

magnetoelectricity (mag-nee-toh-ee-lek-TRIS-i-tee), *n.* electricity induced by magnetic forces.

magnetometer (mag-nuh-TAHM-uh-tuhr), *n.* an instrument for measuring the strength, and frequently direction, of a magnetic field, usually by measuring torque exerted on a suspended magnet.

magnetron (MAG-nuh-trahn), *n.* a 2-element vacuum tube with electron flow controlled from the outside by an applied magnetic field; used in microwave power generation.

magnification (mag-ni-fi-KAY-shuhn), *n.* the enlarged size that an object seems to be when viewed through a lens or lens system, as through a microscope or telescope.

magnify (MAG-ni-fy), *v.* to make an object appear larger, especially when using some lens or combination of lenses.

magnitude (MAG-ni-tood), *n.* **1.** extent of, or degree to which, a property occurs. **2.** the measure of a star's brightness, either as it appears from Earth in relation to other stars, or in absolute terms; see **absolute magnitude, visual magnitude.**

magnolia family (mag-NOHL-yuh), see **Ranales.**

mahogany family (muh-HAHG-uh-nee), see **Geraniales.**

maidenhair tree, alternate name for **ginkgo.**

main-sequence star (SEE-kwents), any of about 90% of all stars when represented on a graph according to absolute magnitude and spectral class; all stars except white dwarfs, supergiants, and most giants fall into a broad, continuous band, the *main sequence;* our sun occurs near the middle. The graph is called a *Hertzsprung-Russell diagram* for the astronomers who first introduced it; see also **absolute magnitude, spectral class.**

mal-, a word part meaning *badly, poorly.*

malachite (MAL-uh-kyt), *n.* a deep-green, copper-containing mineral with hardness 4; basic copper carbonate; often found with *azurite.*

malar (MAY-luhr), *adj.* **1.** of the cheek, or the region around the cheekbone. **2.** the cheekbone or *zygomatic* bone.

malaria (muh-LAIR-ee-uh), *n.* a disease caused by infection with parasitic protozoans *(plasmodia)* transmitted to man, monkeys, birds, fish, and cattle by bite of an infected mosquito; symptoms include recurrent chills, fever, and sweating.

male, *adj.* **1.** in animals, belonging to the sex that produces germ cells capable of fertilizing the ovum of the female and thus starting new individuals. **2.** in plants, relating to any reproductive structure involved in the production of germ cells for fertilization of the related female reproductive structure. *n.* **male.**

male flower, see **flower.**

malignant (muh-LIG-nuhnt), *adj.* describing any disease or infection that is quite serious and may rapidly grow worse or more wide-spread; used especially of tumors (often fatal) that spread to other tissues; contrast with **benign.**

malleable (MAL-ee-uh-buhl), *adj.* able to be worked without breaking; especially, able to be hammered or pressed into shape; used in describing metals.

malleus (MAL-ee-uhs), *n.* a small bone in the ear of many animals, commonly called *hammer;* see **ear.**

mallow family (MAL-oh), see **Malvales.**

malnutrition (mal-noo-TRISH-uhn), *n.* any condition in which the organism does not receive the proper amounts of the proper foods for normal functioning; may be caused by inadequate or improper diet or metabolism disorders.

malocclusion (mal-uh-KLOO-zhuhn), *n.* a condition in which the teeth of upper and lower jaws do not make proper biting or chewing contact when they are together.

Malpighian tube (mal-PIG-ee-uhn), any of several small, tubular outgrowths of the alimentary canal functioning as excretory organs of insects, spiders, and certain other invertebrates.

maltose (MAWL-tohs), *n.* a sweet, colorless, crystalline, disaccharide sugar obtained by enzymatic action of amylase on starch; used as a nutrient and sweetener; formula, $C_{12}H_{22}O_{11} \cdot H_2O$.

Malvales (mal-VAY-leez), *n.* an order of dicot woody shrubs and trees with usually monoecious flowers (bearing both pistils and stamens) that have 5 sepals and petals. Among the 5 families are the mallow family *(Malvaceae)* which yields marsh mallow, okra, and cotton; the sterculia

(1) Musk mallow, *Malva moschata;* (2) poppy mallow, *Callurhoë involucrata;* (3) swamp rose mallow, *Hibiscus moscheutos;* (4) okra, *Hibiscus esculentus;* (5) upland cotton, *Gossypium hirsutum*

family *(Sterculiaceae),* source of chocolate; the linden family *(Tiliaceae),* including jute; and the bombax family *(Bombacaceae),* source of balsa.

Mammalia (muh-MAY-lee-uh), *n.* a class of vertebrates with warm blood, hairy bodies, mammary glands to secrete milk for feeding young, and, usually, development of young within the mother; *mammals* include man and all furry animals; see also **Marsupialia.**

mammalogy (muh-MAL-uh-jee), *n.* the scientific study of animals who suckle their young; the study of mammals.

mammary gland (MAM-uh-ree), any of the milk-secreting glands, ending in a nipple, used by female mammals for nourishment of the young.

mammoth (MAM-uth), *n.* any of various large, extinct, elephantlike animals with long, curved tusks and a hairy coat; see **Prohoscidea.**

manatee (MAN-uh-tee), see **Sirenia.**

mandible (MAN-duh-buhl), *n.* **1.** the lower jaw bone of vertebrates; the lower part of the beak in birds; see **skull. 2.** any similar structure in certain insects.

maneuverability (muh-noo-vuhr-uh-BIL-uh-tee), *n.* the ability of a vehicle to change direction rapidly and easily. In aircraft or space vehicles such direction change includes attitude.

manganese (MAN-guh-neez), *n.* a grayish-white, brittle, metallic chemical element; used chiefly to harden steel alloys and somewhat in chemicals; symbol Mn; *at. no.,* 25; *at. wt.,* 54.9380; isolated by Gahn in 1774.

manganite (MAN-guh-nyt), *n.* a dark gray to black, crystalline mineral with a metallic luster and hardness 4; composed chiefly of hydrous manganese trioxide, $Mn_2O_3 \cdot H_2O$; an ore of manganese.

mange (MAYNJ), *n.* a skin disease of animals (sometimes of man) caused by parasitic mites, resulting in scabs on the skin and hair loss.

mangrove family (MAN-grohv), see **Myrtales.**

manifold (MAN-i-fohld), *n.* a system of pipes or ducts, especially one for bringing an air-fuel mixture to an engine or for discharging the exhaust gases from an engine.

manned spacecraft, any space vehicle with people aboard it, whether they operate it or not.

manometer (muh-NAHM-uh-tuhr), *n.* any device for measuring the pressure of gases or liquids.

man-rocket, *n.* a rocket device for carrying one man with equipment, under the user's control.

mantle, *n.* **1.** a part of the body wall in mollusks, with the function of secreting the shell in those forms that have shells. **2.** the soft body wall of barnacles and similar animals. **3.** the part of the earth's interior between the lithosphere and the core. **4.** an asbestos covering for a flame that produces light by incandescence.

maple family, see **Sapindales.**

marble, *n.* a hard, granular or crystalline metamorphic variety of limestone; used as building and ornamental stone; see **limestone, rock.**

marcasite (MAHR-kuh-syt), *n.* a yellowish, lustrous mineral resembling pyrite, with hardness 6-6½; composed of iron sulfide, FeS_2; used as a source of iron and sulfuric acid.

mare, *n.* **1.** (MAY-ree), *pl.* **maria,** Latin, a *sea;* a dark spot visible on the face of the moon or of Mars. **2.** (MAIR), female of the horse family.

marine (muh-REEN), *adj.* of the sea; adapted to salt-water living; *marine* fishes are salt-water fishes, in contrast to fresh-water fishes.

marine biology, the scientific study of all living organisms occurring in the ocean.

marl, *n.* a soft mixture of limestone and clay; used as a fertilizer for adding lime to soil.

marrow (MAIR-oh), *n.* the soft matter filling the cavity of bones; contains connective tissues holding fat cells and nucleated blood cells.

Mars (MAHRZ), *n.* the third smallest planet in the solar system, and just beyond Earth in orbital position; appears as a red star; day is of almost equal length with that on Earth, but year is about 687 of our days; diameter is roughly half that of earth, but gravitational attraction is about one-third that of Earth.

marsh, *n.* an area of wet land, usually caused by poor drainage with few trees or shrubs, but various types of grasses and other plants.

marsh gas, a flammable gas produced by decaying vegetable matter in swampy regions and in coal and oil deposits; composed chiefly of methane; see also **methane.**

Marsupialia (mahr-soo-pee-AY-lee-uh), *n.* an order of mammals having a pouch on the abdomen of the female in which the young are carried and complete their development; *marsupials* include the kangaroo, opossum, koala, and others.

marsupium (mahr-SOO-pee-uhm), *n.* a pouch on the abdomen of female marsupials.

maser (MAY-zuhr), *n.* a device using the natural vibration of atoms or molecules to amplify certain electromagnetic waves; may operate in the visible light range; named for *M*icrowave *A*mplification by *S*timulated *E*mission of *R*adiation.

mass, *n.* in physics, the absolute quantity of matter in a body that is constant regardless of gravitational forces; distinguished from weight, which is affected by gravitation.

mass defect, the mass of an atomic nucleus minus the masses of its component particles; the components weigh more than the nucleus because some of the mass is converted into the energy that binds the nucleus together; sometimes considered the *atomic number* minus the *mass number.*

mass number, the number of nucleons (protons and neutrons) in the nucleus of an isotope; indicated as carbon-14 or C^{14}; contrast with **atomic number.**

mass ratio, in rocketry, the weight of a rocket with its fuel, divided by its weight after the fuel is burned.

mass spectrograph, a device that separates charged particles, sorting them according to their masses,

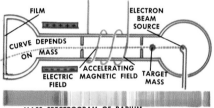

FILM   ELECTRON BEAM SOURCE

CURVE DEPENDS ON MASS

ACCELERATING MAGNETIC FIELD   TARGET MASS

ELECTRIC FIELD

MASS SPECTROGRAM OF BARIUM

in a mass spectrum much as the spectrum produced by a spectograph separates light rays into colors; important for isolating and studying isotopes of chemical elements. If the mass spectrum is recorded electrically, rather than photographically, it is called a *mass spectrometer;* see also **spectrograph.**

mass-twin, *n.* one of a particle-antiparticle pair; a particle having the same mass as another but with the opposite charge, as the positron is the mass-twin of the electron.

masticate (MAS-ti-kayt), *v.* to chew, to reduce to a pulp. *n.* **mastication.**

Mastigophora (mass-ti-GAH-fer-uh), *n.* a class of protozoans having one or more filaments

CUT-AWAY VIEW OF MARSUPIUM

OPOSSUM
Didelphis virginiana

KANGAROO
Macropus rufus

KAOLA BEAR
Phascolaretus cinereus

TASMANIAN DEVIL
Sarcophilus harrisii

TASMANIAN WOLF
Thylacinus cynocephalus

BANDICOOT
Thylacomys lagotys

KANGAROO RAT
Dipodomys ordii

STAR-NOSED MOLE
Condylura cristata

(flagella) used for locomotion; as the euglena and trypanosome; see also **Euglenophyta.**

mastodon (MAS-tuh-dahn), *n.* any of various large, extinct, elephantlike mammals characterized by nipple-like elevations of the molar teeth; some inhabited the United States; ancestors of present elephants; see **Proboscidea.**

mastoid (MAS-toyd), *n.* the nipple-like protuberance of the temporal bone behind the ear in most mammals.

materia medica (muh-TEE-ree-uh MED-i-kuh), the branch of medicine dealing with sources and preparation of drugs; see **pharmacology.**

matrix (MAY-triks), *n., pl.* **matrices** (MAY-tri-cees). **1.** in geology, the substance that surrounds a mineral, fossil, etc. **2.** in industry, a mold or die used for casting. **3.** in biology, the substance between cells of a tissue.

matter, *n.* the material particles of a substance; that which occupies space and is perceptible to natural or artificial senses; see also **mass.**

maturation (match-uh-RAY-shuhn), *n.* **1.** the process of completing natural growth and development to the adult stage. *v.* **mature.** *adj.* **mature.** **2.** the reducing divisions in the meiosis of germ cells; see **meiosis.**

maxilla (mak-SIL-uh), *n.* **1.** a bone that forms the greater part of the upper jaw in vertebrates; see **skull.** **2.** in segmented invertebrates, one of the pairs of mouth parts behind the mandibles.

maximum (MAKS-uh-muhm), *n.* **1.** the greatest quantity possible or known, as *maximum* lifespan. **2.** the highest point possible or known, as the maximum temperature. **3.** in astronomy, a variable star's magnitude while at its greatest brilliance.

maxwell, in the electromagnetic system of units, one line of magnetic force.

Md, symbol for **mendelevium.**

mean, *n.* **1.** the middle point in a series or between extremes. **2.** the arithmetic *average,* found by dividing the sum of a series of numbers by the number of items in the series.

meander (mee-AN-duhr), *n.* **1.** the turning or winding course of a stream or river; common in old valley or plain stages of erosion. **2.** the river that follows such a course.

mean solar day, the average time required for Earth to make one complete rotation on its axis with respect to the sun; defined as 86,400 seconds or 1.0027379 sidereal day.

measles, *n.* an infectious disease occurring mostly in children, caused by a virus; symptoms include fever, congestion of nose and throat, and an itchy skin rash of flat, red spots which spread over the body; complications are rare but serious; medically called *rubeola;* see also **German measles.**

measure (MEZH-uhr), **1.** *n.* **a.** the length, capacity (volume), size, quantity, etc., of anything. **b.** a standard used to determine length, etc., as a yard is a *measure* of length. **c.** a system of measure, as a linear *measure.* **2.** *v.* to determine the length, capacity, size, etc., of anything; see measurement tables on page 214.

mechanical (muh-KAN-i-kuhl), *adj.* done by a machine; automatic; relating to physical work of any kind.

mechanical advantage, 1. *actual* advantage: the ratio of resistance (or load) to effort in a simple

machine. **2.** *theoretical* advantage: the ratio of the distance the effort moves to the distance the resistance (load) moves. *abbr.* **MA.**

mechanical energy, energy present in an object *(mass)* because of its position *(potential)* or its motion *(kinetic);* measured in foot-pounds, gram-centimeters, or ergs; contrast with **radiant energy.**

mechanics (muh-KAN-iks), *n.* the study of the effect of forces on matter; divided usually into *statics,* concerned with matter at rest; and *dynamics,* concerned with matter in motion.

medial (MEE-dee-uhl), *adj.* located in the midline or middle; central.

median (MEE-dee-ahn), *adj.* pertaining to the middle or center, as the *median* score.

medical (MED-uh-kuhl), *adj.* relating to the practice of medicine.

medication (med-uh-KAY-shuhn), *n.* **1.** the application or use of substances for treatment of a disease. **2.** a substance used for curing or treating a disease.

medicinal (muh-DIS-uh-nuhl), *adj.* having the curative properties of a medicine.

medicine (MED-uh-suhn), *n.* **1.** any curative or healing substance used in treating a disease; any useful drug. **2.** the practice and science of preserving health and curing defects and disease.

medium (MEE-dee-uhm), **1.** *n.* in biology, a sterilized substance (as agar) used to grow bacteria, viruses, etc. **2.** *adj.* pertaining to the middle position or state, as of quality, size.

medulla (muh-DUH-luh), *n.* **1.** the soft, marrow-like interior of bones and organs such as the kidneys and adrenals. **2.** a region in the brain, the *medulla oblongata.* *adj.* **medullary.**

medulla oblongata (ahb-lawn-GAH-tuh), *n.* the portion of the brain with centers for controlling vital, involuntary processes such as respiration, heart action, swallowing, and others.

medullary sheath, alternate term for **myelin.**

medusa (muh-DYOO-suh), *n., pl.* **-dusae.** the body form of jellyfishes, having a soft, gelatinous, umbrella-like structure and long, trailing tentacles; see also **polyp.**

mega-, a word part meaning either *one million* or *very large.*

megacephalic (meg-uh-suh-FAL-ik), *adj.* with a larger than average (1550 cubic centimeters) cranial capacity—said of skull measurements.

megacycle (MEG-uh-sy-kuhl), *n.* in physics, a unit equal to one million cycles.

megaspore (MEG-uh-spohr), *n.* a plant spore with haploid number of chromosomes which develops into the female gametophyte.

megatherium (meg-uh-THEE-ree-uhm), *n.* any of the extinct, giant, slothlike mammals which walked on the outer edges of their feet; knuckles had long claws bent inward; about 20 feet long.

Reconstruction of a megatherium of the Pleistocene

megaton bomb

megaton bomb (MEG-uh-tun), a bomb with the same explosive force as that in one million tons of TNT, said of nuclear bombs.

meiosis (my-OH-sis), *n.* a basic type of cell division; the process of sexual cell division in which the chromosome numbers are reduced one half; produces mature, haploid spermatozoa from diploid spermatogonia in the male, and ova from oogonia in the female; complete meioses producing the ovum occurs only if the oocyte is fertilized; also called *maturation* or *reduction division;* contrast with **mitosis.** *adj.* **meiotic.**

is delicate and highly vascular; next is the spongy *arachnoid;* then the outer, tough *dura mater.*

meningitis (men-uhn-JY-tis), *n.* **1.** inflammation of the meninges. **2.** one of the diseases characterized by inflammation of the meninges and resulting in headache, stiff neck, vomiting, and often delirium and coma; frequently due to bacterial infection but may have other causes.

meniscus (men-NIS-kuhs), *n.* the curved upper surface of a liquid in a tube. It is convex when the liquid does not stick to the tube, and concave when it does stick; see **capillarity.**

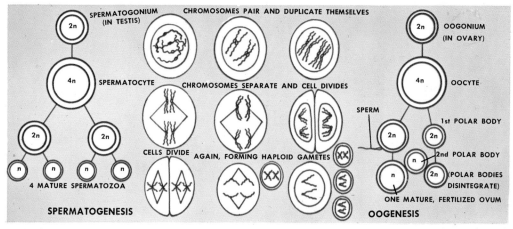

melanin (MEL-uh-nin), *n.* the dark pigment occurring in the skin and hair of man and certain other animals, as well as in some plants.

melting point, the temperature at which a substance changes from a solid to a liquid state; *abbr.* **MP** or **m.p.**

MELTING POINTS OF SOME COMMON COMPOUNDS	
Compound & Melting Pt.	Compound & Melting Pt.
Water, 32°F (−0°C)	Methyl alcohol, −144°F (−97.8°C)
Acetone, −138.6°F (−94.8°C)	
Ammonia, 171.9°F (77.7°C)	Monel metal, about 2417°F (1325°C)
Babbitt metal, about 392°F (200°C)	Naphthalene, 176.2°F (80.1°C)
Calcium carbonate, 2442.2°F (1339°C)	Paraffin wax, 134.6°F (57°C)
	Pewter, 563°F (295°C)
Carbon dioxide, −69.7°F (−56.5°C)	Soldium chloride (salt), 1473.1°F (800.6°C)
Formaldehyde, −133.6°F (−92°C)	Solder, about 410°F (210°C)
	Stainless steel, about 2642°F (1450°C)
Heavy water, 38.9°F (3.82°C)	

membrane (MEM-brayn), *n.* a thin layer of organic tissue which lines or surrounds organs and connects parts and has numerous other functions in all living organisms. *adj.* **membranous.**

mendelevium (men-duh-LEE-vee-uhm), *n.* a man-made radioactive chemical element in the actinide series; symbol Md; *at. no.,* 101; mass number of most stable isotope, 256; first made at the University of California in 1952.

Mendel's laws (MEN-duhl), the fundamental principles of heredity, discovered by Gregor Mendel, stating that pairs of factors (genes) for inherited characters separate from one another and recombine *at random* in the germ cells.

meninges (muh-NIN-jeez), *pl. n.* the 3 connective tissue membranes covering the brain and spinal cord: the *pia mater* adhering to the cord

menopause (MEN-uh-pawz), *n.* the period of irregular menstrual cycles prior to the end of all menstruation; caused by a sudden, natural decrease in ovarian hormone production; usually occurs after about 45 years in women.

menses (MEN-seez), *n.* the monthly discharge of blood and mucosal tissue from the uterus; occurs only in primates that are not pregnant; see also **estrous cycle.**

menstruate (MEN-struh-wayt), *v.* to discharge the menses (blood and cells from the tissue lining the uterus). *n.* **menstruation.**

menthol (MEN-thawl), *n.* a white, crystalline alcohol with a cool, minty odor and taste, derived from peppermint oil; used in medicines, perfumes, and flavoring; formula, $CH_3C_6H_9(C_3H_7)OH$.

Mercator projection (muhr-KAY-tuhr), a map projection made by extending every point on the earth's spherical surface onto a cylinder enclosing the sphere, then opening up the cylinder into a plane surface; the meridians become parallel lines so polar areas appear enlarged.

mecurial barometer, a barometer that shows the air pressure by the height of a column of mercury contained within it; see also **barometer.**

mercuric (muhr-KYOO-rik), *adj.* containing a mercury ion, Hg^{++}.

mercurochrome (muhr-KYOOR-uh-krohm), *n.* a red liquid used as an antiseptic; a 2 per-cent water solution of merbromin, a compound of green crystals; formula, $C_{20}H_8Br_2HgNa_2O_6$.

mercurous (muhr-KYOO-uhs), *adj.* containing a mercury ion, HG^+.

mercury (MUHR-kyoo-ree), *n.* a silvery-white, poisonous, soft metallic chemical element; a liquid at room temperature; expands and contracts uniformly with temperature change, making it useful in thermometers; also used in mercury-vapor lamps; symbol Hg; *at. no.,* 80; *at. wt.,* 200.59; known since ancient times.

Mercury, *n.* **1.** the smallest of the planets near the sun, with a diameter of about 3,000 miles; moves in orbit nearest the sun (average distance, 36,000,-000 miles); often appears as an "evening" or "morning" star; it displays phases similar to the moon since its orbit lies inside the orbit of Earth, always turning the same side toward the sun; takes about 88 days to complete one revolution about the sun. **2.** an American aerospace project, using the small, 1-man *Mercury* space capsule; used by astronauts from 1961 to 1963 in suborbital and orbital flights.

mercury-vapor lamp, a lamp operated by passage of an electric arc through a tube filled with mercury vapor; electrodes conduct current

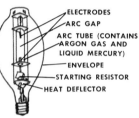

Mercury-vapor lamp: vaporized mercury emits a greenish glow, usually lacking red wavelengths

ELECTRODES
ARC GAP
ARC TUBE (CONTAINS ARGON GAS AND LIQUID MERCURY)
ENVELOPE
STARTING RESISTOR
HEAT DEFLECTOR

through argon gas, lowering resistance in the gap; an arc is set up that vaporizes mercury; tube is glass-walled if used for illumination; quartz if used as a source of ultraviolet light; often serves to convert alternating current to direct current; light is blue-green-white.

meridian (muh-RID-ee-uhn), *n.* **1.** in geography, a line running north-south on the surface of the earth and ending at the North and South poles. The *prime meridian* which passes through Greenwich, England, is the meridian from which longitudes are measured. **2.** in astronomy, a great circle passing through the poles of the heavens and cutting the equator at right angles; see also **longitude.**

meristem (MAIR-uh-stem), *n.* actively dividing cells which increase a plant in length or circumference depending upon their location; found in root tip, stem tip, and vascular and cork cambiums. *adj.* **meristematic.**

mesa (MAY-suh), *n.* a small, high, flat-topped area with steep sides, often covered with rock; usually stands alone in a plain.

mesenchyme (MEZ-uhn-kym), *n.* a diffuse tissue composed of irregularly shaped cells loosely joined in a meshlike network; forms the connecting tissues, bones, cartilage, and other special tissues in vertebrates.

mesentery (MES-uhn-tair-ee), *n.* a thin tissue lining the body cavity and attaching the intestine and other organs to the wall of the body; numerous modifications found in the various animal groups; part of the mesothelium.

meso-, a word part meaning *in the middle.*

mesocarp (MEZ-uh-kahrp), *n.* the middle layer of a pericarp in the fruit of plants; often the fleshy part of the fruit; see **fruit.**

mesoderm (MEZ-uh-duhrm), *n.* the middle germ layer occurring in the embryo of animals; such structures as muscle, connective tissue, blood

vessels, and the inner skin layer are derived from it; contrast with **ectoderm, endoderm.**

mesoglea (mez-uh-GLEE-uh), *n.* a layer of unorganized material containing specialized cells derived from the ectoderm and endoderm in hydra, jellyfish, and certain other invertebrates.

Mesolithic (mez-uh-LITH-ik), *adj.* describing the period intermediate between the Paleolithic and Neolithic cultures, about 6,000 years ago, during which man used flint tools and boats.

meson (MEZ-ahn, MEES-), *n.* any unstable nuclear particle with a mass between those of a proton and an electron; several types exist; see also **pi-meson.**

mesophyll (MEZ-uh-fil), *n.* the tissues forming the interior of leaves, consisting of the top layer of *palisade* cells and a lower layer of spongy *parenchyma.*

mesophyte (MEZ-uh-fyt), *n.* any plant growing in soils containing moderate amounts of water; most plants are mesophytes. *adj.* **mesophytic.**

mesosphere (MEZ-uh-sfeer), *n.* that portion of the earth's atmosphere above the stratopause and below the ionosphere; the region from about 20 to 60 miles above Earth, characterized by low temperatures and ozone formation.

mesothelium (mez-uh-THEE-lee-uhm), *n.* a tissue, originating from mesoderm, which lines the body cavities.

mesothorax (mez-uh-THOH-raks), *n.* the middle section of the 3 sections of an insect's thorax, to which are attached the second pair of legs and the first pair of wings.

Mesozoic (mez-uh-ZOH-ik), *n.* the geologic era of the dinosaurs, conifers, and flying reptiles, which began about 225 million years ago and lasted about 155 million years: divided into *Triassic, Jurassic,* and *Cretaceous* periods; see also **geologic time table.**

Messier-82 (MES-ee-uhr), *n.* an exploding galaxy about 10 million light years away; the oldest astronomical explosion, only recently became visible.

meta-, a word part meaning *among, after, behind, following* in many scientific words; in chemical usage, it often means *obtained by loss of water.*

metabolism (muh-TAB-uh-lizm), *n.* the sum total of the chemical processes occurring within a living organism or a single cell; includes processes which change food into protoplasm or break it down to release energy for cellular use; see also **anabolism, catabolism.** *adj.* **metabolic.**

metabolite (muh-TAB-uh-lyt), *n.* **1.** any substance produced during metabolism. **2.** any substance required so that metabolism can proceed; may be a vitamin, mineral, enzyme, etc.

metacarpal (met-uh-KAHR-puhl), *adj.* referring to several bones in the hand or forefoot of vertebrates; see **skeletal system.**

metagenesis (met-uh-JEN-uh-sis), an alternate for **alternation of generations.**

metal (MET-uhl), *n.* any of a group of chemical elements as iron, silver, copper; generally characterized as ductile, malleable, lustrous, forming positive ions, and having the ability to conduct heat and electricity. *adj.* **metallic.**

metalloid (MET-uh-loyd), *n.* an element resembling a metal, but reacting chemically as both a metal and nonmetal, as arsenic, silicon.

metallurgy

metallurgy (MET-uh-luhr-jee), *n.* the process or technology of separating metals from their ores, refining them. and preparing them for use, such as development of alloys for special purposes.

metamere (MET-uh-meer), *n.* one of the segments of the body of a worm or other segmented animal; also called *somite.*

metamorphic (met-uh-MAWR-fik), *adj.* **1.** characterized by or relating to change of form. **2.** in geology, referring to those rocks whose structure is modified by heat, pressure, or absorbed chemicals; see **rock.**

metamorphosis (met-uh-MAWR-fuh-sis), *n.* the development of an organism after birth or hatching, involving changes in form and growth and usually accompanied by a change of environment; as in some insects, *complete* metamorphosis includes egg, larva, pupa, and adult stages; *incomplete* metamorphosis includes egg, naiad, and adult stages; *gradual* metamorphosis includes the change to an adult by a newly hatched insect that resembles the adult.

GRADUAL, OR DIRECT, METAMORPHOSIS OF SILVERFISH, *Lepisma saccharina*

INCOMPLETE METAMORPHOSIS OF GRASSHOPPER, *Orchelimum vulgare*
WINGS APPEAR
MOLT

COMPLETE METAMORPHOSIS OF FROG, *Rana catesbeiana*
DEVELOPING EGG
THREE STAGES IN DEVELOPMENT OF TADPOLE
HIND LEGS APPEAR
MATURE ADULT
LUNGS AND FRONT LEGS DEVELOP
TAIL IS ABSORBED

COMPLETE METAMORPHOSIS OF MONARCH BUTTERFLY, *Danaus plexippus*
CATERPILLAR (LARVA)
PUPA OR CHRYSALIS
MATURE BUTTERFLY EMERGING FROM CHRYSALIS
MATURE BUTTERFLY (IMAGO)

metaphase (MET-uh-fayz), see **mitosis.**

metastasis (muh-TAS-tuh-sis), *n.,* *pl.* **-ses.** the transmission of microorganisms or diseased cells from one part of the body to another through blood, lymph, or membranous surfaces; commonly applied to cancerous cells. *adj.* **metastatic.**

metatarsal (met-uh-TAHR-suhl), referring to certain bones in the foot; see **skeletal system.**

metathorax (met-uh-THOHR-aks), *n.* the posterior section of the 3 sections of an insect's thorax; bears the last pair of legs.

Metazoa (met-uh-ZOH-uh), *n.* a subkingdom including all multicellular animals; all animals above the unicellular Protozoa (or, according to some authorities, above sponges) are *metazoans.*

meteor (MEE-tee-uhr), *n.* a meteoroid entering the earth's atmosphere at high speed (11 to 72 kilometers a second); it becomes white-hot from friction, and therefore visible to the naked eye; commonly called *shooting star.*

meteorite (MEE-tee-uh-ryt), *n.* a small solid that has fallen on the earth from space.

meteoroid (MEE-tee-uh-royd), *n.* any small solid body that is traveling through outer space and that becomes a *meteor* when it falls to the earth.

meteorological satellite (mee-tee-awr-uh-LAHJ-i-kuhl), an artificial satellite such as *Tiros, Aeros,* or *Nimbus,* which takes, or is planned to take,

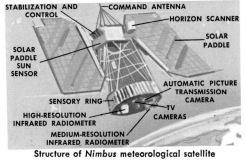

STABILIZATION AND CONTROL — COMMAND ANTENNA — HORIZON SCANNER — SOLAR PADDLE SOLAR PADDLE SUN SENSOR — SENSORY RING — HIGH-RESOLUTION INFRARED RADIOMETER — MEDIUM-RESOLUTION INFRARED RADIOMETER — AUTOMATIC PICTURE TRANSMISSION CAMERA — TV CAMERAS

Structure of *Nimbus* meteorological satellite

photographs of and relay information about weather conditions; also called *weather satellite.*

meteorology (mee-tee-uh-RAHL-uh-jee), *n.* the scientific study of the atmosphere, weather, and climate; interpretation, prediction, etc.

meter (MEE-tuhr), *n.* unit of length in the mks system of units and in the decimal (metric) system: 1,553,164.13 times the wavelength of the red cadmium spectrum in air at atmospheric pressure; in the English system, 39.37+ inches. *abbr.* **m.**

-meter, a word part indicating measurement of quantities, as in the names of devices: a *thermometer* measures heat, a *voltmeter* measures electrical pressure, an *ammeter* measures electric current.

meter-kilogram-second system, see **centimeter-gram-second system.**

methane (METH-ayn), *n.* a colorless, odorless, flammable gas, the simplest hydrocarbon; the chief part of marsh gas, natural gas, and coal gas; used as a chemical intermediate and fuel; formula, CH_4.

methane series, a group of hydrocarbons with the general formula, C_nH_{2n+2}. Methane is first of the series; also called *alkane* or *paraffin* series.

methanol (METH-uh-nawl), alternate term for **methyl alcohol.**

methyl (METH-uhl), *n.* the methane hydrocarbon radical, CH_3^-.

methyl alcohol, a colorless, flammable, poisonous organic compound; used as a chemical intermediate, solvent, and aviation fuel; formula CH_3OH; also called *wood alcohol* and *methanol.*

methylate (METH-uh-layt), **1.** *n.* any compound derived from methyl alcohol where the hydrogen attached to the oxygen is replaced by a metal ion. **2.** *v.* to mix with methyl alcohol or "denature," as mixing with ethyl alcohol in order to make it undrinkable. *n.* **methylation.**

methylene (METH-uh-leen), *n.* the hydrocarbon radical $CH_2=$.

metric system (MET-rik), a decimal (10) system of measurement; the 3 basic units are: the *meter* (39.37+ inches) for length, the *gram* (equal to 1/1000 of the international *kilogram,* or 1 cc of water at 4°C) for mass, and the *liter* (1 cubic decimeter, or 61.025 cubic inches) for volume. The basic units are converted into larger or smaller practical units by multiplying or dividing by 10s, indicated by a prefix: *myria-* = 10,000, *kilo-* = 1,000, *hecto-* = 100, *deca-* = 10, *deci-* = 1/10, *centi-* = 1/100, *milli-* = 1/1000; see measurement tables on page 214.

metrology (muh-TRAHL-uh-jee), *n.* the science concerned with weights and measures, their verification, accuracy, etc.

mev, abbreviation for *million electron volts;* see **electron volt.**

Mg, symbol for **magnesium.**

mho (MOH), *n.* the unit of electrical conductance: the conductivity of a system having a resistance of 1 ohm; the reciprocal of the ohm (and *ohm* spelled backwards).

miacis (MY-uh-sis), *n.* a prehistoric carnivore of the Paleocene, probably an early ancestor of the cat family; lived more than 55 million years ago; may have closely resembled the weasel.

mica (MY-kuh), *n.* any of a group of complex silicate minerals with varying composition; mostly found in igneous and metamorphic rocks; crystallizes in thin, clear layers; see **muscovite.**

micro-, a word part meaning *very small;* in measurements, often used to mean *one-millionth:* a *microsecond* is a millionth of a second.

microbe (MY-krohb), *n.* a germ or bacterium, particularly one causing disease; disease microorganism.

microbiology (my-kroh-by-AHL-uh-jee), *n.* the branch of biology dealing with microorganisms.

microcephalic (my-kroh-suh-FAL-ik), *adj.* referring to anyone with an abnormally small head, or to anyone with very small cranial capacity.

microfilm (MY-kruh-film), *n.* film containing information (as documents) that is reduced in size for convenient handling and storage; special apparatus enlarges it to size for viewing.

microgamete (my-kroh-guh-MEET), *n.* in reproduction, the smaller of the 2 uniting gametes, usually considered to be the fertilizing male sperm cell.

micrograph (MY-kruh-graf), *n.* **1.** a device used to write, draw, or engrave on a small scale. **2.** a device that records very slight movements of a diaphragm. **3.** a photograph or other picture of what is seen through a microscope.

micrometer (my-KRAHM-uh-tuhr), *n.* **1.** an instrument used on telescopes and microscopes for measuring tiny lengths or angles. **2.** *micrometer calipers,* calipers having a micrometer for highly accurate measurements; see also **caliper.**

micromicrocurie, *n.* a unit for expressing the activity of a radioactive material: one-millionth of a millionth of a curie; used especially in measuring fallout.

micron (MY-kron), *n.* a unit of length in the metric system equal to one millionth of a meter.

micronucleus (my-kroh-NOO-klee-uhs), *n.* a small nucleus in many one-celled organisms, usually accompanying the larger, or *macronucleus;* believed to carry the genes for inheritance.

microorganism (my-kroh-AWR-guh-nizm), *n.* a living organism so tiny that a microscope is needed for observing it.

microphone (MYK-ruh-fohn), *n.* any device for converting sound waves into electric current for transmission, recording, amplification, etc.

micropyle (MY-kruh-pyl), *n.* **1.** in some animals, a small opening in the covering of an ovum through which spermatozoa enter in fertilization. **2.** in plants, the duct formed when the integuments (outer layers which later form the seed coat) of the ovule grow beyond the ovary body; in mature seeds, a tiny opening that admits water as seed germinates.

microscope (MY-kruh-skohp), *n.* an instrument used to enlarge the image of very small objects, as the cells of an organism. It consists of a convex lens or combination of such lenses, a stand,

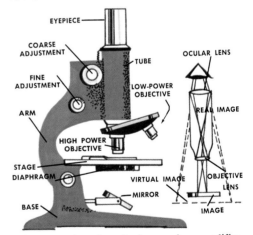

and an eyepiece for viewing; various modifications use light, electrons, fluorescence, etc.; also called *optical microscope;* see also **electron microscope, field ion microscope.**

microscopic (my-kruh-SKAHP-ik), *adj.* **1.** too small to be seen by the eye alone; refers usually to objects at least 150 millimicrons in diameter (within the range of the regular optical microscope). **2.** pertaining to a microscope.

microscopy (my-KRAHS-kuh-pee), *n.* the study of very small structures and organisms with a microscope.

microseism (MY-kruh-sy-zuhm), *n.* a small, rhythmic vibration in the earth, generally due to weather or ocean effects, that tends to interfere with proper readings on seismographs.

microsome (MY-kruh-sohm), *n.* one of the tiny granules found in the protoplasm of animal and plant cells active in the manufacture of proteins.

microspore (MY-kruh-spohr), *n.* a plant spore with haploid number of chromosomes which develops into a male gametophyte.

microtome (MY-kruh-tohm), *n.* an instrument used to cut very thin sections of tissue or other material for study under a microscope.

microwave, *n.* an electromagnetic wave with a very short wavelength, usually less than a meter; generally, those waves that are shorter than radio waves but longer than infrared waves; see **electromagnetic spectrum.**

midbrain, *n.* the middle vesicle of the brain, the *mesencephalon;* gives rise to 2 cranial nerves and has reflex centers for muscle tone.

midget (MIJ-uht), *n.* any person unusually small but well-proportioned; any unusually small form of a plant or animal; see **dwarf.**

midnight sun, the appearance of the sun above the horizon at midnight; occurs north of the Arctic Circle on June 21, south of the Antarctic Circle on December 21.

midrib, *n.* the central and usually largest vein of a leaf; internally, the vein consists of a dense mass of parenchymal cells surrounding the vascular bundles; see **leaf** picture.

migraine (MY-grayn), *n.* a severe headache, usually on one side of the head, and often accompanied by nausea and visual disturbances; cause is unknown though there are many theories.

migration (my-GRAY-shuhn), *n.* the usually periodic movement of an animal or group of animals to another place for getting food or breed-

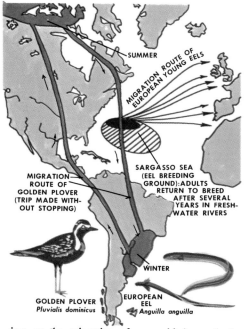

SUMMER

MIGRATION ROUTE OF EUROPEAN YOUNG EELS

MIGRATION ROUTE OF GOLDEN PLOVER (TRIP MADE WITHOUT STOPPING)

SARGASSO SEA (EEL BREEDING GROUND):ADULTS RETURN TO BREED AFTER SEVERAL YEARS IN FRESH-WATER RIVERS

WINTER

GOLDEN PLOVER
Pluvialis dominicus

EUROPEAN EEL
Anguilla anguilla

ing, as the migration of many birds south for winter, or the green turtle to sea coasts for laying eggs. *v.* **migrate.** *adj.* **migratory.**

mildew (MIL-doo), *n.* **1.** any of various parasitic fungi causing a discoloration on plants and some fabrics; *powdery* mildew and *downy* mil-

dew occur in 2 different classes; see **Ascomycetes, Phycomycetes. 2.** a plant disease caused by these parasitic fungi.

milk of magnesia, a cloudy white suspension of magnesium hydroxide, $Mg(OH)_2$, in water; used as an antacid and laxative.

milk sugar, a common term for **lactose.**

milk tooth, any of the first, temporary set of teeth in man and some other mammals; in man, there are 20 milk teeth: 4 incisors, 2 canines, and 4 molars in each jaw; all are replaced before adulthood by permanent teeth; also called *baby tooth* or *deciduous tooth;* see also **tooth.**

milkweed family, see **Gentianales.**

Milky Way, a broad, luminous band of stars that runs across the sky; consists of innumerable stars and nebulae; includes our solar system; also called *the Galaxy.*

millerite (MIL-uh-ryt), *n.* a crystalline, pale yellow mineral with a metallic luster and hardness 3-3½; consists of nickel sulfide, NiS.

milli-, word part meaning *one-thousandth.*

millibar, *n.* a meteorological unit of pressure equal to 1000 dynes per square centimeter.

millipede (MIL-uh-peed), see **Diplopoda.**

milt, *n.* the fluid secretion of male fishes containing the spermatozoa which fertilize the eggs laid by the female.

Insect mimicry: the bumblebee hawkmoth (*Hemaris diffinis*) is protected during flight by its mimicking similarity to the stinging bumblebee (genus *Bombus*)

mimicry (MIM-ik-ree), *n.* the similar appearance, in color or form, of one animal to another, or to a plant or the surroundings; usually for protection; common in insects. *v.* **mimic.**

mineral (MIN-uh-ruhl), *n.* **1.** a naturally occurring, inorganic substance with a definite chemical composition, characteristic crystalline structure, and distinctive chemical properties; see also **crystal. 2.** any naturally occurring solid substance that is not of vegetable or animal origin, such as clays and earths. **3.** loosely, any similar substance (including those of organic origin), if found in the earth, as petroleum.

mineralize, *v.* in general, to supply or to replace part or all of an object with minerals, as in fossils, *n.* **mineralization.**

mineralogy (min-uh-RAHL-uh-jee), *n.* the science that deals with minerals. *Mineralogists* may work in following branches: **crystallography—**study of crystalline minerals; **physical mineralogy—**study of physical properties that identify minerals; **chemical mineralogy—**study of the chemical composition of minerals. *adj.* **mineralogical.**

mineral oil, any colorless, tasteless oil derived from petroleum; used as a laxative and lubricant.

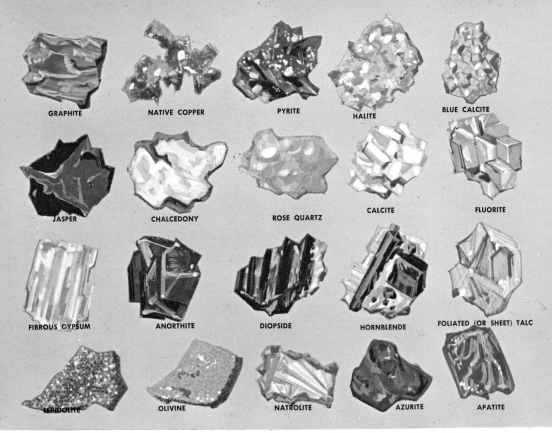

GRAPHITE   NATIVE COPPER   PYRITE   HALITE   BLUE CALCITE

JASPER   CHALCEDONY   ROSE QUARTZ   CALCITE   FLUORITE

FIBROUS GYPSUM   ANORTHITE   DIOPSIDE   HORNBLENDE   FOLIATED (OR SHEET) TALC

LEPIDOLITE   OLIVINE   NATROLITE   AZURITE   APATITE

miniaturize (MIN-ee-uh-chuh-ryz), *v.* to design and make equipment of extremely small size, usually for the sake of reduced weight, as in space vehicle construction. *n.* **miniaturization.**

minim (MIN-uhm), *n.* the smallest measure of liquid volume, equal to 1/60 of a fluid dram; about a drop.

minimum (MIN-uh-muhm), *n.* **1.** the smallest possible quantity, number, etc., as the *minimum* number of calories required per day by an adult. **2.** the lowest known degree or point, as absolute zero is *minimum* temperature. *adj.* **minimal.**

minitrack (MIN-i-trak), *n.* an electronic tracking system for following the course of a rocket or satellite by its radio signals to a series of stations on Earth.

mint family, see **Polemoniales.**

minute **1.** *n.* (MIN-uht), a measurement of time equal to 60 seconds or 1/60 of an hour. **2.** a unit equal to 1/60 of one degree of an arc. **3.** *adj.* (my-NOOT), very tiny.

Miocene (MY-uh-seen), *n.* a unit of geological time between the Oligocene and the Pliocene; the third epoch of the Tertiary Period; lasted from 20 to about 12 million years ago; characterized by the development of large mountain ranges of the world; see **geologic time table.**

mirage (mi-RAHZH), *n.* an optical phenomenon in which the observer sees unreal objects in the distance, as what appears to be blue water, when no water is present; caused by reflection of light when it strikes dense warm air near the earth's surface.

miscible (MIS-uh-buhl), *adj.* able to be mixed; used especially of the degree to which 2 or more liquids can be mixed; see also **mixture.**

missile (MIS-uhl), *n.* **1.** any object that can be thrown or projected, as a spear, arrow, or bullet;

see **projectile. 2.** any self-propelled weapon with built-in guidance and control systems; ordinarily unmanned; see also **rocket.**

missile range, a specified course over which missiles are flown for testing purposes, with observation and tracking stations on the ground.

missing link, a presumed connecting species between animals such as the ancestors of anthropoid apes and of humans; the Java man, *Pithecanthropus erectus,* is often considered a missing link.

Mississippian (mis-i-SIP-ee-uhn), *n.* a period of geologic time in North America, a phase of the Carboniferous period; began about 310 million years ago, lasted about 35 million years; conifers and ferns developed; amphibian life became fairly common; see also **geologic time table.**

mist, *n.* a mass of condensing water vapor near the earth's surface, similar to, but less dense, than fog.

mistletoe family (MIS-uhl-toh), see **Santalales.**

mistral (MIS-truhl), *n.* a cold, dry, northerly wind that blows over the Mediterranean coast of France and surrounding regions.

mite, see **Arachnida.**

mitochondrion (my-toh-KAHN-dree-ahn), *n., pl.* **-dria** (-dree-uh). any of various-shaped structures—rods, threads, and granules—found in the body of cells; functioning to release energy from digested food and storing some of it in the energy-storing compound ATP.

mitosis (my-TOH-sis), *n.* the basic type of cell division occurring in all cells except germ cells forming gametes; yields 2 daughter cells with the same number of chromosomes as the parent cell had. Mitosis consists of several stages: in *interphase,* chromosomes duplicate themselves and centrioles separate; in *prophase,* nuclear membrane breaks down, coiled chromosomes condense around centromeres and separate, centrioles form poles; in *metaphase,* chromosomes separate at the cell equator and move toward the poles (*anaphase*); in *telophase,* cytoplasm separates, nuclear membranes form, and chromosomes uncoil; process is also called *duplication division;* contrast with **meiosis.** *adj.* **mitotic.**

Stages of mitosis: resting stage or interphase (1 and 2), prophase (3 and 4), metaphase (5), anaphase (6), and telophase (7 and 8)

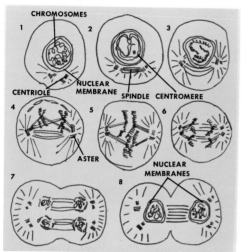

mitral valve (MY-truhl), the valve between the left atrium and ventricle of the heart; prevents blood from flowing back into the atrium; also called *bicuspid valve;* see **heart.**

mixed nerve, a nerve composed of both sensory and motor neurons; a *sensorimotor* nerve.

mixture (MIKS-tuhr), *n.* a substance containing 2 or more elements or compounds but, unlike compounds, they are not chemically united and can be separated by physical means, as air or clay.

mks system, abbreviation for *meter-kilogram-second system;* see **centimeter-gram-second system.**

Mn, symbol for **manganese.**

Mo, symbol for **molybdenum.**

moa (MOH-uh), see **Dinornithiformes.**

mock sun, an alternate term for **parhelion.**

mock-up, *n.* a model, as of an airplane or missile, built to full size; may be of wood or other easily shaped substance.

moderator (MAH-duh-ray-tuhr), *n.* any substance used to slow down a reaction; especially, graphite or other substance used to slow down the neutrons in a nuclear reactor.

modification (mah-duh-fi-KAY-shuhn), *n.* **1.** a change, or alteration, in characteristics or properties. **2.** the act of making such a change, as the *modification* of parts in an aircraft after testing. **3.** in biology, an adaptation to environmental conditions that is not inheritable. *v.* **modify.**

modulate (MAH-juh-layt), *v.* to produce variation in such characteristics of a signal or carrier wave as frequency, amplitude, or phase.

modulation (mah-juh-LAY-shuhn), *n.* variation in frequency, amplitude, or phase of a signal or carrier wave; controlled to produce desired effects; see also **amplitude modulation, frequency modulation.**

module (MAHJ-yuhl), *n.* **1.** an interchangeable unit of design or construction; much electronic circuitry is built of modules which can be replaced as units when repair is needed. **2.** a unit or system within a larger system, as the *lunar excursion module* which was of the *Apollo* spacecraft. It served as a separate vehicle for landing on the moon. *adj.* **modular.**

modulus (MAH-juh-luhs), *n.* a number which is a ratio or proportion between 2 measurements; as the *modulus of elasticity,* or Young's modulus, the ratio of unit stress to unit deformation or strain.

Moho, *n.* short term for the *Mohorovicic discontinuity,* the boundary between Earth's crust and the mantle. It may lie only 3 miles below the surface of the ocean and as much as 20 miles or more under the surface of mountains.

Mohs hardness scale, in mineralogy, a practical scratching test series, ranging from 1 to 10, to measure hardness of minerals: talc H1, gypsum H2, calcite H3, fluorite H4, apatite H5, orthoclase feldspar H6, quartz H7, topaz H8, corundum H9, and diamond H10; if a mineral has hardness 5, it will scratch apatite and all other minerals of less hardness; and will be scratched by harder minerals; named for Friedrich Mohs, German mineralogist (1773–1839).

moisture (MOYS-tuhr), *n.* a liquid such as water that causes a dampness or wetness.

molar (MOH-luhr), **1.** *adj.* in chemistry, containing one mole (one molecular weight in grams) of substance dissolved in one liter of solution. **2.** *n.* any of the large grinding teeth; see **tooth.**

mold, *n.* any of numerous fungi which form either masses of dense, downy, threadlike growths or slimy growths on vegetable and animal matter; often produce decay; see **Phycomycetes.**

mole, *n.* **1.** in chemistry, a unit of quantity equal to the amount of a substance in pounds or grams that corresponds to its molecular weight. **2.** a local growth on the skin that is usually pigmented, rounded, and slightly raised; may or may not be malignant. **3.** a small insectivore; see **Insectivora.**

molecular (moh-LEK-yoo-lahr), *adj.* pertaining to, composed of, or produced from, molecules.

molecular formula, see **formula.**

molecular motion, the motion of molecules in the 3 states of matter (gas, liquid, and solid). The higher the temperature, the more rapid is the motion; see **kinetic theory.**

molecular weight, the sum of the atomic weights of all the atoms in a molecule based on carbon-12 being exactly 12. Thus, the molecular weight of chlorine, Cl_2, is 70.906 (atomic weight of chlorine being 35.453). *abbr.* **mol. wt.**

molecule (MAHL-uh-kyool), *n.* the smallest part of any substance that retains all the properties of the substance. *Monatomic* molecules, such as argon and helium, contain only one atom. *Diatomic* molecules contain 2 or more atoms, as Cl_2 is a molecule of chlorine gas, and CH_3COOH, a molecule of acetic acid. *adj.* **molecular.**

Mollusca (moh-LUSK-uh), *n.* a phylum of invertebrates with soft, unsegmented bodies (except for one order) covered by a fleshy mantle which usually secretes a shell; well-developed head in

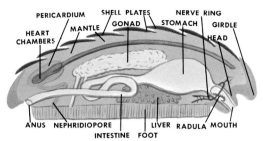

Structures of a typical mollusk, chitin, *Acanthopleura granulata*, shown in longitudinal section

some, but reduced or absent in others; massive muscular foot. Examples of *mollusks* are snail, clam, oyster, mussel, squid, and octopus.

molt, **1.** *v.* to lose hair, skin, feathers, or a shell which are replaced immediately or after change of season. **2.** *n.* such a process of losing hair, feathers, etc.; also called *ecdysis.*

molten (MOHL-tuhn), *adj.* **1.** melted or made a liquid by using heat, as *molten* iron. **2.** produced by being melted or cast in a mold.

molybdenite (muh-LIB-duh-nyt), *n.* a scaly, bluish-gray mineral with a metallic luster, MoS_2, with hardness 1-1½; chief source of molybdenum.

molybdenum (moh-LIB-duh-nuhm), *n.* a hard, gray, metallic chemical element; used in X-ray tube targets and to harden alloys; symbol Mo; *at. no.,* 42; *at. wt.,* 95.94; isolated by Scheele in 1778.

moment (MOH-muhnt), *n.* **1.** the magnitude of the rotational effect of a force on an object; especially, the product of the force times its distance from the axis where applied. **2.** an instant of time.

momentum (moh-MEN-tuhm), *n.* the product of a body's mass times its velocity; see also **Newton's Law of Motion.**

monad (MOH-nad), *n.* **1.** any simple organism, especially a protozoan with flagella. **2.** any chemical substance with a valence of one.

monatomic (mahn-uh-TAHM-ik), *adj.* **1.** consisting of one atom, as a molecule of argon is Ar. **2.** pertaining to an atom or radical with a valence of one, as H^+, NO_3^-. **3.** pertaining to an atom or radical that has only one valence, as O^-, CH_3^-.

monazite (MOH-nuh-zyt), *n.* a yellowish to reddish-brown phosphate mineral, with hardess 5-5½, containing cerium, lanthanum, thorium, and other rare-earth metals, with impurities of iron and silica; an ore of rare-earth metals and thorium, found as grains in sand.

mongolism (MAHN-guhl-izm), *n.* the abnormal condition of a child born with a wide-flattened skull, narrow slanting eyes, squat nose, short stubby fingers, and mental deficiency.

mongoose (MAHN-goos), see **Carnivora.**

mongrel (MAHN-gruhl), *n.* an animal or plant whose parents were of different breeds or varieties; a cross or hybrid.

monitor (MAHN-nuh-tuhr), *n.* **1.** any of various devices used to give experimenters or operators a check on the effects they are trying to produce. **2.** any of several iguana-like lizards.

monkey, see **Primates.**

mono-, a word part meaning *one, single.*

Monotremata

monochromatic (mahn-uh-kroh-MAT-ik), *adj.* having light waves of only one wavelength; *monochromatic* light is produced by filtering out all the rays of undesired wavelength.

monoclinic (mahn-uh-KLIH-nik), *adj.* referring to any crystal with 3 unequal axes: 2 intersect at a non-right angle (obliquely); the third intersects perpendicularly to the other 2; see **crystal system.**

monocot (MAHN-ih-kaht), short term for **monocotyledon.**

monocotyledon (mahn-uh-kaht-uh-LEE-duhn), *n.* any angiosperm of subgroup *Monocotyledoneae* with only one cotyledon or seed leaf in the seed

Typical leaf and stem section of a monocotyledon

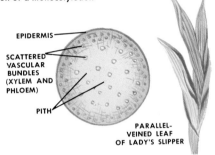

embryo, usually long, narrow, parallel-veined leaves and herbaceous stems; includes grasses, lilies, and cattails. *adj.* **monocotyledonous.**

monocular (mah-NAHK-yuh-luhr), *adj.* looked at with only one eye, as a *monocular* microscope; contrast with **binocular.**

monoecious (muh-NEE-shuhs), *adj.* referring to individuals, particularly plants, with both male and female reproductive organs, as an oak; usually termed *hermaphroditic* in animals.

monomer (MAHN-uh-muhr), *n.* a molecule or compound with low molecular weight, simple structure, and generally containing carbon; see also **polymer.**

monomial (moh-NOH-mee-uhl), *adj.* having only one name; in scientific classification, referring to an obsolete system making use of only one name instead of 2; contrasts with the 2-name system (binomial) regularly used in taxonomy of plants and animals.

mononucleosis (mah-noh-noo-klee-OH-sis), *n.* an infectious disease characterized by fever, sore throat, swelling of the spleen and lymph nodes, and a sharp increase of white blood cells with only one nucleus; course of the disease is usually mild, lasting 2 to 4 weeks; cause is unknown; also called *infectious mononucleosis* and *glandular fever.*

monoplane (MAH-nuh-playn), *n.* an airplane with one pair of wings.

monopropellant, *n.* a substance, such as hydrogen peroxide, which by itself can be decomposed by heat or a chemical agent in a rocket, thus raising the temperature of the resulting gas and producing thrust; no extra oxygen source is needed.

monosaccharide (mahn-uh-SAK-uh-ryd), *n.* a simple sugar that cannot be broken down by hydrolysis, as $C_6H_{12}O_6$ (glucose, fructose).

Monotremata (mahn-oh-TREE-muh-tuh), *n.* an order of primitive, egg-laying mammals. *Mono-*

125

tremes occur in the Australian area; the only surviving members are the duckbill platypus and echidna or spiny anteaters.

Representative monotremes: (left) Australian echidna, or spiny anteater, *Tachyglossus;* and duckbill platypus, *Ornithorhynchus anatinus* (right)

monoxide (mohn-AHKS-eyd), *n.* a compound containing only one atom of oxygen, as carbon monoxide, CO.

monsoon (mahn-SOON), *n.* a seasonal wind that reverses its direction from winter to summer and generally affects the climate of the region. The most notable is the monsoon of the Indian Ocean and southern Asia that blows southwesterly from April to October (bringing heavy rains), and northeasterly for the rest of the year.

moon, *n.* **1.** the body or satellite that accompanies Earth on its yearly revolution around the sun, and revolves around Earth about once every 28 days. The moon is about 238,860 miles from Earth and about 2160 miles in diameter. **2.** any similar body of other planets.

moon-mobile (MOON-muh-beel), *n.* any self-propelled vehicle planned for operation on the moon's surface.

moonstone, *n.* a milky-white, translucent variety of feldspar used as a gemstone; see **orthoclase.**

moor, *n.* an area of wasteland usually composed of marsh or peat and covered with heath plants; the term is used mainly in Great Britain; also called *heath.*

moraine (muh-RAYN), *n.* a mass of rock material that has been transported by a glacier; see **lateral moraine, terminal moraine.**

morbidity (mawr-BID-uh-tee), *n.* **1.** the condition of being sick or diseased. **2.** the proportion of sickness among a given population.

mordant (MOHR-duhnt), *n.* a substance that can unite with both dyes and fiber so that it helps hold the dye to fabric; a dye-fixative.

morel (MOHR-uhl), see **Basidiomycetes.**

morning-glory family, see **Polemoniales.**

morphine (MOHR-feen), *n.* a poisonous, white crystalline alkaloid derived from opium; used as an analgesic and sedative but can be habit-forming; formula, $C_{17}H_{19}NO_3 \cdot H_2O$.

morphogenesis (mawr-fuh-JEN-uh-sis), *n.* the structural or anatomical development of an organism from the embryo.

morphology (mawr-FAHL-uh-jee), *n.* the study of the form and structure of plants and animals; in geology, the study of the external shape of rocks and the forces creating the shapes.

mortar (MAWR-tuhr), *n.* **1.** a laboratory vessel made of a heavy, hard material, as glass or porcelain, used for grinding or pulverizing materials, usually with a heavy, club-shaped instrument called a *pestle.* **2.** any material, as cement, that binds things together, especially building materials such as bricks.

morula (MAWR-yuh-luh), *n.* an unorganized mass of cells formed by the first few divisions of a fertilized egg in embryonic development; the stage before blastula.

mosaic (moh-ZAY-ik), *n.* **1.** in electronics, the photoemissive surface in TV camera tubes, such as a phosphor layer. **2.** in genetics, different genetic makeup of adjoining tissues, as in grafted parts of plants. **3.** any of several virus-caused plant diseases that show in light and dark spotting, or mottling of leaves.

mosquito (muh-SKEE-toh), *n.* any of certain insects of order Diptera; females use their long proboscis to puncture the skin of man and draw blood; some species (as *Anopheles*) transmit certain diseases such as malaria and yellow fever; see **Diptera, Insecta.**

moss, see **Bryophyta, Musci.**

moth, see **Lepidoptera.**

mother-of-pearl, *n.* a shiny, hard substance coating the inside of mollusk shells, secreted by the mantle and containing calcium carbonate and organic material; also called *nacre;* see **pearl.**

motile (MOH-tuhl), *adj.* capable of moving; having structures for locomotion, as some single-celled plant spores and all animals.

motion (MOH-shuhn), *n.* the change of any object's position from one point to another along any path.

motor (MOH-tuhr), *n.* **1.** any machine which produces motion, as an automobile or outboard

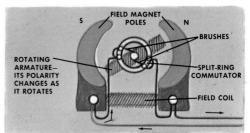

FIELD MAGNET POLES
S
N
BRUSHES
ROTATING ARMATURE— ITS POLARITY CHANGES AS IT ROTATES
SPLIT-RING COMMUTATOR
FIELD COIL

motor; engine. **2.** in strict use, a machine which converts electrical energy into mechanical energy. *adj.* **3.** producing or pertaining to, motion.

motor nerve, a nerve composed of motor neurons or *effectors* that carry impulses from nervous system centers to muscles or glands; contrast with **sensory nerve.**

mountain (MOWN-tuhn), *n.* *a raised area on the earth's surface, often with steep sides, and higher than a hill.*

mouse, see **Rodentia.**

mouth, *n.* **1.** any opening by which food is taken into an organism. **2.** any opening, as of a stream into a bay.

MP, m.p., abbreviation for **melting point.**

mph, abbreviation for miles-per-hour, a unit used to describe speed in the fps system.

mucin (MYOO-sin), see **mucus.**

mucosa (myoo-KOH-suh), alternate term for **mucous membrane.**

mucous (MYOO-kuhs), *adj.* relating to, composed of, similar to, or secreting, mucus.

mucous membrane, a lubricating or mucus-secreting tissue on a bed of connective tissue, lining various internal canals, cavities, tracts, and organs; made of epithelium; also called *mucosa.*

mucus (MYOO-kuhs), *n.* a clear, slimy, viscous secretion, primarily mucin; a type of protein produced by animals which lubricates and moistens certain regions of the body; also serves as a continuous cleaning system in body parts open to the outside.

muffler, *n.* a device for reducing or eliminating the noise produced by the explosive discharge of waste gases from an internal-combustion engine's exhaust; since it slows down the gas discharge, it reduces engine efficiency to some degree.

mulberry family (MUL-buh-ree), see **Urticales.**

mulch, *n.* a loose layer of organic matter such as straw or grass clippings, placed on the ground around cultivated plants to protect them from extremes in temperature or drought.

multi-, a word part meaning *many.*

multicellular (mul-ti-SEL-yuh-luhr), *adj.* composed of more than one cell.

multiple fruit, a fruit composed of the ripened ovaries of a flower cluster on a single stalk as in fig and pineapple.

multiple sclerosis (skluh-ROH-sis), an organic disease of the central nervous system characterized by degeneration of nervous tissue in various areas; cause is unknown.

multiple star, 3 or more stars that seem close together in the sky, often forming a system that revolves around a single center of mass.

mumps, *n.* a contagious disease common to childhood caused by a virus, characterized by inflammation and swelling of the parotid glands; serious complications often occur in adults.

muriatic acid, alternate term for **hydrochloric acid.**

Musales (myoo-ZAY-leez), *n.* an order of monocot tropical plants having a very irregular perianth, a seed with endosperm, and pinnately veined leaves. The 4 families are the banana

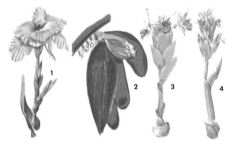

(1) Golden canna, *Canna flaccida;* (2) banana, *Musa paradisiaca sapientum;* (3) ginger, *Zingiber officinale;* (4) turmeric, *Curcuma longa*

family (*Musaceae*); the ginger family (*Zingiberaceae*)—source of ginger, turmeric, and cardamom; the canna family (*Cannaceae*); and the arrowroot family (*Marantaceae*); order is also called *Scitaminales.*

Musci (MYOO-see), *n.* a class of bryophytes containing the mosses, small plants usually growing in moist habitats; plant body is a leafy-type thallus with rhizoids; gametophyte generation is erect, as the familiar sphagnum, with the less complex sporophyte attached and dependent on female plant.

muscle (MUS-uhl), *n.* an organ composed of a bundle of contracting fibers (*myofibrils*), held together by sheets of connective tissue; produces movement in parts of the body; see also **voluntary muscle** picture.

muscle sense, alternate term for **kinesthetic sense.**

muscovite (MUHS-kuh-vyt), *n.* a colorless or variously light-colored mineral with a silky luster in the mica group, $KAl_2(AlSi_3O_{10})(OH)_2$, with hardness 2-2½; used as an electrical insulator.

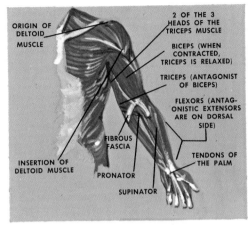

General structures of the muscular system

muscular (MUHS-kyuh-luhr), *adj.* **1.** pertaining to or resembling a muscle. **2.** having healthy and strong muscles.

muscular dystrophy (DIS-truh-fee), a hereditary disease commonest in males, resulting in improper muscle metabolism, especially lack of creatine, a muscle chemical. The victim has a waddling gait, protruding abdomen, and atrophied muscles regulating movement of extremities and spine.

muscular system, the entire system of all voluntary or skeletal muscles in the body; also called *musculature.*

mushroom, see **Eumycophyta.**

Musculature of the human body

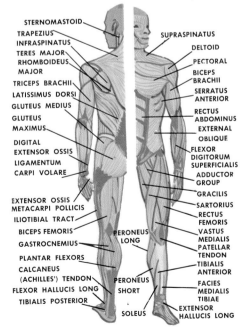

musk, *n.* **1.** a reddish-brown solid derived from the secretion of abdominal glands of the male musk deer; has a very penetrating odor, and is used as a fixative in perfumery. **2.** a number of plants with musk-scented parts.

mussel (MUHS-uhl), see **Pelecypoda.**

mustard family (MUHS-tuhrd), see **Papaverales.**

mutant (MYOO-tuhnt), **1.** *adj.* resulting from or undergoing mutation. **2.** *n.* a new kind of animal or plant produced as a result of mutation.

mutation (myoo-TAY-shuhn), *n.* a sudden, inheritable or lethal change in a gene, producing traits that differ from those of the parents. These inheritable changes in offspring tend to be increased, in breeding livestock and experimental animals or plants, by exposure to X-rays, radioactive elements, heat, and certain other environmental factors. *v.* **mutate.**

mute (MYOOT), *n.* a person unable to speak due to a variety of physiological or psychological reasons.

mutualism (MYOO-chuh-wuhl-izm), *n.* a condition of exchange or balance between 2 or more organisms, as in symbiosis, resulting in benefits to both or all organisms; see also **commensalism.**

my-, myo- a word part meaning *muscle.*

myasthenia (my-uhs-THEE-nee-uh), *n.* an abnormal condition of muscle weakness, especially in the face, resulting in complete paralysis due to a lack of conduction between motor nerve and muscle; cause is unknown.

mycelium (my-SEE-lee-uhm), *n.* a mass of threadlike structures or *hyphae* which form the body of a fungus or its fruiting structure.

mycology (my-KAHL-uh-jee), *n.* the branch of botany dealing with fungi.

myelin (MY-uh-lin), *n.* a whitish, fatty sheath surrounding some nerve cell axons; also called *medullary sheath;* see **neuron.**

myocardium (my-uh-KAHR-dee-uhm), *n.* the muscular tissue forming most of the heart.

myofibril (my-oh-FY-bril), *n.* any of the contracting filaments in muscle fibers or cells; in smooth muscle, they are colorless and homogeneous; in striated and cardiac muscle, they show as alternating light and dark bands.

myology (my-AHL-uh-jee), *n.* the study of muscles, a specialized branch of anatomy.

myoma (my-OH-muh), *n.* a tumor found in, or involving, muscular tissue.

myopia (my-OH-pee-uh), medical term for *nearsightedness;* see **nearsighted.**

Myriapoda (mir-ee-uh-POH-duh), *n.* an alternate grouping including centipedes and millipedes; now placed into 2 separate classes; see **Chilopoda, Diplopoda.**

Myricales (mir-i-KAY-leez), *n.* an order of dicot plants containing the bayberry or sweet-gale fam-

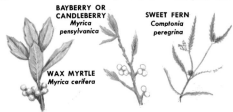

ily (*Myricaceae*), aromatic shrubs which bear flowers with 2 stigmas or forked in short, scaly catkins. The nutlike fruit is thickly coated with a wax used in making candles; includes only 2 species, with the useful plants all in *Myrica.*

myrrh (MUHR), *n.* an aromatic resin from various east African and Arabian shrubs, used for incense and in perfumes.

Myrtales (muhr-TAY-lees), *n.* an order of dicot trees, shrubs, and some herbs often having the base of the flower parts fused into a cuplike receptacle; stamens in 2 whorls often on the perianth. The 12 families include the evergreen

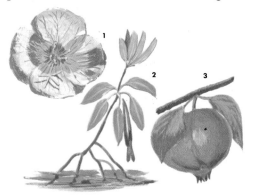

Representatives of order Myrtales: (1) evening primrose, *Oenothera runthiana;* (2) mangrove, *Rhizophora mangle,* sprouting roots; (3) pomegranate, *Punica granatum*

myrtle family (*Myrtaceae*), the mangrove family (*Rhizophoraceae*) which has prop roots, the evening-primrose family (*Onagraceae*), and the pomegranate family (*Punicaceae*). Other families yield Brazil nuts, bay rum cloves, allspice, and water chestnuts.

myrtle family (MUHR-tuhl), see **Myrtales.**

myxedema (mix-uh-DEE-muh), *n.* a condition in adults when the thyroid gland does not secrete enough hormone; shows in severe edema and dry skin; comparable to *cretinism* in the young; see **hypothyroidism.**

myxomycete (MIX-uh-my-seet), alternate term for a slime mold; see **Myxomycophyta.**

Myxomycophytes during the nonmobile, fruiting-body stage; orange structures contain numerous spores

Myxomycophyta (mix-uh-my-KAHF-uh-tuh), *n.* a division of thallophyte plants including the slime molds; *myxomycophytes* have a mobile plant body of a mass of protoplasm, naked, and with many nuclei called a *plasmodium,* formed by the fusion of many zygotes; grow on decaying wood and humus soil; all slime molds are in one class, *Myxomycetes.*